Mastura Raheel.
Summer 1984.

THE GUIDE TO
TEXTILES
FOR INTERIOR DESIGNERS

THE GUIDE TO TEXTILES

FOR INTERIOR DESIGNERS

Dianne R. Jackman
Mary K. Dixon

1983

PEGUIS PUBLISHERS LIMITED
482 HARGRAVE STREET
WINNIPEG, MB R3A 0X5
CANADA

Canadian Cataloguing in Publication Data

Jackman, Dianne R. (Dianne Rose), 1934-
   The guide to textiles for interior designers

   Includes index.
   Bibliography: p. 162
   ISBN 0-919566-95-2

1. Textile fabrics in interior decoration. 2. Textile
fabrics. 3. Textile fibers. I. Dixon, Mary K.
(Mary Katherine), 1936-   II. Title.

TS1765.J3   677   C83-091197-9

Book and cover designs: Pat Stanton
Drawings: Brenda LeBlanc, Avril Goodall

Printed and bound in Canada

TABLE OF CONTENTS

PREFACE

Textiles hold society together. If this seems too bold and general a statement, try to imagine a world without them! From swaddling infants to identifying armies, from catching the wind with a primitive sail to clothing the astronauts, some form of textiles are involved. If you were to write down all the materials you encountered in one day, not forgetting those subtly used or hidden —nylon belted tires, backings, linings, fiber insulated electrical wires, rag-content paper, felt tips on pens, bead strings—the length and diversity of the list would be surprising.

Our day to day contact with textiles is taken for granted. Our clothing, bedding, linens, carpeting, drapery and furniture coverings are both necessities and luxuries. The fabrics we meet during the day—the postman's uniform and the clothing choices of others—serve to shape and identify our world. The textiles in other environments—homes, offices, stores, restaurants, schools —are full of diversity and may appall or delight, or just 'be there' like the automobile upholstery we casually slide over as we get in the car.

This book focuses on the environmental textiles, those essential fabrics and coverings which provide not only visual color and texture to an interior, but also meet the human needs for warmth, privacy, comfort and quiet. Basically, it will take the reader from fiber to finished goods and through the process of intelligent selection of particular textiles for specific applications.

The history of textiles is a fascinating story. While it is not essential for the modern designer to know that indigo dye was being produced by a not uncomplicated process some six thousand years ago, or that civilizations have risen, prospered, and fallen because of textiles, it certainly adds to an appreciation of the medium.

The industry is a dynamic one, combining natural science, social science, high technology and art in a field that is changing daily, converting ancient fibers, new fibers, and unlikely elements into finished goods for wide use in clothing, furnishings and industry. The production of textiles is a world-wide industry, and almost every country values it as part of its economy. In some of the less well developed areas of the world, the primitive spindle is still used to spin natural fibers into yarn and fabrics are woven, knitted, or crafted by hand. In developed countries (where such handwork has graduated to hobby or art form) the mass of textile products are manufactured by industries fully abreast of technological change.

Textile science as it now exists has developed as part of the tremendous expansion in knowledge and technical achievement in this century. Textile machinery can now be computer programmed, permitting designs to be translated from drawing paper to fabric in as little as ten minutes, and in an infinite range of patterns and colors. Fabrics may be woven with streams of air and cut with laser beams. Fiber properties may be scientifically augmented, deleted, or changed altogether. New textiles may be created, or 'engineered', with qualities and characteristics to suit specific end uses.

Manufacturing processes are covered in this book only to the extent needed to comprehend and compare advantages and shortcomings of various materials. The chemistry of the new textiles will be confined to those essentials necessary to differentiate materials for appropriate selection. More detailed information on both these subjects can be found in books listed in the bibliography.

Like other disciplines, textile science has its own language, terminology and methods of classification. This book 'translates' where necessary but generally attempts to stay clear of jargon.

The interior designer's work has sometimes been regarded as dealing with superficialities, the planning of 'a look'. Certainly, aesthetic considerations — the creation of style, mood and character of a total space — are the essential contribution of the designer, but any material selected for appearance only may turn out to be a detriment to a carefully designed scheme if it does not stand up to functional expectations. The designer who selects a textile product based solely on aesthetics does only half a job and possibly a very poor one. The practical considerations, reflecting the use for which a textile is intended within a space, are equally important, and we attempt to familiarize the designer with the essentials of fibers and weaves, and with emphasis on such practical considerations as stability of color, resistance to soil, overall quality and ease of maintenance.

The greater part of this book deals with the selection of textiles. The range of products available for the interior designer seems infinite. Within each category — carpeting, draperies, casements, upholstery and wall coverings — the range of choice is immense. It is essential that the designer have enough basic information regarding each family of textiles to efficiently and quickly narrow the field of possibilities to a workable size. At the same time, for the designer's aesthetic purposes, the requirements of the application, and the client's pocketbook, no possible workable solution to a design problem should be eliminated. A delicate balance indeed! The factors for aesthetic choice — the achievement of harmony and balance through texture, pattern and color — are included in the selection process. This information is so basic to a designer's total education and expertise that no particular guidance on aesthetic choice is offered.

The charts of fibers and fabrics and their characteristics represent a long gestation and arduous birth, but we are as pleased with this innovation as the most happily expectant parents. We sincerely hope they reduce the complexity of textile selection to a manageable proportion, and we urge the user to take time to become familiar with the terms used in order to obtain maximum benefit from, let's face it, some fairly complicated charts.

The sensitivity needed to understand the successful combination of the aesthetic with the practical and the economic must be carefully developed and supplemented with a considerable knowledge. It is hoped that the student and designer alike will find some of that 'considerable knowledge' in these pages.

Winnipeg, Canada
1983

Dianne Jackman
Mary Dixon

INTRODUCTION

As Interior Designers move forward professionally, it is necessary that specialized literature provide technical and researched information to support the statements that knowledgeable individuals must make.

Without such a library of information we cannot lay claim to equality with professionals in other fields. Those of us who deal with the education of future Interior Designers know how few are the reliable, up-to-date references in our areas of learning. Those who encounter clients requiring substantiated details about materials they are considering know how frustrating it is to have only partial answers.

In this book, under one cover, there is a complete file of information about textiles. A quick review of the headings and general type of knowledge will identify the many areas under consideration. While principally a text, this book's continuing use will be as a reference. Index and glossary should be used extensively in order to identify the terms and characteristics of the textile world.

We have all wanted to be more efficient in this area, and identification of the problems is the first step. The index provides this information in a practical, easily retrieved system. Check lists direct the pattern of thinking; the individual and locale of the practice, the environmental and financial constraints, and the availability of merchandise will make the specifying of actual textiles obvious.

The direction that this book takes makes it most valuable in the reference library of every practicing Interior Designer, every student and every para-professional in the soft furnishing field.

Winnipeg, Manitoba   Joan Harland, F.I.D.E.C.
1983   Professor Emeritus

I THE FABRIC OF HISTORY

The development of textiles can truly be said to be the fabric of history. Man's social, cultural and economic progress is closely interwoven with cloth in all its forms. Exploration and settlement, trade routes and transportation, industrialization and labor practices, the wealth of nations and the exploitation of others, work ethics, culture and society, democracy and individual rights, all have had as part of their roots the finding and trading of raw materials and the manufacturing and selling of cloth.

Textiles are a key element not only in history itself but in agriculture, economics, politics, medicine, physics, chemistry, archeology, engineering and anthropology. They are integral to the development of clothing, the home sciences, architecture and interior design. The visual arts are recorded, literally, on the canvasses of the great artists, and the tapestries of thousands of unrecorded weavers, and literature and music would indeed be the poorer without the easily recognized references to textiles and the visions and moods that are universally associated with individual fabrics.

The chronological overview that follows will touch only briefly on the major developments of textiles in each century. The abbreviated 'connected histories' will hint at the extent of the interweaving of textiles with civilization.

1 TEXTILES IN HISTORY

No one knows how early humans discovered that they could make felt, a flat warm material made of matted wool fibers, but this was probably the first cloth. Man's first attempt at weaving might have been interlaced limbs to form a shelter, or baskets, or fishing nets. Made from reeds, grasses, or strips of animal hides stiff enough to be plaited, this weaving predated the discovery of methods of forming crude fibers and the subsequent weaving of cloth. When this hallmark of civilization took place is not known, but records of spinning fiber and weaving cloth can be traced back nearly 6000 years.

Sufficient proof has been found to authenticate that the art of textiles was known in the earliest era of the Stone Age, that period of the mammoth and the cave bear. In the ruins of the prehistoric Swiss Lake Dwellers (an archeological discovery of 1853-54) yarns of linen and wool were found in plaited and woven construction, as well as string, cordage and rope.

Sheep were kept in the cradle of civilization in the Tigris-Euphrates basin (now the Iranian Gulf) around 4000 B.C. and wool trading had begun. Around 3000 B.C. people in Britain wore crude forms of woolen garments. As early as 2640 B.C., according to Chinese legend, the Empress Hsi-Ling-Chi discovered that a particular caterpillar produced an incredible thread with which to make its cocoon. By planting mulberry trees and nurturing the precious moths, the first silk industry was begun.

Egyptian tombs have been a source of historical textiles. Linen cloths measuring some five by sixty feet, date from approximately 3000 B.C., and the quality, reportedly, compares with today's fine sheeting. Tomb drawings, dating from 2000 B.C., depicted ornamental textiles, believed to have their designs either painted or embroidered on plain woven textiles.

The Judea-Christian scriptures hold many references to sheep, shepherds, cotton, linen, wool, weaving, as do the sacred writings of other religions. India was raising cotton, spinning yarn, weaving fabric and trading in the goods by 1500 B.C. By 1000 B.C. traffic in the Mediterranean area was considerable, with the Phoenicians the principal seafarers and traders in raw wool and all

Ancient production of cloth (from the left): pulling the fibrous plant, transporting a bundle from the field, pulling the stalks through a device to remove the seed heads, hand spinning the fibers into yarn, twisting and drawing the yarn, and weaving cloth on a primitive loom.

An ancient silk-winding technique: Burning wood heated a pan of water in which a handful of cocoons were placed. The loosened filament ends were caught, twisted slightly and wound onto the reel at left.

types of woven goods. Their 'exclusive' though was the coveted purple dye which was extracted from the *Murex Brandaris* and *Purpura Haemastoma* molluscs, taken from the Mediterranean around ancient Tyre. This was possibly the first permanent dye and was so costly and rare that only those of royal or imperial rank could wear robes of purple. In the early Roman Catholic Church, centuries later, 'elevation to the purple' meant promotion to the rank of Cardinal. Their robes are still the purple-red color of the ancient mollusc dye. Around 700 B.C. wool dying was established as a craft in Rome, and an ancient dye works with scrap piles of mollusc shells was discovered at Pompeii.

When Alexander the Great invaded India in 327 B.C. he was taken with the extent and beauty of the cotton prints, and cotton soon became the main apparel fabric along the Mediterranean shores.

The Silk Road, a 6000 mile trail from Italy to the Far East, opened around 125 B.C. and was the transport route for silk from China to the Roman Empire. Environmental textiles, bed draperies, window coverings, and household linens, were common in affluent homes, and in 63 B.C. cotton awnings were devised and made their first appearance in Rome.

Ovid, Pliny and Seneca all wrote on facets of the early textiles. The raising and breeding of sheep, the culture of cotton, speculations about silk, all came under their scrutiny and out in their writings. While silk was known and coveted, its origins were a well-kept secret. Seneca thought the lustrous threads were gathered from trees. Pausanias, a traveler of the era, believed that silk came from a spider-like insect twice the size of a large beetle which, he thought, the Chinese fed on green reeds until they burst, whereupon the filaments were extracted from the body. As late as the 4th century, a Roman historian advanced the theory that Chinese soil itself was so soft it could be watered and combed and somehow made into silk cloth.

In the second century, cotton production began in Greece, the first European country to grow the crop. India remained the principal source of this fiber however. Arab traders dealt in calico, muslin and other cotton fabrics, through the Red Sea and overland to the Mediterranean ports and thence to Europe. The source of cotton fiber was also a great mystery to early peoples, and speculations similar to those about silk fibers were common.

The fall of the Roman Empire brought an abrupt end to the demand for innovation and quantity production of textiles. While the techniques developed moved into homes so that the skills were not lost, the impetus for progress was gone and was not to be fully revitalized for another one thousand years.

By the third century, Japan was learning sericulture (silkworm farming and silk harvesting) and provided an expanded source of the precious material. A pound of silk at that time was worth its weight in gold. Silk culture started in India in the fourth century when, according to legend, a Chinese princess given in marriage to an Indian prince, brought him silkworm eggs and mulberry tree seeds hidden in the lining of her headdress. The same sort of devious action brought silk culture to Europe when two Nestorian monks hid eggs and seeds in their hollowed-out canes and presented this bounty to the Emperor Justinian in 552. Under the monks' guidance black mulberry trees were planted near Constantinople, eggs were hatched and a silk centre began to grow.

In 768, Charlemagne saw the possibilities

of a textile industry and established manufacturing centers in Lyons and Rouen, France. Lyons is still an eminent silk designing and fabric weaving center. Soon after, Charlemagne instituted cloth fairs throughout western Europe, and these centers still serve as clearing houses for world textile trade. An England-France trade agreement, in 796, granted English pilgrims in France a charter to trade in English wool.

China had stayed in the forefront of luxury fabrics by devising the method of wax elimination dyeing, now known as batik, which allowed them to produce beautifully patterned silk. In the ninth century, however, civil unrest resulted in the destruction of some of the major silk exporting centers, and silk culture, as a result, was extended in a few European cities.

It must be remembered that all this activity up to the year 1000 was labor intensive to a degree hardly imaginable today. The nurture of the animals, insects or plants, their care and feeding, and the shearing or harvesting were all done by men, women and children with virtually no mechanical help. Spinning and weaving were arduous and time-consuming. Transport was by animal drawn caravans or wind powered ships. Fabrication into clothing or household goods was done not by sewing machines but by needle and thread and human endeavor, by natural light or oil lamps. A new cloak of woven wool was thus the result of thousands of hours' work from many people.

From the eleventh century to the present, the growth in population, nationhood, travel and learning quickens. Textiles were closely connected to all aspects of this varied and increasingly complex history, sometimes reflecting other factors of progress but as often causing particular events or developments. The following textile 'connections' form part of the overall history of the industry. Taken separately, they may be viewed as interesting vignettes of civilization. Taken as a whole, they support the view that textiles are indeed the 'fabric of history'.

Agricultural Patterns

Because early textiles were exclusively natural, agriculture and animal husbandry formed the base for the industry. Sheep raising for wool, crops for the natural dyes, mulberry trees for the silkworms, and the growth of flax and cotton, were the principal agricultural pursuits alongside the production of food for human consumption.

Wool was the favored fiber in Europe and sheep, the source, a valuable commodity. By 1275 the necessity for wool was so great that even serfs averaged fifty sheep per family. By the fourteenth century, sheep raising was England's most profitable pursuit. In Spain, Pedro IV imported Barbary rams for use in crossbreeding to improve the wool staple fiber, which was evidently successful, as

Spanish wool was reputed to have the highest quality by the 1500's. The Spanish Conquistadores had taken sheep to Mexico and native Indians, particularly the Peublo and Navajo, began to use their considerable artistic skills to weave their distinctive blankets. Spain's Merino sheep were closely guarded as a monopoly until the defeat of the Spanish Armada by the English in 1588. It was not until 1765, however, that other nations managed to secure Merinos from Spain.

Sheep began to enter the new world in quantity at the beginning of the seventeenth century. In 1607, the London Company sent a flock to Virginia; in 1625 the Dutch East India Company sent a flock to New York City; the Massachusetts colony received its first sheep in 1633, which were distributed among the settlers; and in 1635 Dutch Texel sheep were bought from Holland to improve the breed. By 1640 there were some three thousand sheep in the colonies.

Skilled English weavers managed to get through the various English embargoes and settled near Lowell, Mass. in 1656, where they received land grants and in return taught their skills to the colonists. The islands around Nantucket were veritable sheep havens in 1665, safe from the Indians and also the British Crown. The colonists were by this time nearly self-sufficient in raw wool and finished garments, much to the dismay of England.

Indian uprisings in the southwest drove the Spaniards out of those territories around the mid-1600's, but wool production by the Indians carried on, with raw wool being traded to white traders. The sheep industry grew in this area, and scientific crossbreeding began about the time of the Civil War.

Wool production in Europe proceeded apace, and exploration and settlement was taking place in other parts of the world. The Dutch occupied South Africa by 1724, and Merino sheep raising was introduced. The venture was not successful until the colony was ceded to Great Britain. In the next two hundred years, the breeds were gradually improved and the industry grew. At present, some thirty-eight million head are raised there, accounting for about six percent of world production of wool.

Sheep were first introduced to Australia in 1780 with the earliest settlers from England. One Captain Macarthur was instrumental in the start of Australia's strong wool industry, purchasing rams and ewes of various types for crossbreeding and for adaptation to the particular climate. He founded and promoted the Pastoral Company of English Investors to help with his plans for colonization and to further his aims to make Australia a world wool-raising area.

Spanish sheep were introduced into the Argentine in 1794; earlier, Empress Maria-Theresa of Austria-Hungary had negotiated with Spain for Merinos to be established on a royal experimental farm.

By 1765, American sheep were numerous enough to trade to the West Indies for molasses, sugar and rum. In 1770, George Washington imported Merino lambs to increase and improve his Mount Vernon flock.

Sometimes, mistakes were made. One Andrew Craigie of Cambridge, Mass. received a gift of three Spanish Merino sheep. Not knowledgeable of the true value, the Craigies enjoyed the sheep very much—for dinner! Ten years later, Mr. Craigie paid $1000 for one Merino ram.

The War of 1812 threw the United States entirely on its own, and the mainly household textile industry was hard pressed to supply cloth and blankets for the army. Broadcloth sold for $8-$12 per yard, and wool rose to $4 per pound. Sheep husbandry gained new impetus, and by 1814 the sheep population was roughly fourteen million head. After the war, increased cotton production in the east, and the growth of towns and cities, led to a gradual move west for sheep farming where free public land for grazing and little need for shelter and fodder made the production

of wool in the southwest a profitable venture. Texans began sheep raising in earnest, along with California and Oregon. By 1865, thirty-six million sheep were estimated. Household production of wool had all but vanished; machinery powered by mules, or water or steam, placed textile production in the factories. The raising of sheep continues world-wide as a viable, profitable agricultural venture.

While silk was being produced in China, Japan, India and other areas east of the Mediterranean, it was just being introduced in Europe in 1000. In 1147, the first white mulberry trees were brought from Syria and were planted in France, in readiness for an attempt at sericulture. This modest venture was successful and, in 1520, Francis I had more silkworms brought from Milan to the Rhone Valley where they have been cultivated ever since.

As soon as the New World was discovered and settled, schemes for silk production began. An attempt was made to start sericulture in Virginia in 1607, and plantation owners were to be fined ten pounds sterling if they did not produce at least ten mulberry trees for each one hundred acres. By 1656, silk production was still being encouraged, and the Virginia Assembly offered 10,000 pounds of tobacco to any planter who exported raw silk or cocoons to the value of two hundred pounds per year. No claims were presented. Threats and encouragement had obviously worked better in Georgia as the Governor was able to take eight pounds of silk as a presentation to Queen Caroline of England. South Carolina was also vigorously promoting silk production. By 1759, Georgia was able to produce some 10,000 pounds of silk cocoons for the silk filature which had been established in Savannah. Tobacco and cotton growing was much preferred though, and by 1772 Georgia's silk industry was nearly extinct.

In 1633 there was still disagreement about the origins of cotton fibers when the great diarist Samuel Pepys wrote, "Sir Martin Noell told us of the dispute between him as a farmer of the additional duty and the East India Co., whether calico be linen or no; which he says it is, having been ever esteemed so; they say it is made of cotton woole that grows upon trees, not like flax or hemp. But it was carried against the Company though they stand out against the verdict."

Cotton was indigenous to North America, of course, and in 1650 the first cotton plantation was established in the colony of Virginia. The first mention of cotton growing in Georgia was in 1735. The indigo plant, used for the production of indigo blue dye, was a profitable crop in South Carolina and continued to do well until after the American Revolution, when indigo imports from the East Indies were found to be cheaper. Cotton planting and harvesting were a principal occupation in the southern areas of America, and the need for field workers was the rationale for the extensive slave trade that existed at that time. The War of 1812 meant a boom in production of all textiles, and cotton growers by 1820 produced approximately 125 million pounds in that year. The cotton industry never really looked back, disruptions such as the Civil War, two World Wars and a depression, merely caused pauses in production. Even the inroads of man-made fibers have not seriously affected cotton, the largest and most profitable crop in the American southeast.

Economic Value

In the earliest days, the textile industry was labor intensive, to say the least. Virtually every step of the process of making finished cloth was done by the physical effort of men, women and children. As early as 1300 several thousand persons were involved in the silk business in cities such as Bologna, Genoa and Milan, not including those whose principal work was the farming of silkworms.

Jewish communities had long been in textile trading and, while any form of money lending or financing was forbidden to Christians, Jewish merchants developed what was later to become 'capital financing' and 'bank drafts' for the necessary funding of raw textile production and the sale of finished goods. The Italians, around 1300, were the first to start Christian financing and are usually given the credit for founding the system of banking. The first banking law on record was passed in Venice to protect depositors in textile transactions, and the great Italian merchant banks came into being. In 1285, Florentine banking houses were making cash advances to English abbeys in return for their entire raw wool output. This successful business was terminated by Edward II in 1311 on the pretext that foreign creditors must be abolished. The English king confiscated all of the English property of these 'financial aggressors'; by 1320 most of the Florentine merchant bankers had left England, and their considerable financial interests there. The Medici family banking houses were pre-eminent at that time, and are usually credited with the founding of 'world scale' banking.

Textile production and the attendant labor and financing, continued through the fifteenth century with controls over production and processing becoming increasingly restricted to the various textile guilds. By 1620, one of the periodic financial depressions overcame Europe; prices dropped, exports were reduced, and unemployment, particularly in England and the European textile centers, was rampant. Fortunes were lost and it was not until after 1630 that recovery began.

The New World had begun to be a force in textiles by this time and the Massachusetts Bay Colony by 1675 was trading wool for linen with France, and wool for wine with Portugal and Spain. This did not please England, needless to say, and restrictive laws proliferated. These provided a thorn for the American colonies but hardly cut back on their endeavors to become independent. England had to diversify its textile industries and did this through its linen mills in Ireland and a silk business begun in 1718 by John Lombe in Derby, who had gone to great lengths to become knowledgeable in silk. His early 'industrial espionage' involved his going in disguise as a laborer to work in leading silk throwing mills in Italy. There, surreptiously, he made drawings of machines and took careful note of procedures. His efforts were discovered in the early 1700's and after many harrowing events, he managed to escape on a ship bound for England.

England was importing cotton, though this was limited to some 200,000 pounds a year, and restrictions against further import, formulated to protect wool, were rife.

By 1800, Ireland's exports in linen fabric reached 25 million yards. The Irish mills, as has been detailed in sociological surveys, histories and historical novels, were truly 'sweatshops' of the worst kind, with women and children working twelve to fourteen hours a day under conditions that present health and safety standards could hardly imagine, let alone allow. By 1821, exports had reached 43 million yards, and all spinning and weaving of fabric were done with little mechanical help.

In young America, meanwhile, the woolen textile industry was burgeoning; homespuns, tweeds and broadcloths of several types were produced and the price of Merino grease wool went from 75¢ to over $3.00 a pound by 1812. With the war over, British wools again made an appearance in America, forcing a decline in prices and a subsequent decline in sheep raising in the northeastern states.

In 1818, the first mill for the weaving of silk ribbons, trimmings and fringes was established in Philadelphia by William H. Horstmann. There were some 170 textile mills in America then and an estimated 135,000 spindles in operation. Mechanical power had just come into widespread use, England had some 2400 power looms in operation by 1816, and the first power-loomed goods were being sold in Massachusetts.

By the 1840's, the women's clothing industry had 96 plants, mostly in New York and Boston, with over 90% of the workers being women. Woolen carpet production was also a growing industry, and the value of machine knitted goods (a development of 1851) rose to seven million dollars in 1860. With the end of the Civil War, all textile industries boomed; the silk industry alone rose in value from twelve million to eighty-seven million dollars in the 20 years between 1880 and 1900. Demand for textile goods of all types was very high. In the U.S. capital investment in silk alone was assessed at one hundred and fifty million dollars, and the industry employed some 100,000 persons.

The world depression of the 30's saw a further demise of many small or household textile industries, and also the introduction of the first commercial synthetic or man-made fibers and fabrics. In 1939, America produced 325 million pounds of rayon, the highest production figure in the world. Agricultural pursuits and the spinning and weaving of natural textiles were joined by textile engineers, machinery technicians, technologists to devise new materials of manufacture, and capital financiers, factory builders and advertisers of the 'new' materials. While acceptance of the man-made fabric was great, cotton remained a premium textile. By 1950, the cotton industry in the U.S. had grown to an annual business of 15 billion dollars—growing, producing, handling, buying and selling—and employing some 14 million.

Textiles and Politics

Textiles, as a major economic facet of each nation, were, naturally enough, subject to the vagaries of politics. Innumerable laws to encourage, to protect, to restrict, to curtail, were passed by rulers anxious to see the best economic return from the industry for their country, and, if the laws could prevent development of the current 'enemy's' economy, so much the better!

In 1111, Henry I of England established the Scottish woolen industry at the mouth of the Tweed River. In 1221, Henry III, in an effort to foster home production of wool, ordered the Mayor of London to burn every piece of woolen cloth which contained Spanish wool. In 1261, this same monarch prohibited the export of 'any or all English wools'. Edward II further forbade all use of foreign cloth. By 1337, King Edward III declared wool a Crown commodity, and announced he would buy all English wool. Not all producers were in favor of this action, and, refusing the edict, were subject to having their wool seized in return for promissory notes. Parliament passed laws prohibiting export of raw wool, which led to such a spate of smuggling that it is said to have contributed greatly to the rise of the British merchant navy. The struggle between the Crown and English woolen producers lasted well into the 15th century. In 1483 Edward IV ended the controversy by reversing the laws regarding non-exportation and allowed shipment of raw wool out of the country, provided it was sent to Calais for distribution.

In order to curry favor with Henry of Castile, Edward IV allowed the shipment of English sheep to Spain. Not wanting to give too much of an advantage to this sometime enemy, however, the sheep designated for export were of poor quality, far below the Spanish Merino. Spain at the time was a textile power, particularly in fabrics, but this advantage gave way to other political concerns. In the 1490's, in the grip of a periodic purification of religious beliefs, Ferdinand V banished some 100,000 woolen workers of Saracen origin. Soon after, Philip III, continuing this trend, drove out some 700,000 'heathens', many of them skilled Jewish and Islamic textile workers.

Columbus discovered, after crossing the Atlantic, that the Indian natives had cotton cloth, and this was a prized sample of a new world commodity that went back to Europe on the discovery ships. Later forays into the Americas by Pizarro and Cortez found the 'little white flower' used in abundance, and discovered that block printing of designs and the coloring of cotton textiles was a well-developed craft. Red cochineal was taken from Mexico and Peru and became a new 'Spanish' textile dye. Pizarro, in fact, in 1533, declared that the Peruvian woven fabrics were superior to those made in Spain and equal to the fine linens made in Egypt.

Back in England, Henry VIII was on the throne engaged in his landmark dispute with

Catholicism. One of his actions, in 1539, was the suppression of some 200 abbeys and monasteries which resulted in the demise of England's famed Monastery Wool, and a great loss of income.

Northern Ireland, having been taken over by England and settled with English and Scottish Protestants, supported a strong flax spinning base for the English mills in Manchester. The Irish mills employed women and children in deplorable conditions, profits were siphoned to the English owners, and this is one of the Irish memories which contribute to the present troubles in that country.

During Oliver Cromwell's era in England (1653-58) the export of sheep, raw wool and yarn to the American colonies was forbidden. This action was designed to limit the growth of the colonies' strength. Instead, it led to increased trade between America, Holland and Spain and to the strengthening of the colonies' independence. This trade and the growing power in textiles was alarming to England, and in 1669 a British law was passed forbidding all export of wool or textile products from the colonies, and even prohibited the trade in textiles between colonies. Needless to say, it could not be properly enforced, and trade continued. This law was followed in 1698 by similar legislation forbidding the shipment of wool from the colonies to England, even though England by this time was in need of raw wool for her own use.

England's relations with Ireland had also deteriorated. England had tried to upgrade their Irish-based flax and linen business but had met with failure. As a political move, they ceded the failing industry to Ireland, who proceeded to turn it into a success. England then forbade the import of woolens from Ireland and any Irish goods found in England were to be confiscated and destroyed.

The cotton industry had meanwhile been growing in America, and in 1700 cotton goods were forbidden in England in an effort to enforce the exclusive use of British woolens by the English people. In 1701, silk imports to England were also forbidden. These restrictions obviously were not effective and in 1712 England forbade the wearing of cotton fabrics. By 1716 there were thirty separate laws prohibiting the import of calico alone, yet the prints continued to gain in popularity.

The many restrictions had little effect on the colonies' growth in textiles; it was noted in 1768 that all the graduates of Harvard College wore colonial made fabrics. In 1770 Ben Franklin was in the forefront of encouraging many facets of American textile manufacturing. England tried another tack at this time and in 1774 forbade the export of cotton textile machinery to America.

America's Civil War (1861-65) saw a great surge in the woolen industry with blankets and uniforms required for the armies on both sides. The end of the conflict saw a thriving garment industry in New York, and the beginnings of America's great textile mills in the south. England finally came to terms with the new political order. There, and throughout Europe, trade increased in textiles during the remainder of the 19th century and into the present.

Textile Workers

Employment, work ethics, and labor laws are intimately connected with textiles. The provision of shelter, food, clothing and transportation were the main concerns of the mass of people for centuries. Textiles played a part in all of these areas. Shelter was rudimentary for most, glass was not yet known, so textiles were necessary for window coverings and for interior comfort on benches and beds. Food production was limited, with grains being a staple of diet and these were of course stored and traded in sacks of woven cloth. Transportation overseas depended on ships powered by the wind, and here sailcloth was the textile medium involved. It was in the making of cloth for clothing that most labor took place, however, and the numbers of people involved in that era of little or no mechanical assistance was incredible. Whole families and generations worked in the many facets of textile production. People were 'labor units' and, as will be seen in the following, often were either settled or dispersed by a country's ruler.

In 1100, Flemish families moved to England seeking work, and Henry I accepted them but scattered and relocated them among the villages and hamlets so that their textile skills could increase knowledge throughout the country.

In 1128, the Cistercian monks arrived in England from France and by 1143 some fifty abbeys, led and peopled by either monks or nuns, were in existence, and led the country in wool production. Sheep counts of 10,000-15,000 per abbey were not uncommon.

On the continent, a skirmish between the rulers of Sicily and Greece resulted in the capture of many Greek silk weavers and artisans, who were resettled in Palermo to aid the silk industry there.

Persecution of the Jews, a fact of their lives for some 600 years by 1150, led them to flee Flanders and settle in England, where they were active traders in wool. By 1271, the king declared that all workers, male and female, were welcome in England "there to make cloth."

By the 14th century, Venice had over 17,000 woolen cloth workers. Florence had about 200 wool dyers, fullers and cloth cutters, or tailors. Louvain, in Flanders, boasted of 150,000 journeyman weavers. Edward III offered protection to all foreigners working in the wool industry in England, and took an active part in promoting commerce in woolen goods. In this century, too, the Black Death visited England. In the resultant chaos, the people complained that sheep raising had become too popular because meadows, woods, cornfields were all being eaten up by the sheep.

Flemish rulers decided that the quality of their cloth was diminishing and set up Cloth Examining Boards. The resultant slow-down in production forced many weavers to seek work in England. Fortunately, they were allowed to stay. The Protestant Reformation caused general disruptions in England and Europe. Edward VI urged Protestants to come to England to work in the textile industry. Workers came from Germany, France, Italy, Poland and Switzerland. In the 16th century Elizabeth I did much to consolidate the English woolen industry, welcoming textile workers from the Netherlands who were fleeing the Spanish invasion, and symbolically, instituting the practice that those gaining knighthood must kneel on a woolsack to remind them of England's economic base. The Spanish invasions in Europe under Philip II caused thousands of workers to flee for their lives. Many went to Ireland, others to parts of France as well as England.

By 1763, silk throwing had developed in England and some 40,000 men, women and children were employed in and around London.

Settlement of the New World was under-

way by this time, and householders were required, by decree, to spin yarn and weave cloth in proportion to the number of females in the family, giving rise to the term 'spinster'. Mennonites from the Rhenish Palatinate immigrated to America in numbers, and soon set up textile weaving and knitting operations in Germantown, then part of the city of Philadelphia. The War of 1812 brought about the introduction of trousers, a symbol of revolt against the British, whose men dressed in knee breeches and hose. The waves of Irish immigrants fleeing famine in their homeland early in the 19th century included many skilled linen workers. By 1850, many had found work in the 1,600 woolen plants in the U.S., which employed some 50,000 workers. While all this indicated labor and wages, conditions were deplorable and hours long. A start towards alleviating some of these conditions was made in 1852 when New York State passed a law aimed at eliminating child labor. A technical advance provided another boon; the development of the self-threading shuttle in 1868 eased the hazard of contracting the 'kiss of death', a respiratory disease caused by the practice of sucking the filling through a hole to thread the shuttle.

Labor unions were gradually winning a place in society, often with long and bitter struggles. In 1900 the International Ladies' Garment Workers Union was formed. New York City at that time had 475 shirtwaist factories, employing 18,000 workers, mostly girls. The boom was due to the current 'Gibson Girl' fashion.

The expansive economy of this era was followed by the crash of '29 and the depression of the thirties. New York City lost 1,100 dress houses between 1929 and 1932, and contract shops were down 80%. The Second World War led to a renewal of the textile industry, with production needs suddenly high and employment opportunities better than ever. The growth of unions and a generally better attitude towards all workers following the war made life easier for most textile employees.

2 THE TEXTILE INDUSTRY

The production of cloth was the first large-scale human endeavor to undergo industrialization. The constant and growing demand for the product and the repetitive nature of many of the steps of cloth manufacture, made it a logical focus for the inventors of early steam and electric powered machinery. The demand factor has never abated; fully automated today for the most part, the industry world-wide produces trillions of yards of fabric per year and employs millions of people.

This chapter will briefly review the breakthrough 'inventions' which caused significant progress in the textile industry, and review the basics of the textile industry today.

Early Industrialization

1516 — Leonardo da Vinci invented the spinning flyer — considered the first continuous movement in cloth manufacture, powered, of course, by hand.

1533 — German woodcarver Johann Jurgen invented the bobbing-wheel, later called the Saxony Wheel, from sketches done by Leonardo da Vinci.

1589 — William Lee of England invented the knitting frame which could knit woolen stockings. In 1598, Lee made the first pair of silk stockings and presented them to Queen Elizabeth I.

1634 — John Pearson of Massachusetts built America's first fulling mill for treating woolen cloth.

1638 — Pearson established the first woolen cloth manufactory.

1643 — First cotton manufactory, also by Pearson in Massachusetts.

1661 — World's first power loom invented by a citizen of Danzig, Poland. The Polish government, fearful that the invention would create disruption among the workers, suppressed the machine and drowned the inventor!

1707 — Courtrai, Belgium, became the flax retting capital of Europe. Still holds this position.

1733 — John Kay, England, invented the fly-shuttle.

1737 — Invention of drawing rollers to draft fibers so that spinning by machine could be done, by John Wyatt and Lewis Paul, England.

1738 — Paul invented the spinning machine.

1748 — Wyatt and Paul invented the revolving cylinder, later to become an essential part of the carding machine.

— Daniel Bourn, England, patented a carding machine, inspired by the necessity of feeding Paul's spinning machine.

1760—Invention of the drop box loom by Robert Kay, England.

1767—Spinning jenny invented by James Hargreaves, England.

1769—Sir Robert Arkwright invented the spinning frame, with partners Jedediah Strutt and Samuel Weed. Horses were used to power the turning of the rollers.

1770—Copperplate printing of calico devised by Thomas Bell, England.

1771—Edmund Cartwright, England, invented the power loom and comber frame.

—First American carpets manufactured in Philadelphia.

1779—Samuel Crompton, England, combining ideas from Hargreaves and Arkwright, invented the mule spinning frame. The name does not indicate that mules were used, but that the system was a hybrid, or mule, of Hargreaves' spinning jenny and Arkwright's spinning frame. Mule spinning still exists.

1782—Invention of the steam engine by James Watt, Scotland.

1785—Cartwright patented second power loom, and invented the warp stop motion for a loom.

—Steam power first used in textile industry.

1787—Kendrow and Porthouse, England, patented a machine for spinning yarn from hemp, tow, flax or wool.

1789—Samuel Slater left England and began building textile machinery from memory, since exportation of machinery and plans from England was not allowed. Built Slater Mill in Pawtucket, R.I.

1791—Eli Whitney invented the cotton gin, America.

1792-1801—Invention of the Jacquard loom to form intricate patterns while weaving, by Joseph-Marie Jacquard of France.

1809—Bobbinet lace-making frame invented by John Heathcoat, U.S.

1822—First cotton mill in Lowell, Massachusetts.

1823—Asa Arnold devised the compound gear, a great improvement to the machine for winding cotton yarn onto the bobbins.

1824—New method for manufacturing velvet devised in America. Woven face to face and then cut in two.

1828—First sewing machine devised in France by Barthelemy Thimmonier. Workers, fearing for their jobs, destroyed the chain-stitch machine. The opposition caused Thimmonier to give up his inventions.

1832—Walter Hunt, at his little shop in downtown New York City, built a sewing machine.

1835—Axminster carpets suffered loss in market due to lower costs of Brussels carpeting.

1840—William Crompton invented the first loom for weaving fancies.

1846—Elias Howe, 26 year old Bostonian watchmaker, patented his sewing machine, which could sew 250 stitches a minute.

—Isaac Singer also perfected and patented a sewing machine.

—The new sewing machines began to be used in factories. Both Howe and Singer profited enormously from their inventions.

1850—Design and set-up of modern carding machines perfected; no fundamental changes since.

1863—Ebenezer Butterick made first paper pattern for home sewing.

1870—James McCall in paper patterns as well.

1890—Sewing machines electrified.

1889-1895—Perfection of the power loom by James Northrop, Englishman employed in the U.S. The loom supplied filling automatically, supplied the thread automatically, incorporated a practical warp stop-motion, did away with the right and left hand motion, automatically supplied filling before exhaustion of the running supply, and was the first with automatic bobbin changing. Used for years by the Gaffney Manufacturing Company in Gaffney, South Carolina, the loom was restored and is now in the Smithsonian Institute in Washington D.C.

Today's Textile Industry

In the recent past, the textile industry was composed of three distinct areas: fiber producers, textile producers and product manufacturers. Today, the textile complex encompasses a much more diverse group of related businesses, producing a wide variety of 'raw materials', processing at the various stages of production, manufacturing textile goods, manufacturing thousands of finished textile products, and marketing. In addition, 'connected industries' manufacture textile machinery, dyes, chemicals, resins, etc., and all engage in research and advertising. The scale of the industry is immense, with the largest sector being the automated mass producers of 'grey goods'—basic cloth which can be converted by a variety of processes into a multitude of finished textiles. Environmental textiles form only a small percentage (estimated at about 10% in the U.S.) of the total industry.

Textile firms within the industry may be single task oriented (for instance, spinning raw cotton into its first stage basic yarn). This 'one aspect producer' is known as a **horizontal operation**, producing at one level only and selling to a variety of users.

Other firms may be **vertical operations**, combining, in one producing factory or mill, several steps of the textile manufacturing process.

The largest of these vertical operations are generally known as **conglomerates** because of the size and scope of their operations, which may include everything from fiber processing to marketing finished goods, and sometimes having diversified interests in textile machinery, retail outlets, transportation equipment, or other such areas.

For ease of understanding, the following will assume each step to be executed by a horizontal operation.

Production

All textiles start as raw materials, either natural or man-made, so the first step is to produce usable fiber. In the case of a natural fiber like cotton, the seed head is picked, sent to the **gin** which removes the fibers from the seed and presses them (called **lint** at this stage) into 500 pound bales. Other natural fibers receive specific basic treatments to get them to a relatively clean fiber stage. (These are more fully explained in Part II). In the case of man-made fibers, the first operation involves blending of the chemical components and spinning of continuous filaments by a choice of methods (see Chap. 5). The filaments may be sold as is, or be cut into staple lengths for further spinning into yarn.

The next step towards finished goods is the **spinning mill**, which transforms raw fibers into yarn. This sector includes firms who simply spin cleaned raw wool into yarn (or similar fairly straightforward operations), and firms who manufacture totally synthetic yarns or sophisticated blends. The firm may be large or small scale. Generally, the yarn producer knows the particular market, and produces a specific range of fibers accordingly.

Yarns are next sent to a specific mill which produces woven fabric, knitted fabric, carpeting, or any of a wide range of goods. The mill may produce a basic fabric which is to be further processed (these are called **grey goods**) or, working closely with their buyers, may produce a cloth of specific weight, weave and design. Mills sell to converters or jobbers.

If the mill has produced grey goods, these are destined for purchase by **converters**. Fabric conversion involves all the post-construction technology—bleaching, dyeing, finishing, printing, and texturizing, along with chemical treatments to enhance or modify performance. The converter must be abreast of current trends in colors and patterns, and sensitive to market fluctuations. The converter's production is finished goods which will be used by manufacturers of textile products. Many converters also manufacture such items as towels, sheets, ready made draperies and bed covers, etc. Converters may operate on a huge scale, or may apply their techniques to small quantities for special or exclusive use. (As discussed in Part II, the scope of fabric conversion by modern methods is truly staggering).

The textile **jobber** buys from the mill or the the converter. The name derives from 'job lot' which is the quantity produced at one production run. In modern terms this may be tens or hundreds of thousands of yards. Firms involved in jobbing buy and stock goods, cut and distribute samples to a particular range of textile product manufacturers and regional jobbers, and then sell **piece goods**, that is, one or more bolts, to these customers.

The **regional jobbers** who buy multiple bolts of finished goods sell **cut orders**, or specific yardages, to regional manufacturers, designers or local retailers. Not wanting to be left with unsold goods, the smaller regional jobber usually stocks fairly safe, popular, middle priced lines.

The big regional jobbers, such as those located in Manhattan, Chicago, or Atlanta, are generally classified as **fabric houses**. These fabric houses may specialize in a particular price range or type of goods, or may carry a wide general range. In New York City, probably the world's largest textile exchange center, fabric houses are classified as **downtown** or **uptown**. Downtown houses sell to retailers, furniture manufacturers, regional houses and uptown houses, and may also have contract divisions specializing in institutional or hotel work. Uptown houses sell cut orders 'to the trade', interior designers, architects, special order retailers, contract departments of major department stores, and furniture manufacturers who in turn sell to the trade. Uptown houses sell only decorative fabrics through showroom samples. Whether 'open' or 'closed' sales are only made to the trade.

While all of the above deals with U.S. produced goods, a thriving business is done in most countries with **imports**. Imports may enter a country at any stage from fiber to finished goods. **Import houses**, similar to the fabric houses mentioned, deal exclusively in imports of finished goods, and are an extension to the range of goods available.

Marketing

One of the most important factors in the textile industry is the buying and/or selling done at each stage of production.

Fibers are marketed as **commodities**, as **brand name fibers**, or as **controlled brand name fibers**. Fibers marketed as commodities are used without identification of source and are sold to any buyer on the open market. A drapery fabric labelled '100% polyester' has been made with commodity polyester fibers. Brand name fibers are identified by source through the brand name used. The fiber producer spends much promotion money to establish his brand name, and expects manufacturers, wholesalers and retailers down the line to take advantage of it. The fiber producer, however, frequently does not have complete control over the use of his brand name after the mill has purchased the fiber.

The controlled brand name approach enables the fiber maker to rigidly control the subsequent use of the fiber. Controlled brand names usually infer licensing. Under a licensed brand name, the licensed producer allows its brand name or trademark to be used by subsequent companies in return for a specified remuneration. In some cases, the final product is carefully checked for quality by the licensed fiber producer. The licensed brand name is an assurance to consumers that the product has satisfactorily passed various tests related to its end use. The tests are specified by the licensor, and requires the maintenance of a quality control program to insure certain levels of performance.

In today's market, user assurance is more vital than ever because of the proliferation and confusion of brands, claims and performance characteristics. Frequently there is no apparent difference in a carpet or drapery fabric, yet performance can vary significantly. In addition to the manufacturer's desire to produce a quality product, and one that will attract repeat business, various government departments and independent consumer groups act as watchdogs to make sure that claims for performance and longevity are not erroneous or overstated.

Finished goods are marketed either by written specifications or from samples. If a fabric is purchased based on written specifications, then the seller must ship the fabric exactly as specified. Such details as yarns per inch, weight, thickness, breaking strength, degree of color fastness, are examples of possible specifications.

If fabrics are purchased from a sample, the seller is required to deliver an almost identical fabric. Piece goods salespeople use various sample forms to show their products:

COLOR CARD: a card on which swatches of each color or print of the textile is pasted. A print fabric is usually sold in only three or four different colors, while a solid textile may be sold in many different colors.

SALES TYPE OR CAP SET: pieces of the same fabric showing different color combinations of a design held together with a section of cardboard.

HEADENT: a piece of fabric usually full width and about one quarter of a yard long.

BOOK: a set of swatches about 4"x 6" (10x15 cm.) fastened together.

SQUARE: pieces of material usually measuring 12"x 12" or 24"x 24" (30 x 30 or 60 x 60 cm.) which show the full pattern.

ONE YARD PIECE OF FABRIC: used to show the full repeat of a pattern, and the draping quality of the material.

II

FROM FIBER
TO FINISHED
GOODS

The abundance of textile goods we see around us are built of infinitely small fibers—hairlike tendrils—which are gathered together and eventually become factories full of fabrics. This sort of amalgamation is common in nature, and in man's production of food, but to produce lasting goods by this method is unique to textiles.

Different fibers take different paths to finished goods. The natural fibers, although one might assume they have a 'head start', generally take longer than man-mades to process into textiles. Speed and efficiency are the hallmarks of modern manufacture. The degree of control and automation in an integrated raw-material-to-finished-fabric factory permits phenomenal production speeds, capable of supplying the world's population with the wealth of cloth it has come to expect.

Many people have begun to question the abundance of synthetics, for many reasons. A new interest in naturals—a renewed interest for many—is a trend that will guarantee the position of respect that fibers of wool, silk, cotton and linen have always held.

3 FIBER BASICS

Fibers are the basic components of textiles. As such, their characteristics and particular properties form the basis for determining the final character of the textile. In today's advanced state-of-the-art, however, it can be said that yarn and textile manufacturers choose the fiber or fibers that most closely meet the requirements of the planned textile, and then proceed to modify, maximize, or minimize those properties to suit their purpose and may, in addition, add totally new properties. In other words, fiber, yarn, method of textile construction, and finishes are all interdependent and together give the finished product its final distinguishing characteristics.

A common error is to search for a mythical fiber absolute, one that does everything well. No single fiber has the capacity to meet all needs; often the functions overlap and the performance of one fiber must be compared to the slightly different performance factors of another. This 'knowledgeable juggling' results in the selection of the best fiber(s) for a particular purpose.

Familiarity with the fibers and their basic properties helps the designer to anticipate the performance that a particular fiber will contribute to a textile.

Fibers used to make textiles fall into two general categories: one, classed as NATURAL, is found in nature itself and the product (like cotton, wool or silk) is used pretty much in the form in which it is found. The other, MAN-MADE, contains products from other substances found in nature (such as oil and wood) which are changed drastically before being made into fibers.

Fiber Composition

A fiber is like a hair—a pliable strand having a minute diameter in relation to its length. All fibers are composed of simple molecules, or monomers, built in a chain-like formation to form giant molecules called macromolecules, or POLYMERS. The process of forming polymers from molecules is called polymerization, and the degree of polymerization (dp) identifies the number of molecular units joined together to form the macromolecule, or polymer. Fibrous polymers are characterized by a high degree of polymerization, usually between 500-10,000. (The number indicates the quantity of specific molecular units which combine to form the macromolecule.) The size and complexity of the marcomolecules means that their properties are radically different from those of the individual molecules. (As an example, sugar and cotton are both composed of glucose units. Sugar is a relatively simple combination of glucose elements, and may be dissolved in water. The cellulose which forms cotton is composed of up to 10,000 glucose molecules joined by polymerization and produces a product that is not only water insoluble but is also resistant to many strong chemicals.) Other characteristics of a polymer are high molecular weight, great stability, and a high degree of intramolecular force that prevents easy destruction.

The polymerization of various chemicals into fibers occurs in nature to produce cotton, wool, silk, etc. The same process is induced and amplified in the laboratory, and transferred to the factory, to produce man-made fibers.

FIBER QUALIFICATIONS

To be suitable for use as a textile fiber, a polymer must meet the following basic qualifications:

— High length-to-breadth ratio;
— Adequate strength, or tenacity;
— Flexibility, or pliability;
— Cohesiveness, or spinning quality;
— Uniformity.

High Length-to-breadth Ratio

A minimum of 100:1 is usually considered essential, and most fibers have much higher ratios. Fibers shorter than 1.5 cm (approx. 1/2") are seldom used for yarn. The fiber molecules as well as the fiber itself are usually long and extremely thin, bundles of long thin monomers forming long thin chains (macromolecules) which are systematically repeated (polymerization) to become fibers.

STAPLE FIBERS are short, measured in centimeters or inches, and range in length from 2-46 cm (3/4-18"). All natural fibers, except silk, are in staple form and vary from 1.3 cm to 1 meter (1/2-39").

FILAMENT FIBERS are long, continuous fiber strands of indefinite length, measured in meters (yards) or even kilometers (miles). They may be monofilament (one fiber) or multifilament (a number of fibers). Silk is the only natural fiber found in filament form. It is usually about 1450 m. (1600 yards) long. Natural rubber and metal are made into filament form but are not naturally found in that condition.

All man-made fibers are produced as filaments. Depending on the end use, they may remain in this state, or, alternately, they may be further transformed into short lengths to become staple fibers. The filament-to-staple process involves grouping thousands of filaments together to form a thick rope called a **filament tow** which is then cut or broken into the required lengths before being twisted into yarns.

Adequate Strength, or Tenacity

While this quality varies among the different fibers, the substance must possess sufficient tenacity to withstand processing by machinery, and to give adequate durability in the end use to which it is allocated. The American Society for Testing and Materials (ASTM) defines tenacity as:

"the tensile stress expressed as force per unit linear density of the unstrained specimen."
ASTM Yearbook, Vol. 32, p. 39

Tenacity is determined by mechanical devices and mathematical conversion formulae. It may be expressed as grams of force per denier. (Denier is a unit of yarn measurement equal to the weight in grams of 9000 meters of the yarn.)

Fiber strength does not always indicate comparable yarn or fabric strength. Most fabrics require a minimum fiber tenacity of 2.5 grams per denier (gpd). However, some weak fibers, like wool, which is one of a few fibers with a strength less than 2.5 gpd, can be used in durable textiles due to their having compensating properties such as superior elasticity and resilience.

The strongest yarns, understandably, are those composed of strong filament fibers—staple fibers in yarn having the possibility of slipping under stress.

Flexibility, or Pliability

This is the capacity to bend repeatedly without breaking. This pliability is an important factor in durability. Fiber size may also determine the flexibility of a fabric. Large fibers (relatively inflexible) give crispness, roughness, body and stiffness. Large fibers also resist crushing, important in carpeting. Fine fibers (very flexible) give softness and pliability. Fabrics made with fine fibers drape more easily.

Cohesiveness, or Spinning Quality

May be described as the ability of fibers to stick together in the yarn manufacturing process. The necessary cohesion may occur either because the longitudinal contour of the cross-section shape of the fibers enable them to fit together sufficiently to adhere to each other, or simply because the surface of the fiber is such that the fibers stick together. When the shape or surface do not qualify as having cohesive quality, cohesion is attained by using fibers of sufficient filament length to be easily twisted into yarn.

Uniformity

It is important that fibers be similar in length and width, in flexibility and in spinning quality. Man-made fibers can be controlled during production to maintain a relatively high degree of uniformity. Yarns composed of generally uniform fibers are preferred by textile manufacturers because they have a smooth and regular appearance, handle well in machinery, and accept dyes more evenly. Natural fibers may lack uniformity and vary slightly in quality because they are affected by weather, nutrients, insects and disease. This failing is compensated by blending the same fibers from different sources to mass produce uniform quality yarns and fabrics.

The above five basic fiber properties are determined by the nature of the external structure, the chemical composition, and the internal structure. These properties are so essential that production of yarns does not proceed if they are absent. The designer can therefore safely assume that these qualities are present in any commercially produced fiber or yarn.

Fiber Classification

It is practically impossible to remember all the properties and characteristics of each individual fiber. Since the advent of man-made fibers scientists have arranged or classified them into like groups. The designer needs to become acquainted with the general properties of each group, and then only the additional knowledge concerning special qualities of individual fibers will be necessary for intelligent selection, use, and care of the textile products.

The system for classification generally is based on the following:
 —the origin of the fiber—natural or man-made;
 —the general chemical type—protein, cellulosic, mineral or synthesized;
 —the generic term—whether natural, or as specified by the Textile Fiber Products Identification Act for man-made fibers;
 —the specific fiber name—or trade name.

Fiber Origin

The broad classifications for fiber origin are natural and man-made.

NATURAL Natural fibers are obtained from plants, animals or minerals. Today, fibers from this group are the product of thousands of years of selection and cross-breeding. In all cases, they have been around long enough for their characteristics to be well known. They are produced seasonally and stored until used. Although carefully controlled, they are still to some extent subject to the vagaries of nature—weather, insects, nutrients or the lack of them, etc. Natural fibers are divided into **cellulosic**, plant source; **protein**, animal source; **mineral**; and **natural rubber.**

MAN-MADE From observation of the silkworm building its coccoon, man could see how silk was made. As early as the 17th century, it was predicted that if a proper liquid were squirted through a small aperture and allowed to congeal, a fiber like that of the silkworm might be produced. It was not until 300 years later, however, that the first filament was made from a solution of cellulose, a rather inferior fiber called artificial silk. By 1910, these fibers were in limited commercial production in the U.S. Improvements followed, the fiber was renamed rayon in 1924, and the man-made fiber industry has never looked back.

The process of polymerization, as discussed, forming polymers from molecules, is used to manufacture fibers. The fibers are made from various chemical solutions which are forced through the tiny holes of a **spinnerette**, a device similar to a shower head. (The term was taken from the name of the extrusion system of the moth larvae.) The fine liquid streams of solution harden into continuous strands called filament fibers. The number of holes in the spinnerette, their shape and size, vary with the filament fiber and the yarn desired. A small spinnerette may be the size of a large thimble and have up to ten holes, while

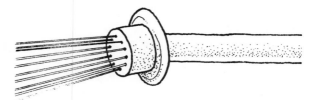

A *simple spinnerette. Adapted from the two-orifice filament-spinning device in the heads of moths and spiders, the spinnerette is the pivotal element in the manufacture of man-made fibers.*

a large one has more than 10,000. The spinnerette is usually round and usually made of platinum or iridium. Extruded filaments may be single, or **monofilament**, such as nylon fishing line. More often the filaments are extruded in groups or bundles known as **multifilaments**. The orifice shape can be varied so as to produce a round, triangular, T-shaped, or some other form. The size is varied to make filaments finer than silk or heavier than horsehair.

Three basic techniques are used to harden the liquid streams and produce the filament fibers. In the **dry spinning method** the polymer solution is combined with a solvent, forced through the holes in the spinnerette into warm air where the solvent evaporates, leaving the liquid stream to immediately solidify. In the **wet spinning method** the polymer solution is forced through the holes into another wet solution where it immediately coagulates into continuous filament. In the **melt spinning method** a solid polymer is melted and forced through the spinnerette into cool air which solidifies it. The straightforward combination of chemicals and mechanical extrusion process often produces a filament that is too smooth or lustrous. This 'artificial look' is sometimes tempered by the addition of a chemical delustering agent to the solution. The effect is usually to pit the surface of the fiber, resulting in a more diffused reflection of light and a softer look. After extrusion, the

Textile Fibers

GENERAL CHEMICAL TYPE	NATURAL GENERIC TERM	SOURCE	MAN-MADE GENERIC TERM	SOURCE
CELLULOSIC	cotton*	seed hairs — cotton	rayon*	wood, cotton
	flax*	flax stalk	acetate*	wood, cotton, modified
	hemp*	hemp stalk		
	jute*	jute stalk	triacetate*	wood, cotton, modified
	abaca	abaca leaves		
	ramie	ramie stalk		
	sisal*	agave leaves		
	coir*	coconut husk		
	kapok	seed hairs — kapok tree		
	pina	pineapple leaves		
PROTEIN	wool*	sheep's hair	azlon	regenerated natural proteins
	silk*	moth larvae secretion	fibrolane	
	mohair*	Angora goat's hair	merinova	
	angora	Angora rabbit's fur	ardil	
	horsehair	horse's mane or tail	vicara	
	alpaca, camel hair, cashmere, llama, vicuna	specialty fibers from named animals' hair		
MINERAL	asbestos	asbestos rock	glass*	silica sand and limestone
			metallic*	various metals
ELASTOMERS	rubber	rubber tree sap	synthetic rubber spandex lastrile	chemicals
SYNTHESIZED			acrylic* andex aramid modacrylic* nylon* novoloid nytril olefin* polyester* saran* vinal vinyon*	manufactured polymers

*commonly used in environmental textiles

molecular chains in the filament must be oriented (made parallel to each other). This is done by a drawing or stretching process, and is important for the ultimate strength and elasticity of the fiber. Man-made filaments may be used for textile production without further processing into yarn, or, conversely, they may be further twisted or spun into yarns, either in their filament form or cut into staple form.

General Chemical Types

Fibers of both natural and man-made origin may be classified in this manner.

CELLULOSIC Natural cellulose fibers are obtained from vegetable sources. These fibers may come from the **stem**, as in flax or hemp, and are called **bast fibers**; from the **leaves**, as in sisal; from the **seed hairs**, cotton; or from nut **husks**, as in coir — a coconut husk fiber used for matting. These sources yield their fibers and are utilized with a minimum of processing. Man-made cellulosic fibers generally duplicate, in part, natural cellulosic fibers but with significant differences in degree and in combination of properties. Fibers in this group burn easily and quickly, are damaged by acids but are resistant to alkalies. They are low in elasticity and resilience. The fibers are soft and absorbent and launder readily, withstand strong detergents and high temperatures.

MODIFIED CELLULOSIC FIBERS combine cellulose with acetic acid. Specific manufacturing techniques and finishes give this group a variety of properties in addition to, or instead of, the basic properties of other cellulose-based fibers.

PROTEIN Most fibers in this group are natural in origin and are derived from animal hair (wool and variants), and in lesser quantity from the secretions of animal life (silk). These fibers, as a group, are relatively weak, and are less resistant to certain chemicals and environmental factors. Protein fibers have good resiliency and elasticity, and excellent moisture absorbency. They burn slowly and are self-extinguishing. Man-made protein fibers have been, and are, produced. However, because the source is protein — or food, in other words — and because of the wide range of fibers produced from non-food sources, converting protein into fibers has not been generally justified. The methods are known, however, and protein not used for human, animal, or fish food may one day be commercially converted to fibers.

MINERAL The most important fiber in the natural mineral group is asbestos, obtained from a fibrous form of serpentine rock mined extensively in Canada. The main property of this fiber is its complete resistance to fire. Man-made mineral fibers such as glass fiber, from silica sand and limestone, or metallic fibers, usually aluminum but sometimes gold or silver, have very specific properties and uses. Variations of both these fibers are used extensively in furnishings.

RUBBER AND ELASTOMERS The liquid sap from the rubber tree (Hevea species) is the source of natural rubber fibers. Man-made elastic fibers are classed as elastomers and are formed of a variety of chemicals.

SYNTHESIZED The generic list which follows indicates the extent of fibers in this category. New developments, new techniques and new combinations are continually being assessed, and new fibers and textiles are the results of this research. Innovation and modification are ongoing activities for textile chemists. They have produced incredible fibers to date and one may expect more wonders in the future. Reputedly 'in the lab' at present are thermo-reactive fibers, capable of responding to temperature changes — becoming warm in winter, cool in summer; color changing fibers; self-cleaning fibers; and fibers that can change from opaque to transparent, and back again!

The significant distinguishing fact about these fibers is that they are 'invented' — devised in the lab and built without recourse to traditional fiber sources. Processes involve extracting molecules from unlikely sources such as petrochemical waste, water and air, inducing the formation of macromolecules, and creating long chain polymers suitable for extruding into fibers. DuPont organized and funded the first research and development in this area in 1928, not knowing what the result of the fundamental investigation would be. The development of nylon, which commenced commercial production in 1939, was one of the results. It has been said, in this regard, that the first pound of nylon fibers cost DuPont 27 million dollars.

Generic Terms

The generic terms for the natural fibers are well known, cotton, wool, etc. It was in the early man-made fiber field that generic terms became confusing. By the mid-fifties a wide range of man-made fibers were being produced, so that in 1958 the Textile Fiber Products Identification Act (TFPIA) was passed in the United States and became effective in 1960. This law established generic, or family names, of all man-made fibers. A generic name is used for a group of fibers having similar chemical composition. New generic names are adopted only when a fiber is developed that is different in chemical composition from other fibers. It also must reflect significantly different properties of importance to the user. The generic classifications are now universal and are always written in lower case. The law also requires textile products, sold at retail, to have labels stating the fiber content.

Specific Fiber Names

Under natural fiber generic terms, origin or additional detail usually comprises the specific name (Indian Head cotton, for instance). Under man-made fiber generic terms, there are fiber trademarks owned and promoted by individual fiber producing firms (e.g., Qiana nylon, a 1968 DuPont introduction). These trade names are given to various fibers manufactured by specific textile firms, and are written as proper nouns.

Man-made fibers are not subject to the limitations of nature, and are usually uniform in quality because the entire production process can be controlled. It can happen, however, when fibers are spun, constructed, finished and styled for the mass market that quality may be short-changed to save time and money. The trade name, therefore, is a good consumer guarantee of quality.

The Classification Chart indicates the range of fibers used for textiles. Specific fiber names, where applicable, will be detailed as each generic term fiber is introduced.

Fiber Properties

Each individual fiber is characterized by a number of inherent properties. These distinctive attributes apply to the basic fiber before it is transformed into yarn and eventually into textile products. The degree to which the final characteristics of a textile agrees or disagrees with the basic characteristics of its component fiber or fibers depends on many factors: the type of yarn produced and treatments applied at that stage; the weave or knit or other method of construction; the weight of the final product; and any of several finishes, dyes or treatments applied to the end product. Specific characteristics or properties may be modified, deleted, or inserted during the transformation from fiber to finished goods. These are not necessarily inherent in the fiber and will be introduced in the chapters on yarn production, fabric construction and finishing. Nevertheless, just as fibers are the 'ingredients' of textiles, so their particular characteristics determine to a large extent the 'flavor' of the final product.

The terms used for identifying fiber properties may be divided into three categories: **inherent characteristics, chemical reactivities** and **environmental sensitivities.** Inherent characteristics as defined in the following box, are those properties which are general, constant, and integral to a fiber **in its fiber state.** Chemical reactivity refers to a fiber's reaction to alkalis, acids, solvents, or other agents. Environmental sensitivities refer to a fiber's sensitivity to sun, heat, fire, water, moisture, microorganisms, insects and aging.

How usable fibers are obtained from natural sources, the method of manufacturing man-made fibers, and the basic properties of each, are detailed in chapters four and five.

Fiber Properties

INHERENT CHARACTERISTICS

FIBER DESCRIPTION   Included in this description is the fiber size, degree of uniformity, natural color, and degree of luster. The width of a fiber is measured in *microns,* one micron being 1/1000 millimeter, or 1/25,400 inch.

Luster is judged on the amount of light reflected by a fiber. High luster indicates a bright sheen, low luster a dull or matte appearance.

STRENGTH   Tenacity is expressed in grams per denier (gpd), with 1.5-2.0 gpd being relatively weak, 2.5-4.0 gpd relatively strong and 5-8 gpd exceptionally strong.

Flexibility is a further aspect of strength and refers to the ability of a fiber to be flexed or bent repeatedly without breaking.

DIMENSIONAL STABILITY   is based on several factors. *Elongation* is a fiber's ability to be stretched or extended, and is expressed as a percentage of the fiber's length taken at *standard conditions* — 21.1°C (70°F) and 65% relative humidity.

Recovery is expressed as a percentage of return to original length after elongation of 2%.

Elasticity is perfect if the recovery after elongation is 100%, but is rated poor if recovery is 75% or less.

Resiliency is the ability to return to shape after bending, compressing or crushing. It is tied to elastic recovery, and rated from excellent to poor depending on the percentage of elastic recovery.

DENSITY   is expressed in grams per cubic centimeter, and indicates the mass per unit volume. The higher the density, the greater the weight of the fiber. Lower density indicates loft, lightness or buoyancy. The range is from 0.9 gpcc, exceptionally low, through 1.3 light, 1.45 medium, to 1.5-2.5 high.

ABSORBENCY   is measured through *moisture regain* and *moisture absorption.* Fibers usually contain a certain amount of water; moisture regain indicates this normal moisture level at standard conditions and is expressed as a percentage of the weight of a moisture-free sample.

Absorption indicates the amount of water the fiber is capable of holding at 100% humidity, and is expressed as a percentage of the weight of the bone dry specimen.

Absorbency influences the dyeability of fibers, and is an important aspect of comfort to human contact. Some synthesized fibers have zero absorbency; natural fibers generally have a higher moisture regain, with wool the highest at 16%. Good absorbency ranges from around 6-14%.

CHEMICAL REACTIVITIES

These refer to a fiber's reaction to *alkalis, acids* and *solvents.*

ENVIRONMENTAL SENSITIVITIES

Each fiber has particular sensitivity to certain elements of the environment. Our concern is with *sun, heat, fire, water, moisture, microorganisms, insects* and *aging.*

4 NATURAL FIBERS

Cellulosic Fibers

Cellulosic fibers are obtained from plants, which are, in turn, composed largely of cellulose. Nearly all plants have parts that are fibrous in nature, and many have been used as fibers. However, depending on the quality of the fiber, the quantity available, and the ease of extraction, certain plants have become staples for fiber production and have, since earliest times, been of great importance to civilization.

Cellulosic fibers in general are soft and absorbent and so are comfortable to human use. They are low in elasticity and resilience, damaged by acids but resistant to alkalis. The fibers burn readily, with a burning paper smell, and leave a fluffy grey ash.

The cotton plant, showing the flower, seed pod formation, and the eventual boll of cotton fibers which surrounds the mature seeds.

COTTON

The most important natural fiber for use in environmental textiles, either alone or as a component of a blend, is cotton, a cellulosic fiber derived from the seed hairs of the plant. Cotton must be grown in a warm climate having sufficient rain or irrigation, with a growing period of from six to seven months and about twelve hours of sunlight per day. It is a bushy annual plant which produces its characteristic boll of fleecy fibers for a 20-30 day period. Hand-picking results in the most uniform and best quality fibers, but this method is rarely used today. Mechanized equipment may be of the picking or stripping type: pickers pull the fibers from the open bolls; strippers pull the entire boll from the plant. The choice of machinery is governed by the evenness and height of growth in the field. Pickers may be used on the same area several times during the season, while the stripper is a once-over operation.

Picked cotton is taken to the ginnery where the **cotton gin** separates the cotton fibers from the seed and removes some of the dirt, twigs and leaves. (The cotton seeds, incidentally, are a valuable product in their own right, from which cattle feed and cottonseed oil are produced.) Samples of the fibers in each bale are removed and the bale classified by **staple length, grade** and **character**. Staple length varies from very short (1.9 cm—less than 3/4″) to extra long (6.35 cm—about 2½″). The grade is based on color (white, gray or yellow), the brightness or dullness, and the quantity of foreign matter. Character is determined by fiber strength, uniformity, fineness, resiliency and cohesiveness. When all of this information has been noted, the quality of the cotton is set, price is determined on the commodity market, and governed by the fluctuations of demand. The ginned cotton is packed in 500 pound bales for delivery to yarn producers or manufacturers.

OPENING, CLEANING AND BLENDING is done as a multi-step continuous process. Several bales of classified cotton fibers are placed at the feed-in point of the opener and blender. 'Opening' in this operation refers to the separation of the mat of fibers into a more loose, or open fiber state. (Imagine this as picking apart a wad of cotton batting with your fingers.) Material from several different bales is fed into the mechanical opener, usually a spiked lattice conveyor which starts the separation process and delivers the partially opened mat of fibers to the picker, where metal 'fingers' pull out tufts of fiber. The mechanical picker is a system of rollers over which the fiber mat passes. Aided by forced air and the action of the fingers, the fibers loosen, dirt and foreign matter is forced out, and the resultant blend of fibers form a 1.5-2 cm (1/2-3/4″) layer which is rolled off onto a collecting cylinder. This roll of fibers (roughly 1.2 x .5 meters, or 45 x 18″) is called the **picker lap.** In an alternate automatic system, no lap is formed but the opened and blended fibers are fed directly into a hopper. In either case, the fibers at this stage are relatively free of dirt, blending of fibers from different bales has occurred, and they are fairly well opened.

CARDING is the next step. The device is somewhat similar to the picker, except that the fiber mat is moved over rotating wire cylinders in which two layers of fine wire pins are anchored. The finer 'fingers' tease out the fibers and the resultant layer is a filmy web which is then mechanically gathered into a soft mass and pulled into a 2.5 cm (1″) thick, loose rope of fibers called a **sliver.** This sliver is then ready for spinning into yarn, or, alternately, for a finer yarn, the sliver of fibers is next combed.

COMBING is a process which is basically a method of culling out any remaining foreign matter and all the short fibers in the carded sliver. It is a three-step operation. First, the carded slivers are fed into a breaker-drawing frame, where several slivers are combined and their fibers once again pulled out into a fine layer before being reformed into a new sliver. Second, 48 slivers are fed through a bank of 3 lapper units which smooths them into a thin layer of fibers and then winds this layer into a wide roll. Finally, this roll of fibers is fed into the comber, where fine metal wires clean out

the remaining short fibers. As much as 20% of the fibers may be removed in this operation. (This 'waste' is called **cotton linters** and is utilized by manufacturers of man-made cellulosic fibers, or by others who can use short fibers, sometimes for non-woven textiles.) The remaining long fibers form a fine web which, at the end of the combing operation, are fed through a cone, under a geared wheel, and emerge as a comb sliver. This superior quality sliver is used to produce the finest cotton yarn and also for blending with other fibers.

Inherent Characteristics

FIBER DESCRIPTION: Cotton is a fairly uniform fiber. 12-20 microns in width, 1/3-6.35 cm (½-2½″) in length. White to pale yellow in color. Low luster.

STRENGTH: 3-5 grams per denier. This is moderate to above average tenacity. When wet, cotton's strength increases by 10-20%. Good flex strength.

DIMENSIONAL STABILITY: Cotton fibers (unlike cotton fabrics) are relatively stable and do not stretch or shrink. Elongation is from 3-7% at the break point. Recovery is 75% or less at 2% elongation. Low elasticity and resilience.

DENSITY: High, 1.54-1.56 grams per cu. cm.

ABSORBENCY: High. At standard conditions, moisture regain is about 8.5%. At 100% humidity, cotton may absorb 25-27% moisture. **Mercerization** (see chap. 9) enlarges the fibers, and absorbency increases; moisture regain varies from 9-10.3%.

Chemical Reactivities

ALKALIS: highly resistant.

ACIDS: Low resistance. Strong acids destroy cotton; hot diluted acids cause disintegration; cold diluted acids cause gradual disintegration.

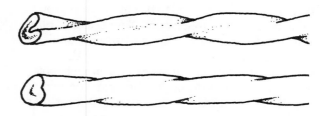

Cotton fiber, greatly enlarged, showing the natural fiber (top) and a mercerized fiber (bottom).

SOLVENTS: Highly resistant to most organic solvents, but no resistance to certain chemical solvents such as cuprammonium hydroxide and cupriethylene diamine.

Environmental Sensitivities

SUNLIGHT: Prolonged exposure causes degradation.

WATER: Not affected by wetting and drying.

MOISTURE: Will mildew, and eventually rot, if kept moist.

FIRE: Burns readily with a smell like burning paper. Leaves fluffy grey ash.

HEAT: Not affected by short exposure to heat up to 149°C (300°F). Long exposure above this temperature causes gradual decomposition. Temperatures above 246°C (475°F) cause rapid deterioration.

COLD: Not affected.

MICROORGANISMS: May be damaged or decayed by fungi, such as mildew and certain bacteria.

INSECTS: Resistant to moths and beetles; susceptible to destruction by silverfish.

AGING: If kept in a dry, dark, cool or temperate environment, will maintain strength and appearance.

Flax fiber form, a polygonal lumen

FLAX

Flax is the plant source of linen, and most flax for fiber (as opposed to flax for seed) is grown in eastern Europe, Ireland and New Zealand. Flax is a **bast fiber**, that is, derived from the stalk of the plant. Flax is pulled from the ground, rather than cut, as the usable fibers extend into the roots. After pulling and drying in the field, the plants are **rippled**—pulled through a special threshing machine to remove the immature seed pods, which are then used for linseed oil.

To obtain the fibers, the outer woody portion of the stalk must be rotted away. This process is called **retting** and can be accomplished by several means. Dew retting simply leaves the flax on the ground to gradually rot; pool or stream retting involves placing bundles of flax in either stagnant or slow moving water. These methods take up to six weeks. Tank retting uses warmed water which hastens the decay of the outer fibers. This takes a few days. Chemical retting involves adding chemicals to the warmed water in the tanks to speed up the process but must be carefully controlled to avoid damage to the fiber.

After retting, the rotted stalks are bundled and passed through fluted rollers to break up the outer woody portions of the stalks (called **breaking**), and then subjected to **scutching** which mechanically separates the usable fiber from the broken outer covering. **Hackling** is the next process, which can be compared to the carding and combing of cotton. This process draws the fibers over increasingly fine sets of pins, which rids the fibers of waste, cleans and straightens them, and finally draws out the fibers—which resemble human hair in gloss and fineness—into a sliver in preparation for yarn manufacture.

Inherent Characteristics

FIBER DESCRIPTION: 15-20 microns in width, 12.7-50.8 cm (5-20″) in length, fairly uniform. Light ivory to dark tan or grey in color. High luster.

STRENGTH: 5.5-6.5 gpd, but may vary from 2.6-7.7. Normally a moderate to very strong fiber. When wet, strength increases by about 20%. Poor resistance to flexing.

DIMENSIONAL STABILITY: Relatively stable. Elongation is from 2.7-3.3% before breaking. Only 65% recovery at 2% elongation. Elasticity and resilience are therefore low.

DENSITY: High, 1.5 grams per cu. cm.

ABSORBENCY: Moisture regain at standard conditions is 12%.

Chemical Reactivities

ALKALIS: Highly resistant.

ACIDS: Resistant to cold diluted acids, but concentrated or hot acid solutions cause deterioration.

SOLVENTS: Highly resistant.

Environmental Sensitivities

SUNLIGHT: Highly resistant to damage, although long exposure causes gradual loss of strength.

WATER: Not affected by wetting and drying.

MOISTURE: More resistant to mildew than cotton, but extreme humidity will allow mildew to grow which will damage the fibers.

FIRE: Burns with a smell like burning paper, leaves a fluffy grey ash.

HEAT: High resistant to heat. Temperatures of 149°C (300°F) may be withstood for long periods with little change in the fiber. Above this temperature long exposure will cause gradual discoloration. Short term exposure to heat up to 260°C (500°F) is not harmful.

COLD: Not affected.

MICROORGANISMS: Highly resistant to most bacteria. Fungi such as mildew will grow on very damp fibers.

INSECTS: Highly resistant.

AGING: Excellent keeping qualities if stored in dry, dark environment.

JUTE

Jute produces a bast fiber, commonly made into burlap, integrated into wall coverings or linoleum, or used as a backing fiber. The plants, grown widely in Brazil, India and Pakistan, grow to a height of 4.6-6.1 meters (15 to 20 feet). Extraction of the fibers is by the same basic method as used for flax, that is, retting, breaking and scutching. The fibers are among the most commonly used in the countries of origin, and in similar countries having a relatively low economic standard.

Inherent Characteristics
FIBER DESCRIPTION: Less uniform than flax, jute fibers are long and produced in a bundle held together by a gummy substance high in pectin. Yellow, brown or grey in color. Fibers may be short and somewhat stiff, or quite long and shiny. High luster.

STRENGTH: 3-5 gpd—strong, but very poor flexibility.

DIMENSIONAL STABILITY: Stable, with low elongation—less than 2% and poor elasticity. A natural roughness prevents slippage when the fibers are used for burlap, bagging, or for backing material.

DENSITY: High, 1.5 grams per cu. cm.

ABSORBENCY: High, 13.7% moisture regain.

Chemical Reactivities
ALKALIS: Highly resistant.

ACIDS: Low resistance.

SOLVENTS: Good resistance. The fibers are difficult to bleach, so are usually left natural or dyed in bright or dark colors.

Environmental Sensitivities
Roughly the same as for cotton and flax, with better resistance to microorganisms and insects.

RAMIE

Another bast fiber, extracted from the ramie plant common to the Orient, but also cultivated now in Egypt, France, Italy and the Soviet Union. Ramie was sometimes known as China Grass, but does not resemble grass. It is a perennial shrub that can be cut several times per season. Fibers are extracted by decorticating to remove the outer woody covering and are degummed in a caustic soda solution to remove the pectins and waxes, then rinsed in dilute acid to neutralize the caustic and bleach the fibers. Ramie textiles may be like fine linen or as coarse as canvas. Because of its stiffness and strength it is often blended with cotton or rayon fibers.

Inherent Characteristics
FIBER DESCRIPTION: Very fine and long, somewhat stiff. High luster.

STRENGTH: Very strong, 5.3-7.4 gpd. Poor flexibility.

DIMENSIONAL STABILITY: Low elastic recovery, poor elongation—3 to 7%.

DENSITY: High, 1.5 grams per cu. cm.

ABSORBENCY: Moisture regain is 6% at standard conditions; relatively low.

Chemical Reactivities
Generally the same as other natural cellulosic fibers, but higher resistance to cold concentrated mineral acids.

Environmental Sensitivities
Similar to cotton and flax, but with excep-

tional resistance to microorganisms, insects and rotting.

HEMP

A bast fiber from a tough, easily grown plant which is cultivated throughout the world. The plants are cut by hand and thereafter handled like flax to extract the fibers.

Inherent Characteristics

FIBER DESCRIPTION: Both coarse and fine fibers are produced, and length varies from 2.54 cm (1″) to several centimeters or inches. Fibers are dark tan or brown and difficult to bleach, but may be dyed dark or bright colors. Hemp fabrics are in limited use in interior design, but some are used in Italy. Low luster.

STRENGTH: Above average, 5.2 gpd.

DIMENSIONAL STABILITY: Low in elongation, poor elasticity.

DENSITY: 1.48 grams per cu. cm.

ABSORBENCY: 12% moisture regain; can absorb moisture up to 30% of its weight at 100% humidity.

Chemical Reactivities

ALKALIS: Hot concentrated alkalis will dissolve hemp; hot or cold dilute, or cold concentrates, will not cause damage.

ACIDS: Resistant to cool, weak acids, but generally mineral acids will reduce hemp's strength and eventually destroy the fibers.

SOLVENTS: Resistant, with careful handling.

Environmental Sensitivities

Generally the same as cotton.

The following cellulosic fibers are of some interest for environmental textiles, but production is regional and limited. Use in North American and European interior design is therefore not of importance.

AGAVE

The agave plant is grown in warm climates and its leaves are the source of **Sisal.** The fibers are obtained from the large evergreen leaves when they are about four years old, and must be separated from fleshy leaf parts. Naturally brown and stiff in character, the fibers do not bleach, but are sometimes dyed. Environmental use is for matting or carpeting.

ABACA

This plant is indigenous to the Philippines and is a member of the banana family. It is also grown as a decorative plant in other warm climates. Fibers are extracted from the leaf stalk and may be as long as 4.5 meters (15′). It has a natural luster and is off-white to dark grey or brown. Main use is for rope and cordage; some regional environmental use for table coverings, or place mats for indoor/outdoor use.

PINA

The fiber is extracted from pineapple leaves and is mainly produced in the Philippines. White or ivory in color, it is fine, lustrous, soft, flexible and strong. Often used for elaborately embroidered table covers, as well as 'peasant type' clothing.

COIR

Obtained from the fibrous mass between the outer shell and the husk of coconuts, coir is a stiff, strong, cinnamon brown fiber. It is impervious to abrasion and weather, and is not affected by water. Use is principally for outdoor carpets, floor mats and patio coverings.

KAPOK

This interesting fiber is obtained from the seed hairs of the Java kapok tree. Difficult to spin into yarn, the fiber is extremely light, soft and buoyant. Once used extensively for pillow filling and upholstery padding, its major use now is for life preservers where it will support up to 30 times the weight of the preserver without becoming waterlogged.

Protein Fibers

Animal life is the source of natural protein fibers. Most are from animal hair coverings, with the secretions from insects as another source.

They have many properties in common. All protein fibers are composed of amino acids formed into polypeptide chains with high molecular weight. All have excellent moisture absorbency and are warmer than comparable plant derivative fibers. All are relatively weak, and weaker still when wet. Despite inroads by man-made fibers, their outstanding qualities in specific areas ensure their continued popularity.

Wool fiber form
—overlapping scales on a central shaft

WOOL

Most wool for fiber use is obtained from sheep specially bred and raised in temperate climates for the quality of their fleece. The wool is sheared from the living animals and is called **fleece** or **clip wool**. Wool may also be pulled from the hides of sheep slaughtered for meat, and is then called **pulled wool**. Pulled wool is usually inferior in quality, due to the breed, the quality of its fleece not being of importance in sheep raised for food. Pulled wool may be successfully mixed with fleece. Preliminary grading of the wool is done at time of shearing (usually once a year) but it is shipped 'in the fleece'—a rolled bundle of the wool sheared from one sheep—to the initial wool processor.

Sorting is then done by an expert grader. Each fleece is opened and fibers pulled and sorted according to fineness, length and strength. The best fibers come from the sides and shoulders. Fine, long fibers are reserved for sheer wool fabrics and for worsteds. Medium fibers are used for woolens, and coarse fibers, whether long or short, are used for carpeting or rough fabrics. **Lamb's wool**, usually reserved for clothing yarns, is sheared from animals under eight months of age.

After sorting, wool is **scoured** or cleaned. The raw wool is given several washes in warm, soapy water and is well rinsed and dried. This scouring removes the natural grease (which is recovered, and eventually becomes purified lanolin for the cosmetics industry) and dirt or excrement that may have adhered to the fleece. The cleaned wool fibers are then **carded** by a similar method to that described for cotton, which removes burrs or twigs, and begins the straightening of the fibers. The carded fiber may be ready for spinning into woolen yarn at this stage, or, if worsted yarn is desired, the carded fibers are passed through a combing machine which further orients the fibers and delivers a pulled, thick, untwisted bundle of fibers called **top**.

Wool Products Labeling Acts, enacted in most western countries, require that wool products bear specific labels. **Wool, new wool,** or **virgin wool**, indicate that the wool has not been used. Virgin wool may only be used as a designation for wool made into yarns and fabrics for the first time.

Wool may indicate that unused wool yarn has been recovered and reconstructed into new yarns or fabrics. **Reprocessed wool** refers to products containing wool fibers reclaimed from unused scraps of fabrics, whether from cuttings or samples. The fabrics are **garnetted**, or shredded back into a fibrous state, and then used to make new yarns. **Reused wool** indicates that the wool fibers have been reclaimed from worn or used wool fabrics. Reused wool is sometimes called **shoddy**. The quality of reprocessed and reused wool is, of course, lower than that of new wool, due to the damage and breaking of the fibers during the garnetting process. However, wool fabrics or blankets of reprocessed or reused wool retain warmth, good durability and fair resilience, and may, in fact, give better service than similar products manufactured from new wool of poor quality.

Inherent Characteristics

FIBER DESCRIPTION: Depending on source (breed of sheep) wool fibers vary from fine (15 to 17 microns) to coarse (40 microns), with lengths ranging from 3.8-38 cm (1½-15″). Some wool fibers are exceptionally coarse (in the 70 micron width range) and stiff. The fibers have a natural three dimensional crimp or waviness, that is, the waves emanate from shaft to tip and also spiral. Most wool is naturally ivory colored; other fibers are grey, black, tan or brown. Low luster.

STRENGTH: 1.0 to 1.7 gpd, dry, 0.8 to 1.6, gpd, wet. This is very weak, but properties such as good resilience can compensate for this weakness when the fibers are manufactured into yarn.

DIMENSIONAL STABILITY: Elongation is about 25% dry, 35% wet, at standard conditions, with excellent elastic recovery—99% recovery at 2-5% elongation. Resiliency and elasticity therefore are exceptionally good. Flexibility is excellent; wool takes reshaping by heat, moisture and pressure and retains such a set.

While these characteristics refer to the fiber, the dimensional stability of wool yarns or fabrics is not good. Moisture or agitation may cause wool yarns to shrink. This may be due to the fibers matting (felting shrinkage) or by the action of moisture releasing the fibers' natural tension and subsequent drying, returning the fibers to an original length which may be tighter than that present when the yarn was spun. Because of wool's easy elongation, it is impossible to spin yarn without inadvertently elongating the fibers, and it is the subsequent elastic recovery after exposure to moisture that causes the shrinkage. Fabrics of wool are doubly stretched in the manufacturing processes, that is both in the yarn and weaving or knitting. Wool fabrics therefore are not considered dimensionally stable.

DENSITY: Low, 1.30 to 1.32 grams per cu. cm.

ABSORBENCY: High. At standard conditions, moisture regain is 13.6 to 16%. Wool will absorb about 30% of its weight in moisture. It has the ability to produce heat as it absorbs moisture, and absorbs heat as it evaporates moisture. This is called hygroscopic behavior. Although it absorbs moisture well, the surface structure tends to repel or shed liquid.

Chemical Reactivities
ALKALIS: Virtually no resistance. A 5% solution of sodium hydroxide will dissolve wool.

ACIDS: Fair resistance to mild or dilute acids. Concentrated mineral acids will decompose the fibers.

SOLVENTS: Resistant to cleaning solvents.

Environmental Sensitivities
SUNLIGHT: Prolonged exposure causes degradation and eventually destruction.

WATER, MOISTURE: See remarks under Dimensional Stability. Wool is not harmed by wetting, however. A 1969 issue of *Textiles Industries* contained an article about a cargo of raw wool which sank with the freighter *Oregon* in 160 feet of water off Nantucket Island. The 16,000 bales were submerged for 22 years, yet when the freighter was salvaged, the cargo was in good condition except for a small quantity which had been saturated with bunker oil! If wet woolen fabric is left to air dry, without wringing, agitation or hanging, it will maintain its former character.

FIRE: Will burn slowly in flame, smelling like burning hair, and will self-extinguish if the flame is removed. It leaves a brittle, bead-like residue.

HEAT: Wet heat causes the fibers to become weak and stiffen. Dry heat, above 132°C (270°F), causes yellowing and decomposition. Heats greater than 300°C (572°F) will cause it to char.

COLD: Not affected.

MICROORGANISMS: Good resistance to bacteria and fungi, although sustained moistrue will lead to mildew and eventual destruction.

INSECTS: As a protein, or modified food product, wool is attractive to many insects and beetles. (Various finishes are used to repel insects).

AGING: Properly protected and stored, age has no destructive effects whatsoever. Wool tapestries and clothing have survived for thousands of years.

SPECIALTY ANIMAL FIBERS
Available in limited quantities, these fibers are desirable for their specific characteristics.

Mohair
The source of this fiber is the Angora goat. The animals are sheared twice a year and produce a fine silky fiber. It is similar to wool in all respects, except for a more lustrous appearance, greater abrasion resistance, better resiliency and good adaptability to complex yarn spinning techniques. Upholstery, rugs and draperies may be of mohair or mohair blends.

Alpaca
A member of the camel family, native to the mountainous regions of South America. The animals are sheared only once every two years, and the fine fibers, when separated from the coarse guard hairs, are used in fabric production. Alpaca is similar to mohair in overall characteristics, with strong glossy fibers sometimes used for plush upholstery. The natural colors range from white to brown and black and are often used without dyeing.

Cashmere
This fiber is obtained from the Kashmir goat, which is combed to yield about 114 grams (4 ounces) of fiber in total, of which only a percentage is the characteristic, very soft, fine product. Yearly production is very small, and is usually limited to apparel production.

Camel's Hair
The Bactrian camel sheds about 2.2 kilograms (5 pounds) of fiber per year. The outer hairs

are used in industry, and for artists' brushes; and the fine, short underhairs are as soft and fine as top quality wool. Very limited environmental use, occasionally in blankets of coarse fibers.

Llama

Similar in characteristics to alpaca. Both are members of the camel family and native to South American mountains. Llamas are sheared once a year. The fibers are weaker than those from alpaca, and most are used by South American Indian weavers. Some fiber is exported and blended with wool, other specialty fibers, or man-made fibers. Limited use.

Vicuna

This is the rarest hair fiber, which is taken from the small, camel-related animal found only in the high reaches of the Andes Mountains. The dog-sized beasts are extremely wild and fiber is only obtained by killing the animal. Attempts at domestication have not been successful, and Peru wisely limits the yearly kill. Each animal yields about 114 g. (4 ozs.) of fine fiber and 284-340 g (10-12 ozs) of shorter, less fine fiber. The fiber is one of the softest known to man and is strong and lustrous. Its limited yield makes it impractical for environmental use, and a coat of vicuna cloth is as costly as a fine fur.

SPECIALTY FUR FIBERS

Angora

The Angora rabbit is raised for its white, fluffy, silky fur. The fur is combed and clipped every three months and provides a fair supply of fine, lustrous and resilient fibers. Principally used in knitting yarns and knitted fabrics, or blended with other fibers to obtain a specific appearance.

Angora and fur fibers derived from any other fur bearing animals are occasionally used for blending with wool, primarily to add softness, color interest, or prestige value.

SILK

Silk is the liquid secretion of the larvae of several moths, hardened on contact with the air, and produced for protection of the chrysalis until it hatches into a moth. This wonder of nature was discovered by the Chinese, reportedly around 2700 B.C., and kept as a carefully guarded monopoly for nearly 3000 years. Today, **sericulture**, the growth and production of moths for their silk, is an industry practiced in many countries and requires skill and considerable labor.

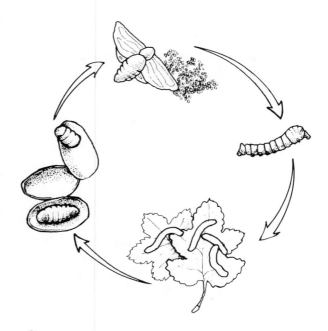

Circle of life of the silk producing **Bombyx Mori** *moth, showing the adult female, eggs, larva, mulberry leaves, cocoon of silk threads and emerging moth.*

Silk is produced by several moth species, but the *Bombyx mori* is the only one commercially raised. Silk 'factories' are really immaculate 'farms' where the insects are raised from egg to moth and fed exclusively on fresh young leaves of the mulberry tree. The female lays up to 700 eggs per month. Naturally, hatch occurs in from 3-7 days, but eggs may be kept in cold storage without damage. There must be a supply of mulberry leaves for the tiny emerging worms to eat. The larva eats and grows for 35 days, increasing 10,000 times in weight, and molting 4 times to an eventual size of roughly 1.3 x 7.6 cm (½ x 3″). At this point, the larva begins to spin its cocoon, extruding silk liquid through two tiny orifices in its head (the spinnerettes). The head moves in a figure eight motion constructing the cocoon from the outside in as the larva decreases in size and finally rests as a dormant chrysalis. Unless the soon-to-be-moth is to be used for breeding, the cocoon in the silk factory is subjected to heat, which kills the chrysalis without harming the silk. Each cocoon is composed of two triangular shaped filaments called **brins**, which lie with two flat sides together. The cocoons are next shipped to a **filature**, to be reeled. There, they are placed in hot water to soften the gummy substance called sericin which surrounds the fiber. The cocoons are then brushed lightly to find the ends of the filaments which are threaded through a guide and wound onto a reel. The reeling is a delicate operation, and uniform reeled silk is the result of experienced workers able to recognize subtle differences in the filaments and to guide the reeling of multiple fiber strands.

Inherent Characteristics

FIBER DESCRIPTION: The smooth filaments are very long and fine; width is from 9-11 microns, length is from 915-2750 meters (1000-3000 yards). Off-white to cream in color, with a high luster.

STRENGTH: Very strong. 2.4-5.1 gpd dry; wet strength is less—80-85% of dry strength.

DIMENSIONAL STABILITY: Good. Elongation varies from 10-25% at standard conditions, 33-35% when wet. Elastic recovery is 92% at 2% elongation. Medium resiliency and good elasticity.

DENSITY: Medium, 1.25-1.35 grams per cubic centimeter.

ABSORBENCY: Moisture regain at standard conditions is 11%. At saturation (100% humidity) regain is 25-35%.

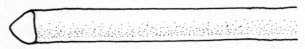

Silk fiber form showing the triangular shape of the silkworm's natural spinnerette.

Chemical Reactivities

ALKALIS: Very low resistance. Heated caustic soda will dissolve silk, although not as quickly as wool. Weak alkalis such as soap, borax and ammonia are not too harmful unless contact is maintained for a long time.

ACIDS: Resistant to organic acids. Little to no resistance to mineral acids which are absorbed rapidly, tend to be held by the molecular arrangement of the fiber, and are difficult to remove.

SOLVENTS: Highly resistant.

Environmental Sensitivities

SUNLIGHT: Low resistance, exposure causes fiber degradation and destruction.

WATER: Not harmed by wetting. Silk tends to absorb and retain salts found in some water however, which may then attack and degrade the fibers. Fabrics of silk may be washed in warm water with mild soap or detergent but there must be minimal handling, thorough rinsing, and air drying out of the sun.

MOISTURE: Highly resistant to damage from mildew, but rot-producing conditions such as soil and moisture will cause it to decompose.

FIRE: Burns in flame, with a smell like burning hair, self-extinguishes when the flame is removed. Leaves a brittle ash.

HEAT: Unaffected by long periods at 135°C (275°F). At 177°C (350°F) scorching and rapid decomposition occurs.

COLD: Unaffected.

MICROORGANISMS: Resistant to mildew, medium resistance to other bacteria and fungi.

INSECTS: Highly resistant to moths, but may be eaten by carpet beetles.

AGING: Oxygen causes gradual loss of strength and decomposition. Silk should be stored in a carefully sealed environment, otherwise it will eventually be destroyed.

WILD SILK

This fiber is collected in the wild in the cocoons of other moth species. The *Antheraea myllita* and *A. pernyi* feed on oak leaves in China and India and produce **tussah silk**, which is tan or light brown, less even than *Bombyx mori* silk, and cannot be bleached. Other moths in warm climates yield silk fiber but the limited quantities are not of significance.

Mineral and Natural Rubber

ASBESTOS

This type of serpentine rock is the only natural mineral found in fiber form. It has been known since Greek and Roman times, and was the basis of many legends. Its total resistance to fire was the outstanding property. While several rock varieties yield the silky fibers, *Chrysotile* is the source of about 95% of textile fibers and this rock is mined in Canada (Quebec and

Ontario), South Africa, the United States (Arizona and California), and lesser quantities in Italy, Turkey, South America and the Soviet Union.

Whether open-pit or underground mined, the fibrous rock is crushed and screened to separate it from surrounding rock layers. The fibers extracted in the crushing/screening process are then cleaned, and graded by length. High capital and labor costs make it a relatively expensive fiber. The cleaned fibers are frequently blended with 5-20% of cotton or rayon, and are then carded for yarn production in much the same way as cotton or wool.

Inherent Characteristics
FIBER DESCRIPTION: A fine, lustrous fiber, which may be quite soft or rather stiff. Staple length is dependent on mining process. White, amber, grey or green.

STRENGTH: Tenacity is high 2.5-3.1 gpd. Excellent flexibility.

DIMENSIONAL STABILITY: Exceptional, no elongation.

DENSITY: Very high, 2.10-2.80 gpcc.

ABSORBENCY: Very low, moisture regain is 1.0% at standard conditions.

Chemical Reactivities
ALKALIS, ACIDS, SOLVENTS: Generally high resistance.

Environmental Sensitivities
SUNLIGHT: Resistant.

WATER, MOISTURE: No effect.

FIRE, HEAT: Resistant. The fiber will fuse with prolonged exposure at 1520°C (2770°F) but brief exposures to temperatures as high as 3315°C (6000°F) without fiber destruction have been noted.

COLD: No effect.

MICROORGANISMS, INSECTS, AGING: No effect.

NATURAL RUBBER

Elastomeric fibers were first produced from natural rubber, the gummy sap of the rubber tree. While the highly elastic property was recognized at an early stage, it was in 1839 that Charles Goodyear found that the addition of sulphur to heated rubber liquid added greatly to the strength and elasticity and also prevented the rubber from becoming brittle in cold—a serious defect pre-

viously. The process was called **vulcanizing**, and vulcanized rubber found its first heavy commercial use for automobile tires when that industry boomed in the early 20th century. In 1920, research by the U.S. Rubber Company found that the liquid could be extruded in filament form, resulting in the first rubber fibers. Rubber filaments were used as yarn core, and were wrapped in another fiber, usually cotton. Today, rayon or nylon are also used as an outerwrap.

Synthetic elastomeric fibers have largely replaced natural rubber because the synthetics have been engineered to overcome some of natural rubber's serious drawbacks.

Inherent Characteristics
FIBER DESCRIPTION: A natural light brown fiber extruded in various diameters from a solution of natural rubber and particular chemicals (classified information). No luster.

STRENGTH: High, dependent to a large degree on form or size. Excellent flexibility, resistant to cutting and tearing.

DIMENSIONAL STABILITY: Extreme elongation— may be up to 800%, and excellent elastic recovery.

DENSITY: Medium, about 1.0 gpcc.

ABSORBENCY: None, impermeable to water.

Chemical Reactivities
ALKALIS, ACIDS, SOLVENTS: Resistance to many chemicals is good, but body oils and petroleum solvents cause damage.

Environmental Sensitivities
SUNLIGHT: No resistance, exposure causes deterioration.

WATER, MOISTURE: Impermeable, not harmed by water or moisture.

FIRE: Melts, and then burns rapidly, with a pungent odor; leaves a gummy black residue.

HEAT: Very low resistance. Temperatures of 93°C (200°F) and over cause deterioration and loss of flexibility.

COLD: Natural rubber by itself becomes brittle in cold. The addition of chemicals and the vulcanizing process used now to produce rubber fibers makes the product resistant to cold temperatures.

MICROORGANISMS, INSECTS: No effect.

AGING: Low resistance, strength and elasticity are gradually lost.

5 MAN-MADE FIBERS

Cellulosic Fibers

The possibility of producing a silk-like filament was first mentioned in 1664 by Robert Hooke of England, but it was not until 1855 that a solution of mulberry leaves and nitric acid was used as a basis for such an experiment. The fiber was obtained by inserting a needle into the mixture and slowly drawing it out. The material drawn out by the needle formed a strand which hardened in the air. It appears that in 1862 a Frenchman named Ozanam copied the moth larva's liquid extrusion system and thereby 'invented' the first spinnerette. This device is the basis for all manufactured fibers. In 1883, J. W. Swan, an English weaver, used a solution of cellulose nitrate in glacial acetic acid to produce fibers, which he exhibited in London in 1884. These fibers, incidentally, were used as the filaments for the first electric light bulbs.

RAYON

Credit for the invention of rayon is usually given to Count Hilaire Chardonnet. He used a cellulose nitrate solution dissolved in alcohol. This solution was forced through the spinnerette, the fibers stretched to introduce strength and were then denitrated to reduce flammability. By 1889, he was able to exhibit fabrics made of this new fiber, and in 1895 his French company enjoyed a limited commercial success.

The first American rayon plant, the American Viscose Company (so named because of the thick viscose solution used to produce the fiber) was opened in 1910, and is still a major force in rayon production as part of the FMC Corporation. Many companies entered the field, and in 1926 American Bemberg introduced the cuprammonium process. Rayon was first used for tire cord in 1937, and is still in wide use for this purpose. Developments since include high-strength rayon, carpet rayon, high-wet-modulus rayon and a flame-retardant version. Rayon is an important environmental textile.

The basic ingredients of rayon today are wood pulp and cotton linters (fibers that are too short for production into cotton yarn). Modern rayon is produced by wet spinning, following one of several exacting and complex methods which transform the raw materials first into sheets of solid pure cellulose, next into a shredded form and, finally, through many processes and aging, into the solution which is pumped through the spinnerette. One of the processes is illustrated.

Improvements on the original viscose process for manufacturing rayon fibers have been made over the years, in general to improve the strength, build in a different 'hand' (or feel), improve on wrinkle resistance, or modify the dimensional stability. These changes are accomplished by the addition or deletion of certain chemicals and/or modifications to the processing steps. The specific chemistry is complex and is unnecessary for the designer's identification and appreciation of rayon fibers. The bibliography, however, contains information on reference texts which contain explicit detail should the reader wish to further explore the field.

Rayon Production *This representation shows the raw material (1), usually wood pulp or cotton linters, which is shredded (2), mixed in a solution (3), filtered (4), aged (5) and finally wet spun into a coagulating bath (6). The formed fibers are drawn (7) and wound on reels (8).*

Rayon is defined by the Textile Fiber Products Identification Act (TFPIA) as

> "a manufactured fiber composed of regenerated cellulose, as well as manufactured fibers composed of regenerated cellulose in which substituents have replaced not more than 15% of the hydrogens of the hydroxyl groups."

This definition of the generic fiber encompasses regular and high-tenacity viscose rayon (BeauGrip, Coloray, Encel, Englo, Fibro, Jetspun, Kolorban, Sayfr), high-wet-modulus rayon (Avril, Nupron, Vincal, Xena, Zantrel 200), Cuprammonium rayon (Bemberg, Cupioni), and Saponified cellulose rayon (Fortisan).

Inherent Characteristics

FIBER DESCRIPTION: Rayon fibers can be produced in any length, and, depending on the shape of the holes in the spinnerette, in a variety of sizes and shapes. Fibers may be less than 12 microns to more than 100. Unless colored pigment has been added at the solution stage, the fibers appear nearly transparent. If a delustering agent has been added the fibers are white.

STRENGTH: Tenacity of rayon varies, relatively low (1.5-2.4 gpd) for regular viscose rayon, medium to high (2.4-5.0 gpd) for medium to high-tenacity rayon, high (3.4-5.5 gpd) for high-wet-modulus rayon, very high (6.0-7.0 gpd) for Saponified cellulose rayon. The tenacity of Cuprammonium rayon is low (1.7-2.3 gpd). All rayons are much weaker when wet, but the high-wet-modulus rayon and Saponified cellulose rayon exceed cotton in both dry and wet strength. Good flexibility.

DIMENSIONAL STABILITY: While the regular viscose rayons are not stable, 15-30% elongation with 82% elastic recovery at 2% (with much less elastic recovery at greater elongation), the stronger rayon fibers have approximately 6-30% elongation and elastic recovery of 95-100% at 2% elongation. Like wool, regular rayon stretches easily in yarn and fabric construction and so are subject to relaxation shrinkage after the first wetting. Finishes (chap. 9) are used on most rayon fabrics to control dimensional stability. Low resiliency.

DENSITY: Medium — 1.50-1.52 gpcc.

ABSORBENCY: High. Moisture regain varies from 10.7-16% at standard conditions, with absorption of 20-27% of weight.

Chemical Reactivities

ALKALIS: Resistant to weak alkalis, strong solutions cause loss of strength.

ACIDS: Resistant to cold dilute acids, hot or cold concentrates cause disintegration, and hot dilute acids cause deterioration of the fibers.

SOLVENTS: Good resistance.

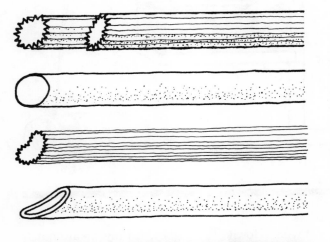

Four forms of rayon filaments (from top): the lengthwise striations and serrated cross-section of viscose rayon; a uniform circular form of cuprammonium rayon; lima bean shape with lengthwise striations; and a collapsed tube form with hollow center.

Environmental Sensitivities

SUNLIGHT: Low resistance, exposure causes gradual deterioration.

WATER: Low resistance, fibers swell in water and lose strength while wet.

MOISTURE: Subject to damage from mildew in conditions of dampness.

FIRE: Like other cellulose fibers, rayon burns readily, leaving a fluffy ash.

HEAT: Resistant to temperatures up to 177°C (350°F), but long exposure to higher temperatures results in degradation.

COLD: Not affected.

MICROORGANISMS: Subject to damage from fungi-forming mildew, especially if the fibers are soiled and damp. Fibers may also be damaged by rot-producing bacteria.

INSECTS: Resistant to all insects except silverfish, which destroy unprotected fibers.

AGING: Good resistance.

Modified Cellulosic Fibers

The first successful cellulose acetate, an ester of cellulose and acetic acid, was developed in 1904 by Henri and Camille Dreyfus in England. Their early product was used for lacquers, films and 'dope' to be used on early airplanes' fabric wings. In 1913, they made the solution into filaments, but it was not until 1921 that production of acetate fibers began in England and, subsequently, in 1924, in the United States.

ACETATE AND TRIACETATE

Acetate and triacetate were at first considered variations of rayon, but this confusion was cleared up in 1951 and a specific definition was written by the TFPIA, namely:

> "a manufactured fiber in which the fiber forming substance is cellulose acetate. Where not less than 92% of the hydroxyl groups are acetylated, the term triacetate may be used as a generic description of the fiber."

Acetate is composed of cellulose, acetic acid, and acetic anhydride, with sulphuric acid as a catalyst. The fibers are formed by the dry spinning method. Triacetate has the same composition; changes to the process result in a fiber with greater stability to aging and resistance to sunlight.

Inherent Characteristics

FIBER DESCRIPTION: As with other man-made fibers, shape and size may be controlled in the manufacturing process. The fiber may be smooth and bright or dull and pitted, depending on chemical solution.

STRENGTH: Low, tenacity is 1.1-1.7 gpd dry, and 0.8-1.0 gpd wet.

DIMENSIONAL STABILITY: Comparatively stable. Elongation is from 23-45%, with 90-94% elastic recovery at 2% stretch. If stretched more than 1%, some permanent deformation takes place. Acetate has poor resiliency; triacetate has good resiliency.

DENSITY: 1.31 gpcc.

ABSORBENCY: Low; moisture regain ranges from 3.2-6.5%. Absorption is 9-14%. Heat-treated triacetate has a moisture regain of 2.5-3.0%.

Chemical Reactivities

ALKALIS: Good resistance to dilute alkalis, concentrated alkalis cause a gradual loss of fiber weight and a stiffening of the fibers.

ACIDS: Poor resistance. Concentrates cause disintegration. Hot dilute acids cause loss of strength or decomposition. With long exposure, cold dilute acids weaken the fibers.

SOLVENTS: Good resistance to dry cleaning solvents, but acetone, phenol or chloroform destroy the fibers.

Environmental Sensitivities

SUNLIGHT: Acetate loses strength and may disintegrate with prolonged exposure. Triacetate has greater resistance to sun—better than silk or rayon.

WATER: Loss of strength when wet.

MOISTURE: Discoloration from mildew.

FIRE: Melts and burns, with a chemical smell. Leaves a hard, black bead ash. May be treated for flame retardance.

HEAT: Acetate is softened by temperatures above 177°C (350°F). Triacetate may be heat treated to withstand temperatures to 232°C (450°F) without damage.

COLD: Not affected.

MICROORGANISMS: Fungi such as mildew will grow on damp fibers and will discolor them. Acetate may be weakened but triacetate retains its strength.

INSECTS: Good resistance.

AGING: Acetate weakens with age; triacetate has excellent resistance to damage from aging.

Synthesized Fibers

Synthesized fibers are truly invented. Manufacturers turned from imitating the silkworm or using known fiber producing elements, like cellulose, to creating fibers through chemistry and their own basic knowledge.

The DuPont organization must be given full credit for initiating and funding, almost without restriction, the development of this entirely new field. The investigative research started in 1928 when Wallace Carothers, a brilliant young organic chemist, was selected by DuPont to head a team to study possible uses for the gummy waste by-products of various existing manufacturing operations. No particular end use was designated, and the basic research team was given *carte blanche* to see what could be developed.

From this study came, among other things, the ability to manufacture controlled linear polymers (macromolecules composed of molecular units linked end-to-end). One of these substances was found, in 1930, to have the ability to form a filament. This was discovered by dipping a glass rod into one of the solutions and drawing out material which did not simply slide off the rod and fall back into the solution but immediately hardened into a solid strand. This strand could be stretched, and the resultant fine thread was attractive, strong and flexible. The next few years were then devoted to improving the polymer solution, finding methods of forming the threads economically, and developing the necessary machinery to produce the fiber in quantity. Concurrently, testing of the fiber itself progressed, and the team soon found it had developed quite a fantastic new filament.

In 1939, DuPont invested in a large-scale plant in Seaford, Delaware, and **nylon** was introduced in a well planned and coordinated advertising and marketing promotion. Nylon stockings were introduced in 1940 and received immediate widespread acceptance. After World War II, development of synthesized fibers was accelerated and is still a vital research field. The following will introduce the generic fibers within this broad category. **Types** of generic fibers may be further identified by numbers or letters (such as nylon 6.6) and these signify a particular chemical formula used by producers to differentiate between the various polymer solutions. The chemistry and production processes of these fibers is available to those interested (see bibliography) but they are not necessary information for the designer.

NYLON

Nylon is classified as a polyamide fiber. It is manufactured in a number of types, and under hundreds of trade names. Early advertising proclaimed that nylon was made of coal, water and air. This simplification certainly caught the public's fancy, and was, of course, accurate—to a degree. The 'coal' used in nylon is the phenol derived from benzene which in turn is a product of the distillation of coal tar, or petroleum. 'Water' and 'air' indicate the elements of carbon, hydrogen, oxygen and nitrogen. Even this breakdown is a simplification, and the actual chemical process to produce nylon is complex and exacting.

A few of the hundreds of trade names for nylon are Anton, Astroturf, Ayrlyn, Blue "C",

Production of Synthesized Polymer Fiber

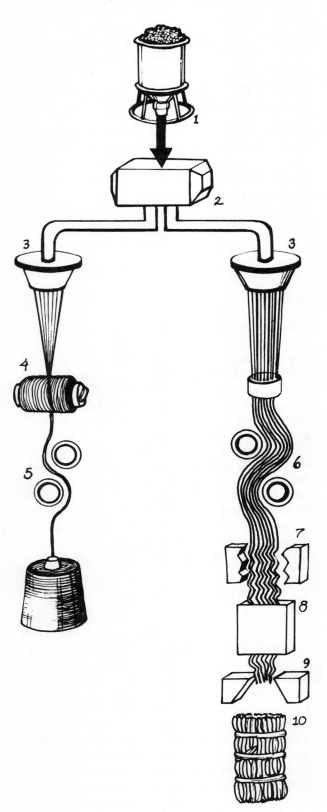

Nylon, polyester and other synthesized fibers are produced on a fast, continuous, controlled basis. Polymerization (1) is the automated combination of specific chemicals and catalysts which are blended and heated to produce the liquid polymer. The liquid is then heated (2) to remove moisture and reduce the liquid to the proper spinning viscosity. The solution is then spun (3) in a variety of ways. For filament yarns (at left) the multifilaments are gathered (4), drawn (5), and wound. For staple fiber (at right) the spun filaments are drawn (6), crimped (7), heat set (8) cut (9) and baled (10).

Cadon, Cantrece, Caprolan, Cedilla, Celanese, Cordura, Cumuloft, Enka, Enkalure, Grilon, Perlon, Phillips 66 and Stryton.

While noting the following properties of nylon, it should be remembered that the manufacturing process, as well as slight variations in the polymer solution, cause significant differences in the fibers produced. However, these are differences <u>in degree</u> and do not change the basic overall properties of the fiber.

Inherent Characteristics

FIBER DESCRIPTION: Manufactured by the melt spinning method. Size is variable (controlled) and the cross-section may be round, irregular, triangular, or some other multilobal shape. Fibers may be produced shiny or dull.

STRENGTH: Exceptional tenacity, from 3.5-9 gpd depending on manufacture. Wet nylon loses 10-20% of its strength.

DIMENSIONAL STABILITY: Excellent. The fiber is highly elastic, ranging from 16-50%, depending on filament size and type, with 100% elastic recovery, although this complete recovery may take several minutes. Warmth and/or moisture improve recovery. Good resiliency.

DENSITY: Low, 1.14 gpcc.

ABSORBENCY: Low; moisture regain is from 3.5-5% at standard conditions, or about 8% at 95% relative humidity.

Chemical Reactivities

ALKALIS: Resistant.

ACIDS: Not resistant to mineral acids, which, even at very weak dilutions, cause damage or destruction of the fibers. Acid fumes may also weaken or eventually destroy nylon.

SOLVENTS: Excellent resistance to most organic

solvents; the exception is phenol, which is found in some disinfectants.

Environmental Sensitivities
SUNLIGHT: Low resistance. Extended exposure causes loss of strength and eventual decomposition. Various finishes can add sun resistance to nylon.

WATER: No effect.

MOISTURE: No effect.

FIRE: Melts, but will not ignite unless temperatures exceed 530°C (980°F); forms a gummy grey or tan residue that hardens when cooling.

HEAT: Nylon is a **thermoplastic** or heat sensitive fiber. Temperatures up to 149°C (300°F) can be withstood for long periods of time, but exceeding this temperature for even a few hours causes discoloration. At 177-205°C (350-400°F) the fiber softens, and will melt at 210-250°C (410-480°F).

COLD: Not affected.

MICROORGANISMS: Not affected by fungi or bacteria.

INSECTS: Highly resistant, although some outdoor insects will eat the fiber if trapped within a fabric.

AGING: No effect.

ARAMID

Aramids are produced by the dry spinning method and are polyamids made of aromatic compounds. Their main overall feature is a magnification of nylon's strength and exceptional heat resistance. The generic term was defined in 1974. Trade names are Nomex and Kevlar.

Aramid fibers have wide industrial use, such as tire cord, aircraft components, parachutes, firefighters' clothing, spacesuits, and as bulletproof armor. (Kevlar will rebound a .38 caliber bullet fired from ten feet away.) Environmental use may develop where safety from fire and/or armed attack is deemed necessary.

Inherent Characteristics
FIBER DESCRIPTION: Fibers are either round or dogbone shaped in cross-section. Size is dependent on manufacturer. Fibers are difficult to dye, but some accept a limited range of medium to dark shades. Solution dyeing (adding color to the polymer solution before spinning) is done in some instances.

STRENGTH: Tenacity may be 4-5.3 gpd, or up to 13-18 gpd. This latter figure is three times stronger than nylon and is in fact stronger than steel of comparable size.

DIMENSIONAL STABILITY: Excellent, elongation is 10-31%.

DENSITY: 1.38-1.44 gpcc.

ABSORBENCY: Very low, moisture regain is 3.5%.

Chemical Reactivities
ALKALIS, ACIDS, SOLVENTS: Resistant.

Environmental Sensitivities
SUNLIGHT: No effect.

WATER, MOISTURE: No effect.

FIRE: Resistant.

HEAT: Resistant. Does not melt; begins to degrade at 370°C (700°F).

COLD: No effect.

MICROORGANISMS, INSECTS, AGING: No effect.

POLYESTER

One of the most successful man-made fibers, polyester accounts for a huge proportion of fibers in use today. While the possibility of polyester fibers was part of the initial DuPont research, the first commercially acceptable fibers were developed in England in 1941. Under the name Terylene, polyester was reintroduced in England after the war. Licensing arrangements with the original inventors brought polyester manufacture to DuPont in the United States in 1951, and many firms now produce polyester fibers. The outstanding property was ease of maintenance and excellent crease resistance. Early promotion of polyester fabric featured a man's suit which was worn for 67 consecutive days without pressing, during which time it was submerged in a swimming pool twice and washed frequently in an automatic washer. It was still presentable, and, at the time, that was a fantastic innovation!

As with all synthesized fibers, polyester is produced from a blend of chemicals, in this case a reaction between dihydric alcohol and dicarboxylic acid. Formulations and methods differ slightly and, as noted previously, are complex and exact. There are currently hundreds of types of polyester, each with slight but significant differences (in degree) in particular characteristics.

Some of the many trade names are Avlin, Crimplene, Dacron, Encron, Fortrel, Guaranteeth, Kodel, Monsanto, Quintess, Spectran, Tergal, Texture, Trevira, Vycron and Zefran, also Fiberfill for pillows and furnishings.

Inherent Characteristics

FIBER DESCRIPTION: Formed by the melt spinning process, the fibers are smooth and uniform, and may be round or variously shaped, depending on manufacture. Fibers are partially transparent, white or off-white, and may be made bright, dull, or with a speckled appearance.

STRENGTH: Variable, dependent on manufacturer. The range is from 2.5 gpd to 9.5 gpd with no loss of strength when wet.

DIMENSIONAL STABILITY: Excellent. Elongation ranges from a low of 8% to high of 67%, but with 75-100% elastic recovery in all cases. This great variability is dependent on type, with the stronger fibers having less elongation and better recovery. Resilience is exceptional, and heat-setting of the finished goods prevents virtually all stretching, sagging and wrinkling.

DENSITY: Generally 1.38 gpcc.

ABSORBENCY: Very low; moisture regain is only 0.4-0.8% at standard conditions, only 0.6-0.8 at 100% relative humidity. A serious drawback of polyester is its **oleophilic quality**—oily materials are easily absorbed and then held tenaciously.

Chemical Reactivities

ALKALIS: Good resistance to weak alkalis, either cool or hot; moderate resistance to strong alkalis at room temperature; hot strong alkalis degrade the fibers.

ACIDS: Excellent resistance to cold or hot acids, but prolonged exposure to boiling acids will destroy or disintegrate the fiber.

SOLVENTS: Resistant to organic solvents, and those used in cleaning and stain removal. Certain phenol mixtures will dissolve the fibers, but these are not normally encountered. Resistant to oxidizing agents and bleaches.

Environmental Sensitivities

SUNLIGHT: Excellent resistance to sun behind glass, but prolonged exposure to direct sunlight will weaken the fiber.

WATER: No effect.

MOISTURE: Exceptionally low absorbency ensures that moisture has little effect. The fibers have a high degree of wickability, so that polyester fabrics may pass moisture from the exterior to the interior or vice versa. This characteristic is generally only of concern in apparel applications.

FIRE: Burns slowly, with a dark smoke and aromatic odor. Fibers of light fabrics first melt and drip away from a single flame. Some fire-retardant finishes are used; this would be clearly labelled.

HEAT: Resistant to prolonged heat up to 120°C (250°F). At 150°C (300°F), the fibers lose 20-30% of their strength. Melting occurs at about 238°C (460°F), forming a hard, golden brown bead. Polyester fabrics may set wrinkles or creases at high temperatures.

MICROORGANISMS: No effect.

INSECTS: Resistant, but trapped insects will cut their way to freedom.

AGING: No effect.

ACRYLIC

The first acrylic fibers evolved out of the early DuPont research, and the first acrylic fabric, Orlon, was introduced in 1950. The fiber was touted as a replacement of either wool, which it could, in staple form, be made to resemble, or silk, which it closely resembled in filament form. Its most significant feature is a warm 'hand', particularly when mechanically 'bulked' and cut into staple length. Early use was largely as a replacement for wool, either in knitted or woven fabrics, where it combined the softness and bulk of wool without the problems of felting and shrinkage. Its use has since greatly expanded to include furnishing fabrics, blankets, carpeting, special flooring, such as tennis courts, and it is often used in blended fabrics.

Some trade names are Acrilan, Creslan, Courtelle, Dralon, Orlon, and Zefran.

Inherent Characteristics
FIBER DESCRIPTION: Produced by either a wet

or dry spinning method, the fiber is the synthetic polymerization of 85% or more of acrylonitrile (vinyl cyanide). Various manufacturers add up to 15% of other chemicals to produce specific qualities. These other ingredients are classified information. Fibers may be round, dumbbell or bean shaped, of various thicknesses, with a somewhat grainy appearance. Lustrous to dull, depending on manufacture. Color is from white to cream, and some are producer-dyed. Acrylics are generally crimped and marketed in staple form.

STRENGTH: Tenacity ranges from 2.0-4.2 gpd, with a very slight loss of strength when wet. Exceptional resilience.

DIMENSIONAL STABILITY: Elongation varies from 20-55%, with elastic recovery at 2% in the 97-99% range. Elongation when wet is slightly higher. With increasing elongation, recovery decreases. Acrylic fabrics need pretreatment and appropriate care to avoid shrinking and/or stretching.

DENSITY: 1.16 gpcc.

ABSORBENCY: Low, 1.0-2.5% moisture regain at standard conditions; only 1-2% greater at saturation level.

Chemical Reactivities

ALKALIS: Good resistance to weak alkalis; concentrates cause fiber degradation.

ACIDS: Good resistance to most mineral and organic acids, but concentrates may cause loss of strength. One cold concentrate, nitric acid, dissolves the fiber.

SOLVENTS: Excellent resistance.

Environmental Sensitivities

SUNLIGHT: Excellent resistance.

WATER: No effect.

MOISTURE: No effect normally, but extreme heat and moisture may cause shrinkage.

FIRE: Burns with a yellow flame, forming a gummy residue that retains sufficient heat to ignite other combustible products; cools to a hard, black, irregular bead.

HEAT: No effect to 150°C (300°F). Higher temperatures cause discoloration, degradation, disintegration, and melting at around 232°C (450°F).

MICROORGANISMS, INSECTS: No effect.

AGING: No effect.

Some typical synthetic filament forms

Circular, uniform

Circular, lengthwise serrations

Lima bean, smooth

Lima bean, serrated

Triangular, rounded edges

Trilobal

Lobular, lengthwise striations

Mushroom

Dog-bone

Ribbon-shaped

Flat, broad

Collapsed tube, hollow center

MODACRYLIC

Modacrylics were introduced in 1956, when Dynel was brought out by Union Carbide. They are similar to acrylics but withstand higher temperatures and do not burn. This resistance to fire is the outstanding property and makes the fiber desirable for draperies, casements, blankets and industrial fabrics, as well as such apparel uses as children's sleepwear, and specialty uses such as 'fake fur', wigs, and molded fabrics as for speaker grilles. Dynel, Verel and SEF are trade names.

Inherent Characteristics

FIBER DESCRIPTION: Produced by the wet spinning method, the fibers are translucent, cream or white, and generally crimped and used in staple form. Shape is usually somewhat flat and irregular. May be bright or dull.

STRENGTH: Moderate, approximately 2.3-3.1 gpd. Very good resilience.

DIMENSIONAL STABILITY: Elongation varies between 30-48%. Good to excellent elastic recovery. No change when wet.

DENSITY: 1.35-1.37 gpcc.

ABSORBENCY: Low, 2.5-4% moisture regain at standard conditions.

Chemical Reactivities

ALKALIS: Excellent resistance.

ACIDS: Excellent resistance.

SOLVENTS: Good resistance, except to acetone and formic acid.

Environmental Sensitivities

SUNLIGHT: Excellent resistance, except for Dynel, which discolors after prolonged exposure.

WATER: No effect.

MOISTURE: No effect.

FIRE: Will not support combustion. If ignited under most extreme conditions, will self-extinguish on removal of the fire source. No dripping occurs, as with acrylics; only a hard black char is left.

HEAT: The fibers are heat sensitive, softening and shrinking at temperatures above 150°C (300°F).

MICROORGANISMS, INSECTS: Resistant.

AGING: No effect.

OLEFIN

Olefin fibers are made from 85% or more of ethylene or propane gas. High pressure and catalysts induce polymerization, and the fibers are produced by the melt spin process, or, alternately, by producing a film or sheet of material which is then cut into narrow strips and twisted to form a yarn similar to a filament fiber. This alternate method is less expensive than melt spinning. In either case, olefin fibers are relatively low in cost, and have characteristics that are desirable for use in upholstery fabrics, and particularly in carpeting, carpet tiles, and carpet backing. The fibers are also often heat formed into various molded applications; one unusual application is the creation of flexible, resilient surfacing for use as artificial ski slopes.

There are numerous trade names, some of which are Chevron, DLP, Fibretex, Fibrilon, Herculon, Loktuft, Marvess, Montrel, Patlon, Poly-bac, Plycrest, Poly-loom, Plymacramé, Poly-ty, Supertuft, Typar, Tyvek and Vectra.

Inherent Characteristics

FIBER DESCRIPTION: Fibers produced by either method are even, and usually round. Ethylene polymers are white and waxy in feel and appearance. Propylene produces a less waxy fiber. Fibers manufactured directly as multifilament yarns, however, have a comfortable, soft hand.

STRENGTH: Depending on manufacturing technique, tenacity varies greatly, from 1.5 gpd (weak) to 8 gpd (strong).

DIMENSIONAL STABILITY: Elongation is also variable, from 20-80%. Elastic recovery is excellent, so that resistance to crushing (as in floor coverings) may be very good to exceptional, depending on carpet structure. The fibers will shrink in heat, so preshrinking is necessary before production of yarns or finished textiles.

DENSITY: Exceptionally low, from 0.90-0.96 gpcc. Olefin fibers will float.

ABSORBENCY: Virtually no moisture regain or absorption.

Chemical Reactivities

ALKALIS: No effect.

ACIDS: Excellent resistance, except to strong oxidizing acids which cause loss of strength.

SOLVENTS: Low resistance. As olefin fibers may be cleaned thoroughly with water, this need not present a problem.

OILS AND GREASE: Fibers stain easily, but water, soap and synthetic detergents, used promptly, will remove the greasy material.

Environmental Sensitivities

SUNLIGHT: Basically no resistance to sunlight, but stabilizing and sunlight inhibiting chemicals may be added during manufacture to increase resistance.

WATER, MOISTURE: No effect.

FIRE: Will burn slowly with a sooty smoke, leaving a hard, tan-colored residue.

HEAT: Very sensitive. Shrinkage occurs at 75°C (165°F). Polyethylene fibers melt at 105-125°C (221-257°F). Polypropylene fibers melt at 170°C (335°F). May be preshrunk and stabilized to some extent, but melting at the above temperatures cannot be avoided.

MICROORGANISMS, INSECTS: No effect.

AGING: No effect.

SARAN

Saran first appeared on the market in 1940, introduced by Dow Chemical. It is a relatively expensive fiber and for that reason production is limited, with olefin fibers a common replacement. Saran fibers are stronger and heavier than olefin, however, are usually tough and durable and are easy to maintain. For particular upholstery, draperies and outdoor furniture applications, they are still desirable. Saran is the major trade name.

Inherent Characteristics

FIBER DESCRIPTION: Fibers are melt spun and cooled quickly in water, and may be white, yellowish, or colored by the addition of pigment to the melt solution. Fibers are round and smooth with a high luster.

STRENGTH: Tenacity is 1.4-2.4 gpd, moderate.

DIMENSIONAL STABILITY: Good. Elongation is from 15-20%, with near perfect elastic recovery. Good resilience.

DENSITY: High, 1.7 gpcc.

ABSORBENCY: Virtually no absorption.

Chemical Reactivities

ALKALIS: Resistant, except to sodium hydroxide, which causes deterioration.

ACIDS: Not affected.

SOLVENTS: Good resistance.

Environmental Sensitivities

SUNLIGHT: Resistant to damage, but white or light colors may darken slightly.

WATER, MOISTURE: No effect.

FIRE: Fibers will melt and burn slowly in direct flame, but will self-extinguish when flame is removed.

HEAT: Sensitive. Fibers soften at 115°C (240°F) and melt at 177°C (350°F).

MICROORGANISMS, INSECTS: No effect.

AGING: No effect. Even in applications such as outdoor furniture, saran will retain appearance and durability for 8-10 years.

VINYON

This 1939 introduction by American Viscose is a polyvinyl chloride fiber produced by either a dry or wet spinning method. It is used principally in industrial applications, but also to heat seal or bond some needle constructed fabrics. Trade names include Fibravyl, HH, Leavil, PeCe, PVC, Phovyl, Teviron, Thermovyl, Valcren, Vinyon.

Inherent Characteristics

FIBER DESCRIPTION: Fibers are smooth, white or semi-transparent, usually round, but also produced in dogbone or dumbbell shapes.

STRENGTH: Great variation, 0.7-3.8 gpd, depending on polymerization process.

DIMENSIONAL STABILITY: Elongation may be anywhere from 12% to 125%.

DENSITY: 1.34-1.43 gpcc.

ABSORBENCY: Practically non-absorbent.

Chemical Reactivities
ALKALIS, ACIDS: No effect.

SOLVENTS: No effect, except for a lack of resistance to acetone, aromatic hydrocarbons and ether.

Environmental Sensitivities
WATER, MOISTURE: No effect.

FIRE: Will not support combustion, but will burn in a direct flame.

HEAT: Very sensitive. Fibers soften at 65°C (150°F).

MICROORGANISMS, INSECTS: No effect.

VINAL

A vinyl alcohol fiber produced in Japan by the dry spinning method. Fibers are smooth but grainy; cross section is usually a bean shape, and color is white, or solution dyed. A relatively strong fiber — 3.5-6.5 gpd, with moderate elongation (15-30%). Density is about 1.26, and moisture regain is 5% at standard conditions, or 12% at saturation. The fibers have moderate resistance to chemicals. Vinal softens at 200°C (390°F) and melts at 220°C (425°F) and does not support combustion. It is resistant to microorganisms and insects.

Principally an industrial fiber (fishing nets, filters, tire cord, etc.) it can also be manufactured in a water-soluble form where it finds specialty applications such as backing for embroidery. When the vinal is dissolved, a cut-out embroidery or exceptionally sheer fabric results. The trade name is Poval.

NOVOLOID

A 1972 introduction, novoloid is a phenol formaldehyde fiber, most noted for its great fire resistance. It is used widely in protective clothing and combined with other fibers to add flame resistance.

Novoloid characteristics include strength of 1.7-2.0 gpd, elongation of 35%, density of 1.25, and a 6% moisture regain. It is resistant to solvents, fairly resistant to weak acids and alkalis but poor resistance to concentrates. Sunlight has little effect; microorganisms and insects have no effect.

The resistance to fire is exceptional; flame temperatures of 2500°C (4500°F) cause it to convert to a carbon textile with no loss in strength and flexibility. It does not melt or shrink.

Mineral and Elastomeric Fibers

GLASS FIBERS

Venetian artisans in the middle ages were the first to draw molten glass into fiber form which they used to decorate blown glassware. Many attempts were made in the 19th century to produce glass fiber, but coarseness, weakness, and lack of flexibility were early characteristics and were certainly not desirable for fabric use. In the 1930's, Owens-Illinois Glass and Corning Glass did considerable separate research on glass fiber production. In 1938, they joined forces as the Owens-Corning Fiberglas Corp. and produced the first commercially acceptable glass fiber, Fiberglas.

The raw materials are silica sand and limestone. In one method, these are combined with small quantities of selected other elements and melted together at about 1650°C (3000°F) to form clear glass marbles, called **cullet**, which is then treated as the single raw material for glass fiber production. In this method, the cullet is reheated to the molten stage and fed by gravity through a rectangular platinum bushing (similar to a spinnerette) with from 400 to 1600 orifices. The filaments harden immediately in the air, and are lubricated, dried and wound. One 28 gram (1 ounce) marble may produce as much as 160 km (100 miles) of glass fiber.

In the direct method, the cullet step is eliminated and the ingredients are automatically measured, blended, and fed through the furnace and extruded as molten glass through the bushing. This method, understandably, is of economic advantage, and conversion to this procedure is widespread.

Although either method produces filament fiber, staple fibers may be manufactured by the addition of high pressured blasts of steam directed at the filaments as they drop from the bushing. This causes breakage into varying lengths 12-38 cm (5-15″) and the resultant staple fibers are collected on a revolving drum, carded, and pulled into a sliver. Short fibers are also produced by chopping.

Besides the well-known use as a sheer casement fabric, glass fibers are utilized in draperies, bedspreads, table coverings, and some upholstery fabrics. The broken or cut ends, however, can be irritating to human contact, and loose fibers may be accidentally ingested. Beta, a 1960 introduction by Owens-Corning, is the finest fiber, and blends well with other fibers. Fabrics of fiber glass launder easily and resist wrinkling. Glass fibers are also widely used in industry as insulation, filters, electrical tapes, fillers, and as reinforcement for various materials such as boat hulls, car bodies, furniture and vaulting poles.

Trade names include Beta, Fiberglas, Ferro, Modiglass, Pittsburgh PPG, Unifab, and Unistrand.

Inherent Characteristics

FIBER DESCRIPTION: Smooth, even and transparent, round in cross section, variable in width. Filament or staple form.

STRENGTH: High; tenacity is 6.3-6.9 gpd. Exceptional resistance to pressure or stress, but lacking in abrasion resistance.

DIMENSIONAL STABILITY: Excellent; elongation is only 3%; elastic recovery is 100%.

DENSITY: High, 2.54 gpcc.

ABSORBENCY: Nil.

Chemical Reactivities

ALKALIS: Poor resistance to cold strong alkalis or hot weak alkalis.

ACIDS: Good resistance, except to hydrofluoric or hot phosphoric acid.

SOLVENTS: No effect.

Environmental Sensititivies

SUNLIGHT: No effect.

WATER, MOISTURE: No effect.

FIRE: Will not burn.

HEAT: Fibers lose strength at 315°C (600°F) and soften at about 815°C (1500°F). With removal from heat, the fibers regain strength, but the shape may be changed.

MICROORGANISMS, INSECTS, AGING: No effect.

OTHER METALLIC FIBERS

Gold, silver and **aluminum** are often used in textile products. The fibers are usually produced by slitting very thin sheets of the metal into narrow ribbons. They are very expensive, and because they are weak and soft, are most often used as a wrapping around a stronger core fiber. Gold tends to discolor and silver to tarnish, so aluminum, colored in a variety of shades, is more commonly used. Polyester may be used as a coating for aluminum fiber to produce fibers such as Mylar. Finely ground aluminum, color, and polyester may be mixed to produce effective, bright, tarnish-free fibers. Metallic-polyester fibers are somewhat delicate. They launder easily, but temperatures above 140°C (285°F) must be avoided. Trade names are Bekinox, Brunsmet, Lurex and Mylar.

Stainless steel is a more recent metallic fiber and its addition to fabrics contributes strength, tear and abrasion resistance, and reduction of static build-up. The fibers are also used as resistance wires which can transmit and radiate heat when connected to a power source.

Ceramic fibers from various mineral compounds are also produced for very specific applications, such as the aerospace industry's rockets, fittings and related structures.

ELASTOMERIC FIBERS

Elastomers are rubberlike substances, and the fiber forms are characterized by exceptional elongation, from 200-800%, with excellent recovery.

SPANDEX

Spandex fibers are composed primarily (85%) of segmented polyurethane. Other elements are added, and production techniques vary considerably. These technical processes are largely classified information. The fiber may be used in its filament form; as a wrapped or core yarn, with other filament fibers wrapped in a spiral around the spandex; or, as a corespun yarn, when staple fibers are fed around the spandex core filament to produce a single yarn.

Trade names in use are Duraspan, Estane, Fulflex, Glospan, Interspan, Lycra, Numa, Spanzelle, Unel, and Vyrene.

Inherent Characteristics

FIBER DESCRIPTION: The fibers are normally white, round or dogbone shaped, and most are formed into multifilament yarns in the production process. The multifilaments usually fuse together at random intervals to produce flexible yarns of various diameters.

STRENGTH: Tenacity of the fibers is low, 0.5-1.03 gpd. However, in the case of elastomers, this is not a factor, as the actual strength in use is greatly increased by the elongation capability.

DIMENSIONAL STABILITY: Elongation is from 500-800%, with nearly perfect recovery.

DENSITY: 1.20-1.25 gpcc, low.

ABSORBENCY: Moisture regain is low, 0.3-1.2%. However, the fibers accept dyes readily.

Chemical Reactivities
ALKALIS, ACIDS, SOLVENTS: Generally good resistance. Concentrated alkalis at high temperatures cause loss of strength, some bleaches cause yellowing and strength loss. Labelling by manufacturers is important here for specific care instructions.

Compared with natural rubber, these fibers have much greater resistance to smog, oils, perspiration and body oils.

Environmental Sensitivities
SUNLIGHT: Resistant.

WATER, MOISTURE: No effect.

FIRE: Burns in flame and forms a gummy residue.

HEAT: Resistant to temperatures up to 150°C (300°F).

COLD: No effect.

MICROORGANISMS, INSECTS, AGING: No effect.

6

FIBER MODIFICATION

Modification of natural fibers is limited to chemical or mechanical treatment of the yarn or fabric made from a particular fiber. These will be discussed in chap. 9.

Modification of the man-made fibers, however, is practically limitless. Now in the 'third generation', these can literally be engineered to fit almost any application. Manufactured fibers were originally made to simulate silk, the only natural filaments. Rayon, nylon, polyester, acrylics, etc., were first made as round fibers spun from a spinnerette having simple round orifices, with only the size of the round hole as a variable.

Modifications

CROSS SECTION

The first modifications (now called 'second generation' fibers) were accomplished by changing the orifice shape in the spinnerette, and trilobal, triangular, rectangular, dogbone, mushroom, pentalobal, and other shaped orifices were designed to produce continuous filaments with these variations. The changes exposed more surface on the fibers and aided in their capacity to be spun into yarns, having a greater range of effects such as sheen, dullness, smoothness, roughness, opacity, and so on, which better matched the characteristics of silk, wool, linen and cotton.

Cross section was further modified by the production of thick-and-thin fibers, which shows variation along the length of the fiber. This modification is accomplished by uneven drawing out of the fibers, and allows for subtle color effects, with the thicker portions accepting greater quantities of dye. Texture, as well, is slightly affected.

MOLECULAR STRUCTURE

The basic strength of a fiber may be modified in two ways: by a change in chemical constituents to increase the degree of polymerization, or by increased stretching of the fiber which results in a greater alignment of the molecules. The speed of extrusion from the spinnerette also affects the strength, with greater tenacity resulting from a faster spin. Low-pilling fibers may be produced by reducing the molecular weight. This reduces the flex life and results in a less strong fiber, but where pilling is an unattractive feature, it is preferable.

COLOR AND PROPERTIES

Where it is desirable to produce color at the fiber stage, as opposed to later dyeing of the yarn or textile, this is done by the addition of compatible pigments to the solution before spinning into filaments. Alternately, a fiber which normally does not accept dyestuff may be modified by the incorporation of dye-catching chemicals to the solution. Further, these chemicals are formulated to accept only certain dyes (basic, acid, disperse, etc., as discussed in chap. 9) so that yarns and fabrics manufactured from a blend of fibers can be given one dye bath with the end result being several subtle tones of color within

Filament fiber before texturizing

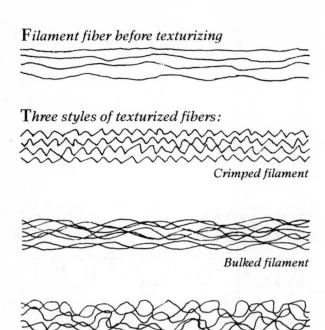

Three styles of texturized fibers:

Crimped filament

Bulked filament

Bulked filament

the one yarn or fabric.

To insert, delete, enhance or minimize inherent characteristics, fiber chemists have devised special techniques. Under this classification are soil release, flame resistance, anti-static properties, and resistance to sunlight. These modifications require the addition of various chemical stabilizers or particular compounds to the solution, and fibers so improved, or modified, are labelled by the manufacturer.

DELUSTERING

The manufacturer often produces a filament with a high degree of luster. In general, this is not a desirable quality, and chemicals may be added to the solution prior to spinning to produce a pitted surface. These are only evident under microscopic examination, but the effect is to dull the reflecting capacity of the fiber and therefore results in a less shiny surface.

TEXTURIZING

To produce bulkier yarns and fabrics, or ones having more loft, filaments may be produced to incorporate more air spaces within the filament or along its length. This may be done by introducing air into the solution, or by the addition of chemical elements which are subsequently evaporated or washed out. Such fibers have a lower density, or weight per unit volume.

Filaments may also be crimped after spinning. This procedure sets a permanent kink, curl or wave in the individual filaments so that when they are gathered together to produce yarn they form a thicker, more resilient strand. (An everyday illustration is the difference between a braid of naturally curly hair and one of straight hair.) The effect of the crimp is to force each filament to make more space for itself within a yarn structure. Crimp may be introduced through modification of the spinnerette shape, adjusting the air flow at the spinnerette, by vibration, or by the addition of chemicals which may produce either immediate or latent crimp. A latent crimp needs an additional process step to produce the effect.

Crimp is also commonly set by heat, and many methods are used. The filaments may be fed through intermeshing gears, or into a variously sized tunnel in such a way as to produce a sinuous set. The stuffer-box method produces the greatest amount of bulk. In this process, filaments are mechanically fed through crimping gears into the stuffer-box, forcing them into a saw-toothed crimp which is then heat set.

These processes may be introduced either at the filament manufacturing or yarn producing stage, and will be discussed further in chap. 7.

Staple fibers

STAPLE AND TOW

While not a modification of the filament per se, cutting the filaments into short lengths, or staple, is often done at point of production. The staple fibers are then packed in bales and sold to yarn manufacturers, where they are treated much like cotton or wool. Alternately, the hundreds of thousands of filaments produced simultaneously may be drawn into thick ropes, or slivers, and packaged in that form, which is called filament tow. Yarn manufacturers then have the option of modifying and/or treating the fibers, processing the filaments directly into yarn, or, of cutting the tow into staple form as part of their integrated yarn production.

Third Generation Fibers

While changes are still being made to fibers under the general classifications described above, the newest technology is focused on the so-called 'third generation' fibers, and here ingenuity and research are producing fibers to meet very particular needs, literally custom tailoring fibers for specialized end uses.

The objective of these third generation modifications is basically to create fibers, or filament yarns, with texture to more closely simulate the unevenness of natural fibers, for desired hand, or appearance, while at the same time maintaining the performance features of strength, soil resistance, shape retention, dyeability, wrinkle-resistance, or other characteristics, that have already been engineered into the basic man-made fiber. Three methods are currently in use to create these effects: 1. bi-component fibers; 2. bi-constituent fibers; and 3. combination filaments.

BI-COMPONENT FIBERS

Bi-component fibers are composed of two generically similar but chemically different polymers, physically joined at the production stage into a single filament. The first conception of this technique was to join two polymers of different shrinkage rates so that in the processing of yarn, as one component shrank more than the other, crimping would occur, giving greater bulk to the processed yarn. The technique for conjugate spinning was developed by American Viscose in 1940 when two rayon solutions, one aged and one unaged, were extruded through a single divided spinnerette. The two halves joined and had a straight configuration until immersed in water, which caused one half to shrink, drawing the whole into a three dimensional helical crimp. Later techniques with other fibers used heat, or a combination of moisture and heat, to produce the desired crimp. Side-by-side bi-components may also be produced with differing dye reactions, so that one dye bath can produce a two-color fiber.

Bi-components are also made by a 'pipe-in-pipe' extrusion procedure, which produces a fiber with a sheath different from the core. Most recent technology has expanded from the two component stage to include multi-component fibers, but the focus must still be on compatible polymers with good surface-to-surface adhesion.

BI-CONSTITUTENT FIBERS

Bi-constituent fibers are composed of two generically different polymers physically joined in the solution stage before extrusion through the spinnerette. The first bi-constituent was devised by Allied Chemical in 1968 and introduced the 'matrix-fibril' technique. One polymer is in solution form—the matrix—while the second is in very short, fine filament form—the fibril. These are combined and extruded together to produce an essentially new fiber. Allied Chemical's innovation produced a 70% nylon, 30% polyester blend called Source.

Bi-constituents are produced in three distinct ways:

— by mixing two polymers to produce an entirely different fiber, as in the matrix-fibril technique;
— by adding chemical ingredients to change a particular function or property of one of the component polymers;
— by adding ingredients which can be removed at a further processing step to leave desired voids in the finished filament. This is often a water soluble ingredient which washes or leaches out in water, leaving pits or hollow spaces on the filament's surface.

The bi-constituent fiber is the most difficult new fiber to engineer.

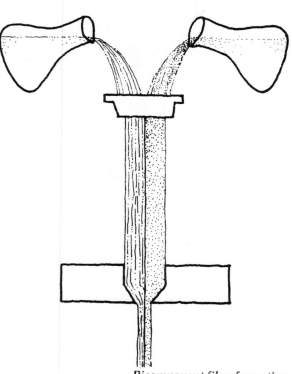

Bicomponent fiber formation

Some Bi-component and Bi-constituent Fibers

SOURCE, introduced by Allied Chemical, is a 70% nylon, 30% polyester, matrix-fibril bi-constituent fiber. Inherent characteristics of nylon have been retained with improvements in appearance, which give the fiber a unique silky sheen and luminosity. It is used in carpeting, and is easily maintained.

MONVELLE, developed by Monsanto, is a side-by-side bi-component fiber with 50% each of nylon and spandex. It is principally used in hosiery.

CORDELAN, a Japanese import, is a matrix-fibril bi-constituent of 50% vinal and 50% vinyon. It retains the inherent characteristics of its two components, and does not absorb stains. It is easily maintained and has a pleasant hand. Most important, it will not support combustion, and does not give off toxic fumes as do many other flame-retardant fibers. Its uses include draperies, bedspreads, upholstery and blankets, as well as children's sleepwear, work clothes and industrial fabrics.

Many other multiple component or constituent fibers are being investigated. Some, such as Arnel Blend 100 (a sheathcore bi-component with a polyester core and a triacetate sheath) have wide acceptance in the apparel field.

COMBINATION FILAMENTS

Combination filaments are composed of man-made filament fibers physically joined after each is produced, not in the production stage as in the bi-component, nor in the solution stage as in the bi-constituent. This method has a greater range of possible combinations than either of the previous two. The combining of component fibers is accomplished by twisting or interlacing in a separate manufacturing step. While production of this fiber does not require the delicate chemical balancing techniques of the bi-component or bi-constituent, its potential for creating new and specialized fibers is broader, and a much greater range can be joined by this method. This technology has added greatly to the whole field of fiber blending.

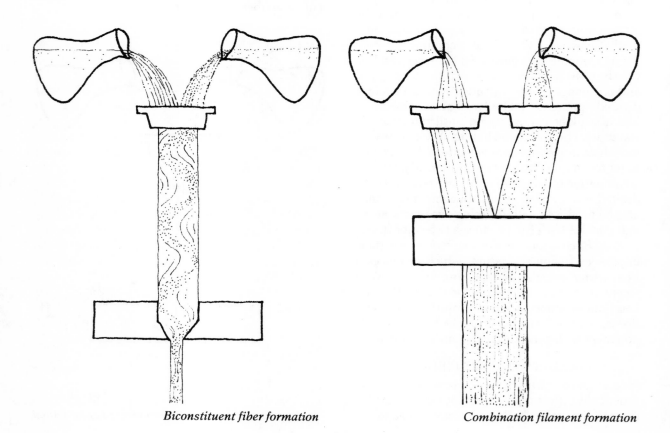

Biconstituent fiber formation   *Combination filament formation*

Fiber Blending

The blending of fibers is certainly not new. First, blends combined different weights of the same natural fiber such as wool, for a new texture or look. Next came blends of naturals, cotton/wool, wool/silk, silk/cotton, cotton/linen, etc., for new textures, new weights, and new performance standards. Viyella, an English blend of 55% wool and 45% cotton, has been a staple fabric for many years. Today, blends of natural fibers, natural with man-made fibers, and blends of different man-made fibers based on the combination filament principle described above, are the dominant factor in the fabric producing industries.

Blends are, by definition, 'intimate blends' in which specific proportions (by weight) of two or more component fibers are combined at the start of the textile process.

There are many reasons for blending fibers:

—to obtain cross-dyed effects;
—to improve uniformity in manufacturing or finishing;
—for economic reasons—extending the effect, or prestige, of expensive fibers by the addition of less costly ones;
—to improve appearance or touch;
—to produce fabrics with improved performance.

While all reasons are viable, the last two are perhaps the most important, and have provided the impetus for most of the significant advances in this area. Fiber characteristics and user needs are assessed, and a combination plotted which will complement each component fiber and meet as many requirements as possible.

Blend levels are an important factor, and this area is the subject of much study. It has been found, for instance, that 15% of nylon blended with wool improves the overall strength of the fabric, but 60% of nylon is needed to significantly improve the strength of rayon. The industry is conscientious in setting its own standards in this area, but it is as well to know that these variables exist.

These performance-based blends produce, in effect, a new fiber which combines functional properties. For instance, the superior hand of one fiber blended with the strength of a second fiber produces a 'new' fiber with hand plus strength. A good example of this is the first successful combination filament, Arnel-plus-nylon. In various proportions, it creates fibers with the bulk, texture and aesthetic qualities of the tri-acetate Arnel, without greatly diminishing the strength that nylon contributes.

Textile chemists have assigned functions to many of the man-made fibers based on outstanding properties or special strengths. These fibers may be depended upon to contribute that particular characteristic to the finished yarn or textile product. Some of the dependable fibers and their functions are as follows:

ACRYLIC provides dimensional stability, creates bulk without weight and adds versatility to surface texturing.

NYLON adds strength and abrasion resistance. Often used as the core of a filament, it gives durability, dimensional stability and press retention to the finished textile.

POLYESTER is the fiber for unrivalled wash and wear performance. It adds wrinkle resistance and press retention, as well as strength and abrasion resistance.

RAYON contributes a 'natural hand', eases processing of a textile, and is easily given decorative effects.

Modern blending is largely an automated process, though four basic methods are still employed depending on size of operation and fibers being combined. **Hand feeding** is the least reliable for establishing exact proportions. As implied, the fibers are hand fed from behind the hopper line. **Sliver blending** combines slivers of staple fibers through a process of doubling and drafting. **Hopper blending** has the different components hand weighed and spread in layers, and then fed into the hopper line from the cross section. **Automatic blending** is the same as hopper blending, except fully automated, and is the most common form of staple fiber blending. All of these methods blend the component fibers before, or as, they are being spun into yarn.

Similar to, but distinct from, blended yarns are mixture yarns, which are less intimate blends of two or more fibers twisted together after each is in strand or continuous filament form.

An additional distinction in this area are mixture textiles. These may be made from mixture yarn, from different component strands laid side by side, from different yarns woven at right angles to each other, or from some other fabric construction method. These will be discussed in chap. 8.

These techniques of blending, along with previous modifications through technology and chemistry, make it possible to design a fiber to order. Textile chemists are able to improve luster, improve hand, modify or improve dyeability, improve flame resistance, reduce static conductivity, improve whiteness retention, reduce pilling, improve laundering performance, increase moisture absorbency, impart stretch, and can manufacture fibers with bulk, moldability, or temperature sensitivity. Having these performance factors 'on order' as it were, gives fibers a staggering range.

The continuing challenge for textile technologists is to be able to combine performance requirements, to produce new textiles in sufficient quantity to meet needs, and to keep costs competitive. As was stated earlier, there is no one fiber absolute, though many of the new synthetic blends do, quite literally, look, feel, and perform perfectly for the required use, and, barring mishaps such as fire or chemical spill, may be easily maintained almost indefinitely. This ageless characteristic is most noticeable in the clothing field, where it is common to find ourselves tiring of a garment long before it has lost its appearance or shown signs of wear.

The fact governing textiles today is that no pre-eminent type of fiber exists. Competition between natural and man-made fibers is a thing of the past, and each fiber is assessed and valued for its own best qualities.

7 YARN PRODUCTION

Yarn is a generic term for a continuous strand suitable for weaving, knitting, or otherwise intertwining to form a textile fabric. It is the medium of construction. By whatever means a fabric is formed its character is determined to a great degree by the type of yarn from which it is made.

Based on the fibers from which it is formed, yarn is of two types: spun yarn, made from staple fibers, or filament yarn, made from filament fibers. Filament fibers may also be spun, after being cut into staple lengths. All natural fibers, with the exception of silk, are staple; silk and all man-made fibers are filament.

Chapters four and five detailed the general characteristics of each of the fibers used for textile production, and discussed how usable fibers are obtained from natural sources. This section will first briefly examine the theory, practice, and current status of spinning. With this basic information in mind, the production and character of yarn in all its diversity will be discussed.

Spinning—Past to Present

Spinning is an ancient capability, predating written history by many centuries. The principle is easily demonstrated by lifting a layer of ordinary cotton batting, gradually pulling the fibers apart, and rolling or twisting them between the thumb and forefinger to form a continuous strand. This method was the basis of early spinning of wool, cotton and flax, and the earliest 'inventions' in the textile industry were 1. simply a stick, called the distaff, to which the mass of raw fibers was tied; and 2. a shorter stick, notched at one end and pointed at the other. Near the pointed end a round of clay or wood, called the whorl, was attached, and this combination formed the spindle. To spin yarn, the distaff was held under the arm, and a lead of fibers twisted out and attached to the spindle. Using both hands to feed out the fibers and form them into a thread, the weight of the spindle drew the strand downward, and it was rotated to impart a firm twist to the attached strand. As the spindle approached the ground, it would be taken up and the yarn wound around it, secured in the notch, and the motion repeated.

Earliest spun yarn was probably rather uneven and coarse, but this simple procedure, like many others, developed into a fine art, and hand spun threads have been discovered which have not been equalled for delicacy since. Dacca muslins were reportedly so fine that they could not withstand the weight of a suspended spindle, but were instead wound on a bamboo needle lightly weighted with clay and rotated on a supporting shell.

The next major invention, the spinning wheel, was not devised for many centuries, and appeared in Europe some time in the fifteenth century. The distaff was mounted in an upright position, and the spindle mounted horizontally within a frame. A wheel that was rotated by hand was connected by a band to the spindle which caused it to revolve. In 1519, Leonardo da Vinci invented a flyer which twisted the strand and a companion device which fed the yarn evenly across a bobbin mounted on the spindle. In 1533, the Saxony Wheel added a foot treadle to operate the wheel, and the first continuous motion spinning was made possible.

The Saxony Wheel was used exclusively for over two hundred years, and is still used for handcrafted yarns. At the beginning of the Industrial Revolution in England, weaving underwent many advances. The increased demand for yarn caused a great advance in spinning techniques, and within forty years, from 1738 to 1779, spinning changed from a home craft to an industrial giant. By 1812, there were five million spindles operating in Britain, giving employment to 70,000 spinners and 150,000 weavers.

Chap. 2 detailed the important inventions in this period, and it will be remembered that four Englishmen—Lewis Paul, James Hargreaves, Richard Arkwright and Samuel Crompton—devised the methods upon which all modern spinning is based. The principles have not changed greatly since that time.

MECHANIZED SPINNING

Some of the first steps in the process of converting fibers to yarn were covered in chap. 4 and 5. Our discussion of cotton, for instance, covered the steps for picking, ginning, baling, opening, blending, lapping, carding, and combing. Although most of these steps, and spinning as well, are now undertaken within one integrated mill, this description of mechanized spinning of yarn from staple fibers picks up at the point of delivery of the carded or combed sliver of fibers to the spinning mill.

Drawing

This step involves the combining and subsequent redrawing out of several slivers. There are usually two passes through this mechanical process and the result is a longer, thinner strand of fibers.

Roving

This operation is generally one continuous step, with the task of further drawing out the drawn sliver and imparting a slight twist. The resulting product is called the roving.

Spinning

In order of their development, there are five methods of spinning now in operation: flyer, mule, cap, ring, and open end.

FLYER This system is in limited use today, usually for spinning flax and jute. Its main disadvantage is lack of speed. The operation is much like the early Saxony Wheel; the yarn is drawn from an elevated delivery roll of roving down to the top of the flyer, where it is twisted around the flyer leg, through an eye, and onto the bobbin. The bobbin rotates at about 3000 revolutions per minute (rpm).

MULE SPINNING is a slightly faster production method, but involves three distinct steps, drawing out of the strand, twisting, and winding. Capable of producing very fine yarns, mule spinning has nonetheless been largely replaced, although cotton waste and some woolen and worsted yarns are still spun commercially by this system.

CAP SPINNING is an adaptation of flyer spinning, with the flyer replaced by a 'cap' or bonnet within which the bobbin rises and falls while spinning. The action of the bobbin is powered from below. The roving is delivered from above the cap and drags over the lower edge to be wound on the bobbin inside, at about 7000 rpm. This method was used extensively for worsted yarn, but it, too, is gradually being replaced.

RING SPINNING is currently the most commonly used system to employ the spindle. Action is fast and continuous and uses a ring and traveler to spin and feed the strand on to the high speed (15,000 rpm) spindle. There is greater strain on the yarn with this system but this is not a serious drawback, and it is the principal method of producing fine yarns.

OPEN END SPINNING is the only new system. It was introduced in 1967 and is the first machine not to use a spindle. Slivers of fibers as opposed to a drawn roving, are fed directly into the spinning frame where suction pulls the fibers into a spinning chamber containing a rotor revolving at speeds as high as 45,000 rpm. The yarn forms continuously inside the rotor, and is simultaneously pulled out and wound onto large packages. The speed, degree of automation, and floor space savings are attractive features to manufacturers, and the system will undoubtedly continue to grow. The major drawback is that only relatively coarse yarns can be produced by open end spinning.

Winding and Twisting

Yarns from the bobbins or tubes employed in the spinning step have finally to be rewound onto large packages suitable for subsequent fabric manufacturing steps. Yarns as they come from the spinning equipment are single strands with a minimum amount of twist, generally just enough to hold the fibers together. In the winding process, they may or may not be given additional twist dependent on the planned end use.

RECENT INNOVATIONS

As might be imagined, increased technology makes almost continuous inroads into yarn production. As this relates to spinning, most progress in the industry has been in compacting the system, integrating steps formerly taken one-by-one into one continuous flow.

Automated Fiber to Sliver

The various steps detailed earlier may be accomplished as one automatic operation involving several types of machinery. All hand operations, packaging and transporting are eliminated. Production speed is greater, labor costs are lower, and an overall cleaner plant makes for healthier and more pleasant surroundings. The product, as well, is more uniform and sometimes stronger as a result of the tight control and high standards possible with increased automation.

Automated Sliver to Yarn

This method eliminates separate drawing, roving, and twisting operations. Each step is performed, but in one continuous automated operation.

In a fully integrated plant, both of the above procedures may be combined to produce yarn from fibers with a minimum of human labor involved.

Automated Tow to Yarn

This system eliminates the separate cutting or breaking of man-made filaments into staple form. In the former system, staple fibers obtained by cutting or breaking man-made filaments were processed like cotton or wool; the individual fibers had to be straightened, carded, and formed into slivers preparatory to yarn manufacture. In the tow to yarn system, the alignment of the mass of filament fibers is not lost; breaking into staple is done by passing the tow through rollers operating at different speeds, and the staple lengths are varied rather than identical. These are distinct advantages. The fibers then proceed through the usual drawing and spinning machinery to become yarn.

The system reduces fiber waste, introduces considerable economy, and produces either very uniform yarns, or, if desired, special effect yarns.

Classification of Yarns

As has been noted, the method of conversion into yarn depends on the form of fiber that is used. Staple fibers become yarn in the ways just outlined.

Silk and all man-made fibers are in filament form, and are used to produce 'thrown' yarns. The origin of the term throwing is Anglo-Saxon and the original word, *thrawan*, meant to twist or revolve. The process of throwing, then, is to twist two or more filaments together to form one yarn. The process originally applied only to silk but now also describes the process of making yarn from man-made filaments.

Yarn is also produced today from tapes, which are exceedingly thin strips of a fine sheet of man-made material. This alternate to extruding a solution through a spinnerette results in a product which is similar to, and treated as, a man-made filament fiber.

Other fairly recent innovations are the manufacture of twistless yarns, which are held together by adhesive rather than twist, self-twist yarns, fasciated, and fibrillated yarns, each of which are manufactured in unconventional ways.

SPUN YARNS

Singles and Plys

Yarn as it comes from the spinning frame is called a single yarn. It may have very little twist and be quite soft and weak, or be moderately twisted to impart more strength and a crisper feel.

Twisting two or several strands together produces a ply yarn, with the number of strands designating the number of ply (2-3-or 4-ply, etc). The individual yarns in ply yarns are usually

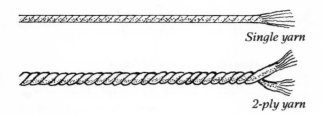

Single yarn

2-ply yarn

slightly more twisted than singles, and the ply yarn has other advantages as well; the fibers do not slip as readily within the yarn, the yarn's diameter is more uniform, and strength is gained both by the additional plys and by reinforcement of any weak spots in individual plys or strands.

FILAMENT YARNS

Filament fibers (silk and all man-mades) are continuous strands of variable size and shape and may be used, as is, in two ways to create yarn, either as a monofilament or a multifilament yarn. They are generally smooth, strong, and lustrous.

Monofilament yarns are, as the name implies, one filament. They may be as thick as fishing line or as fine as a nylon stocking thread.

Multifilament yarns are much more commonly used, and are composed of many fine filaments thrown, or twisted, to form one strand. Most are low twist, as very little is needed to hold the fibers together, but a tight twist may be used to give a special effect in the finished fabric.

Multifilament yarns may be single or ply, but there are few reasons for, or benefits from, ply filament yarn. They do not need plying to increase strength or uniformity; these qualities can be built in with the number of filaments and their comparative strength and size. Plying, in the case of filament yarns, is generally employed to produce specialty yarns, or mixture yarns for special applications.

OTHER YARN METHODS

Technology has added several interesting alternatives to the traditional two yarn producing methods.

Tape Yarns

Tape yarns are also called split film yarns. They are produced by slitting very thin sheets (or films) of polymer into narrow strips. In production, the following steps would be fully automated: extrusion of a polymer sheet, cooling through a 'quench tank' of cold water or other medium, over a set of guides and through a slitting unit, through an oven or over a heat source, around tensioning rolls to draw the tapes, and through separating guides directly to the yarn winders. The polymer film may be as fine as plastic wrap, or coarser, depending on planned end use. The resultant yarn may retain a flat, tape appearance, or, with finer tapes, drawing tends to cause longitudinal breakage (or fibrillation) and the forming of these many long fibrils causes the tape yarn to resemble a coarse filament.

Tape yarns are strong, stable, and have good abrasion resistance. While the system can be used to produce yarns from any man-made fiber polymer, olefin (polypropylene or polyethylene) is the usual material. Tape yarns are used for carpet backing, furniture webbings, awnings and blinds, as well as tarpaulins, sacking, travel goods and swimming pool covers.

Twistless Yarns

Twistless yarns describe a product which is held together by adhesives rather than by twisting. As in spinning, the roving is attenuated into a fine strand; however, rather than being spun and twisted, the strand is passed between rollers which also applies an adhesive. Fibers in twistless yarns lie parallel and the yarns make up into fabrics with excellent covering power and an attractive appearance. The fabrics have good strength. The adhesive may or may not be removed in subsequent finishing operations.

Self-twist Yarns

These are basically 2-ply yarns. The yarn is made by standard methods, except an alternate twist is applied along the length, first left hand (counter-clockwise or Z twist) and then right hand (clockwise S twist). When two yarns so twisted are combined, the alternating twists cause them to 'grab' or twist together, resulting in one 2-ply yarn without a separate twisting operation. Use is limited as the yarns are unstable.

Fasciated Yarns

Fasciated yarns are produced by a mechanical system which ties together a continuous bundle of fibers at irregular intervals. These yarns are surprisingly strong and inexpensive to produce.

Sheath Yarns

These are produced by a system developed by the Bobtex Company which involves extrusion of a polymer core into which loose fibrils are embedded. The extended fibers form a sheath around the filament core.

Basic Yarns—Spun, Filament

Basic yarns are those plain utilitarian yarns that are used to make up most textile products. As a general rule, they are smooth, uniform and stable, with size, quality, and twist as variables. The fibers for spun yarns may be any natural or man-made fibers, or a blend of two or more; for filament yarns the fibers are either man-made or silk.

SPUN YARNS

Cotton, Staple Cut Filaments, and Blends

Yarns of cotton and cotton blends are widely used in environmental textiles. The blending processes, reviewed in chap. 6, provide slivers of fibers meticulously blended by weight. Textiles labelled "70% polyester, 30% cotton" have generally been constructed of such blended yarn. Spun yarns are made in three distinct qualities: staple, carded, and combed. Blended yarns are usually in the combed category.

STAPLE YARNS are those spun from relatively short cuts of a fiber twisted together into yarn.

CARDED YARNS are spun from a carded sliver and have only the very short fibers removed, and the remaining ones brought into general alignment.

COMBED YARNS are comprised of only long fibers laid parallel before spinning, which produces the strongest, smoothest yarn.

Staple and carded yarns are used for napped fabrics or rough textures like bark cloth. Combed yarns are required for shirtings, sheetings, or any smooth, fine fabric.

Woolen and Worsted Yarns

When applied to fabrics of wool, or wool blends, carded yarn is used for woolens, and combed yarn for worsteds. Woolen yarn (and fabrics) are relatively bulky, fuzzy and uneven. Tweed is a woolen fabric. Worsted yarn (and fabrics) are, by comparison, smooth, even, and with little fuzz. Gabardine is a worsted fabric. Combed wool yarn has more twist than carded yarn, and that factor, along with the longer, more even fibers, accounts for the difference between woolens and worsteds. One is not better than the other, each has particular uses, and each is produced in both poor and high quality.

In use, woolen yarns and fabrics provide better insulation and bulk, and have a soft, napped appearance. Worsted yarns and fabrics are firmer and denser, and will hold their shape and creases better. The surface of worsted fabrics clearly reveal the weave, but it is more prone to develop an unwelcome shine from wear or pressing. A 'fulling finish', which slighly naps the surface, is sometimes used on worsteds to subdue the shine problem.

Tow and Line Linen Yarns

Flax produces two qualities of fiber. Tow yarns are composed of the shorter fibers, and is used for rough or homespun type fabrics. Line is the designation for yarns made of the smooth, long flax fibers, and is used for fine table linens, handkerchiefs, etc.

Thread

Thread is a basic yarn, but the term is used to designate a very fine, even, and strong product used to join pieces of fabric rather than to create textiles. It is not, as might be assumed, finer or of smaller diameter than yarn. It is frequently of ply construction. While thread used to be limited to cotton, linen or silk, now it is made of any fiber, man-made or natural, with the most common being cotton, polyester, and polyester/cotton.

Cord (or Cable) Yarns and Crepe Yarns

These are variations of simple ply yarns. Cord is made of two or more ply yarns twisted together. To identify a cord, the number of ply yarns and then the number of their constituent single yarns is given. A 3.5 cord indicates that the yarn is composed of three 5-ply yarns twisted together to form one strand.

Crepe yarns are simply ply yarns which have been given a high degree of twist. Made into fabrics of the same name, crepe yarn produces a characteristic evenly textured surface. A crepe yarn detached from the fabric and slackened will retwist on itself.

Generally speaking, basic yarns produce smooth, plain, durable textiles. However, the generalization must not be taken too literally because differences in fibers, fabric construction, finishes and coloring may also produce uneven, fancy, or delicate fabrics.

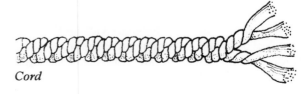

Cord

Textured Yarns

The term 'textured yarns' belongs to:

"that group of filament or spun yarns that have been given notably greater apparent volume than conventional yarn of similar fiber (filament) count and linear density...."

— American Society for Testing and Materials

Wool is the only naturally bulky fiber. The greater volume of woolen yarn and fabrics is mostly a result of wool's inherent kink. First attempts at introducing bulk to man-made fibers came with the early cross sectional modifications, and these had some of the desired effect, but not to a sufficient degree.

It was realized in the 1930s that the thermoplasticity (capacity to soften in heat, harden in cold) of man-made fibers would allow the heat setting of texturing crimp, and this was first done with viscose rayon by the Swiss firm, Heberlein & Co. After World War II, their researchers adapted the process of mechanically crimping and heat setting to nylon, and introduced Helanca stretch nylon. Early success was in the manufacture of ski clothes, and laid the groundwork for accelerated research with other fibers in other countries.

By the 1960s, textured stretch fabrics had gained acceptance and popularity for a wide variety of apparel and furnishing applications.

ADVANTAGES

Stretch and recovery of a finished fabric is only one feature of texturing. There are many other advantageous aspects as well. Textured yarns, or yarns made of textured fibers, make more comfortable, versatile and attractive fabrics than their non-textured counterparts. Regular nylon, for instance, constructed into a moderately firm woven or knit fabric, is sleek and tightly packed, preventing the movement of air and moisture. Texturing the nylon creates bulk and space between the filaments, so that the same construction will result in a fabric that 'breathes', and one that looks less artificial. Textured yarns are more opaque, and therefore cover better than a non-textured yarn of the same weight. Textured yarns are dry and warmer to the touch, without the cool slick feel of straight filament yarns. Fabrics made of textured yarns have greater abrasion resistance and do not pill.

TEXTURING METHODS

Texturing of man-made filaments is an exacting procedure, but one that is now performed quickly and efficiently. New machinery and specific improvements are an on-going process of equipment producers in the United States, Europe and Japan. Generally speaking, the large quantity, high speed conversion of smooth thermoplastic fibers into textured filament yarns is done on continuous (feed-in to wind-up), fully automated machinery. Each texturing procedure has appropriate equipment, and each results in a different texturing effect.

False Twist

This method is used to produce both textured and stretch yarns. Basically, the procedure twists a simple filament yarn around a spindle and sets it with heat. The degree of twist is controllable through the size of the spindle and the closeness of the yarns as they are wound around it. Yarns may be twisted to have 400% elongation and perfect recovery. The twisted yarn is then untwisted and cooled, and is wound on take-up spools. This produces stretch yarn. If the yarn is given an additional heat-set-cool after it is untwisted, the result is a textured yarn with a minimum of stretch, and is called a set or stabilized yarn. As twist is one-sided in this method, there is a tendency towards a torque effect, which may result in distortion. A counteracting procedure twists two simple yarns in opposite directions, to form a 2-ply balanced yarn. Helanca and ARTC are trade names of stretch yarns produced by the false twist method. Set or stabilized yarns textured by this method are Fluflon, Saaba and Superloft.

Knife-edge

Here, the system draws the simple yarn over a heated knife edge which sets a helical twist (like a gift type ribbon curled by drawing against a sharp edge). The twist reverses at random so there is no problem of unbalance. Agilon, a fine yarn used for hosiery, is a trade name example.

Stuffer Box

The Stuffer Box method produces the greatest amount of bulk. Basically, straight yarns are passed through crimping rollers and literally stuffed into a heated box where the saw tooth crimp is set. BanLon is a popular trade name yarn prepared by this method.

Gear Crimping

As the name implies, this method crimps yarns by passing them through heated, rotating, intermeshing gears. The gear sizes are variable and any degree of saw tooth crimp is possible.

Tunnel Crimping

This method feeds yarn into a heated tunnel in such a way that it arranges itself into a sinuous coil.

Knit-Deknit

In this method, texture is introduced by machine knitting yarn into a tube, heat setting the knit material, and then unravelling the yarn and rerolling it.

Air Jet Method

This is one of the few production methods used to manufacture textured yarns which does not employ heat. The system simply passes straight yarn by a turbulent stream of compressed air. This blows the filaments in the yarn apart and forms loops in individual fibers. The result is a bulky yarn, but with no stretch potential. Controlling the air jet allows yarns to be textured to resemble complex yarns, such as bouclé. The special feature of the air jet method is that fibers other than those which are thermoplastic can be textured. Glass fibers, for instance, are bulked by this method. Trade names in this category are Taslan and Skyloft.

Specialty Yarns

This category includes the complex, so-called novelty yarns and yarns designed specifically for their stretch and recovery potential.

COMPLEX YARNS

Complex yarns are manufactured for their appearance. In general, the structure is uneven, rather than even, and deliberate irregularities are built in. They contribute interest and decorative surface to fabrics and are widely used for environmental textiles. Fabrics made of novelty yarns are generally not as durable as those made with even yarns and require greater care in maintenance. Their interesting appearance takes precedence, however, in many applications where hard use is not a prime consideration.

Decorative effects are possible with single or ply yarns.

Magnification of a specialty slub yarn

Single Yarns

SLUB YARNS are staple yarns which have the twist interrupted at irregular intervals. This produces a yarn with softer, bulky sections along its length.

THICK-AND-THIN YARNS are filament yarns composed of fibers which have irregular thick and thin areas along the length, produced by deliberate changes in pressure at the point of extrusion from the spinnerette.

FLOCK YARNS (sometimes called flake yarns) are characterized by nubs or tufts of fiber protruding from the surface. This is accomplished by mechanically inserting tufts at irregular intervals as the yarn is being twisted. The twists hold the tufts in place.

Ply Yarns

The addition of strands or plys makes more complex effects possible. New 'novelty yarns' are produced regularly, but the following complex ply yarns generally cover all types of effects.

BOUCLÉ YARNS are 3-ply, with tight loops projecting from the strand at fairly regular intervals. Construction is as follows: a base yarn remains straight, the effect yarn forms multiple loops, and the binder yarn twists around the base securing the effect yarn.

RATINE AND GIMP YARNS are variations of bouclé yarns, and are formed in the same manner. Ratine yarns have closer set loops than bouclé, which are produced by twisting the finished yarn in the opposite direction. Gimp has loops slightly softer than ratine and is not double-twisted.

LOOP (OR CURL) YARNS are at least 3-ply, and may be more. As in bouclé, an effect yarn forms the loops, which are larger and more pronounced than in bouclé, on a rather heavy base yarn, and is secured by one or more binder yarns.

NUB (SPOT, KNOT) YARNS are ply yarns which are manufactured on a special machine which holds the base yarn securely and wraps the effect yarn in such a manner as to form nubs, or enlarged

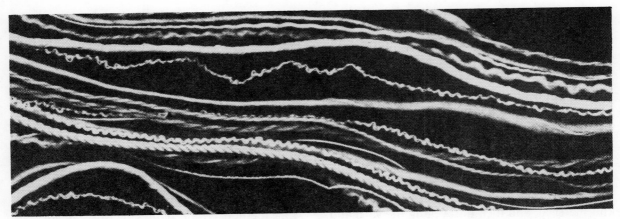

A selection of specialty yarns

segments along the length. Sometimes colored fibers are inserted in the nub, which gives a flocked effect as well.

SEED OR SPLASH YARNS are variations of nub yarns, seed yarns having a very tiny nub, splash yarns an elongated nub.

SPIRAL OR CORKSCREW YARNS are composed of different yarns twisted together. Differences may be in diameter, size, or fiber content. Spiral yarn has two components, a bulky, slack twist yarn which is spirally wound around a fine yarn with a hard twist. Corkscrew yarns twist yarns of different sizes, twist yarns irregularly, or corkscrew a fine yarn around a bulky one.

CHENILLE YARNS are made in an unusual manner: a leno weave fabric (see chap. 8) is constructed and then slit lengthwise into narrow strips which serve as yarn. The soft filling yarns of the fabric form the characteristic fuzzy pile, and the warp yarns prevent the pile from falling apart when the fabric is slit to form chenille yarn. In constructing fabric or rugs with this yarn, the pile can be made to appear on either or both sides.

METALLIC YARNS

Metallic yarns for decorative environmental use are usually constructed by a sandwich, or lamination technique. In the first, aluminum foil and pigment are sandwiched between plastic layers; in the second, metallized polyester is laminated to clear polyester. Both methods then use the tape technique to produce yarn, and in both cases the 'metal' is made durable and tarnish proof.

A core yarn technique is also used, with fine extruded metal being wrapped around a core of a stronger material. This procedure does not protect the metal, however, and dulling and tarnishing are inevitable.

STRETCH YARNS

The principal stretch yarns used in environmental textiles are those filament yarns textured by the false twist method. As was noted, this produces a very reliable, yet unobtrusive, stretch effect in constructed textiles. The 'give' inherent in fabrics made of these yarns is called 'comfort stretch', which implies an easy yielding to body movement or pressure, and good recovery with no loss of appearance. Method of fabric construction and the degree of tension also contributes greatly to the overall stretching and recovery capacity of any textile product.

'Power stretch' is the term given the holding power, high elasticity, and full recovery of fabrics composed all or in part of elastic yarns. These yarns are of two types: bare elastic and covered, or wrapped yarns. **Bare elastic yarns** are simply monofilaments of spandex or anidex, or multifilament yarns of these materials formed as an integral step of elastomeric fiber production. **Covered elastic yarns** are made of spandex, anidex, or occasionally natural rubber, wrapped in the core spun technique with spun or filament yarn, or, by a variety of processes which result in a yarn of combined synthesized elastomers and other natural or man-made fibers.

Generally speaking, these power stretch yarns are used for apparel or specialty applications. However, wherever firm fit or gathered fullness of fabrics is desired, an elastic yarn may be utilized.

Yarn Specifications

Yarns are described in many ways, and a yarn specification may include one or several of the descriptions.

Fiber Content

Fiber content is listed generically and may also include a trade name. If the yarn is made of a blend of fibers, these are stated as percentages.

STAPLE FIBERS (natural fibers, except silk; blends of natural with man-made) are made into spun yarns. The type or quality of the fibers may also be identified (for instance, 100% combed pima cotton). 'Spun' is not stated.

FILAMENT STAPLE FIBERS (silk or man-made) made into spun yarns state 'spun' as part of their description (for instance, spun rayon).

FILAMENT FIBERS (silk or man-made) are made into thrown or filament yarns and here, as well, 'filament' is not stated but is assumed.

SINGLE YARNS AND PLY YARNS have been discussed. To review, a single is the yarn as it is spun or thrown, or otherwise made. Ply refers to the subsequent joining of two or more singles.

Yarn Twist

Yarn twist is the most common method of holding fibers together to form a single strand. The amount of twist to accomplish this holding action depends on the diameter of the yarn, but is relatively low. Twist is measured in **turns per inch (TPI)**. The direction of the twist is designated as S or Z. **S twist** is right-handed, or clockwise, **Z twist** is left-handed, or counterclockwise.

Twist adds strength, and yarn is often twisted considerably more than is needed to simply hold the fibers together. The degree of optimum twist possible for increasing strength is a mathematical computation based on a factor called the twist multiplier (TM) which, in turn, takes in all factors pertaining to a particular yarn. **Balanced yarns** are those in which the amount of twist does not exceed the optimum level. A balanced yarn will hang in a loop without kinking or doubling. An **unbalanced yarn** has too much twist and a torque is set up. Hung in a loop, it will twist on itself.

Yarn Count

Over the centuries, many systems have been devised for measuring yarn for purposes of buying and selling, and for estimating the size of the yarn.

Weight is a factor of reckoning, and **yarn numbers** express a relationship between a particular quantity of yarn and a unit of weight. As can be imagined, these systems evolved over time and were not standard. A direct yarn number is the mass per unit length, while an indirect yarn number is the length per unit mass.

As an example of the indirect yarn numbering system, cotton is numbered by measuring the weight in pounds of one 840 yard hank. In this system the higher the number, the finer the yarn. A 50 spun cotton yarn indicates that 50-840 yard hanks weigh one pound, a 100 count yarn would need 100-840 yard hanks to make up the pound. Woolen yarn is measured by the number of 300 yard hanks, worsted yarn is measured by the number of 560 yard hanks per pound. When identifying spun cotton or cotton blends, the yarn count is followed by 's' if the yarn is a single, or 2, 3, etc. to indicate the number of plys. Wool is described in a reverse fashion with the ply count first, and the yarn count following.

The direct yarn numbering system is used with silk and man-made filament yarns, and is called the **denier system**. (The denier was a Roman coin.) The denier number represents the weight in grams of 9,000 meters of the yarn. 9,000 meters of a 10 denier yarn would weigh 10 grams. In this system, the yarn number correlates directly with the weight, so the higher the number the heavier the weight.

Filament yarns are also expressed by indicating the number of filaments in the yarn. If combined with the denier number, the denier comes first, the filament number comes second, and the degree and direction of twist, if given, comes last. A 300-20-2S nylon yarn indicates that 9,000 meters weighs 300 grams, that the yarn is made up of 20 filaments, and that it has been twisted

Yarn showing an S twist, and the less common Z twist

clockwise two turns per inch. To obtain the denier number per filament, the total denier is divided by the number of filaments. In this example, 15 denier is the yarn count of each filament.

TEX SYSTEM A universal metric numbering system has been devised and was introduced some time ago. This method, called Tex, would determine the yarn number by the weight in grams of 1 kilometer of yarn. The system is in use, but commercial acceptance has not been widespread as yet, and is not enforced by regulatory agencies.

COMPARISON OF PROPERTIES: SPUN AND FILAMENT YARNS

The basic difference between spun and filament yarns, that is, whether composed of short fibers or continuous filaments, accounts for many differences in properties, which may be generalized as follows, based on otherwise equal yarns:

Strength

Filament yarns are stronger than spun yarns for the simple reason that under pulling pressure some of the fibers in a spun yarn will slip apart, leaving fewer fibers to be broken apart. With all fibers in a filament yarn continuous, more force would be needed to break them apart.

Flexibility

Yarns of monofilaments or few filaments are less flexible than comparable spun yarns. However, filament yarns composed of multifilaments are equally flexible to spun yarn, or may be more flexible.

Uniformity

In general, filament yarns are more uniform in diameter than spun yarns, although only visible under microscopic examination.

Smoothness and Luster

Filament yarns are both smoother and more lustrous, because there are no fiber tendrils protruding from the yarn. This may or may not be of advantage, depending on application of a fabric constructed exclusively of either type.

Advantages in Use

Fabrics of spun yarns are generally warm, soft, and light in weight. Fabrics of regular (nontextured) filament yarns are smooth and cool. Some fabrics use both spun and filament yarns to combine the desired qualities of each.

It must be remembered that texturing, finishing, method of construction, and several other factors, can modify any of these generalizations.

8 FABRIC CONSTRUCTION

The construction of fabrics today is a blend of ancient arts and modern technology. Automated equipment and new methods of bonding make possible entirely new fabrics, yet felting and weaving, the oldest techniques, are as viable today as ever.

This chapter will examine each of the fabric construction techniques, and the particular characteristics of the fabrics they produce.

Weaving Techniques

Weaving is the interlacing of two sets of yarn at right angles to each other. It is another of the ancient accomplishments which we have found no reason to replace. The three basic weaves were devised at an early date and samples of expertly woven materials have been found in Egypt, in Europe, in Asia and in South America. These date from around 4000 B.C. Looms are depicted on vases, in wall hangings, and in other pictorial records on all continents, showing that fabric construction by weaving was one of woman's earliest accomplishments.

THE LOOM

Primitive weaving on a loom was a fairly simple procedure. The lengthwise yarns, called the **warp**, were separated and secured at each end of the loom to remain taut. A device called a reed, which resembled a comb with long teeth, was fixed at the weaving end to keep the warp yarns separated, and was used to push each filling yarn into place. The crosswise yarns, called the **filling pick** or **weft** were wound around a stick, woven over and under alternate warp yarns to form the interlacing, and then pushed together with the reed to form a firm cloth. Early improvements in this procedure were the **heddle** and the **shuttle**. The heddle was a wooden bar device which could raise alternate yarns of the warp creating a triangular opening called a **shed**, through which the filling could more easily be passed. The shuttle, an improvement on the ball of filling wrapped around a stick, was a smooth boat-shaped device, pointed at both ends, which held a removable spindle wound with filling yarns. The shuttle could then be thrown through the shed. The heddle would be turned to reverse the position of the warp yarns, and the process repeated.

This procedure, with the addition of power, automation, size and speed, is still followed and is the basis of the textile industry's capacity to supply fabrics of all types to billions of consumers.

Weaving

Modern weaving entails only four separate motions, mechanically performed on a loom with ten working parts. The names of these parts, and their functions, are as follows:

1. The warp beam is the cylinder around which the warp yarns are wound in a parallel

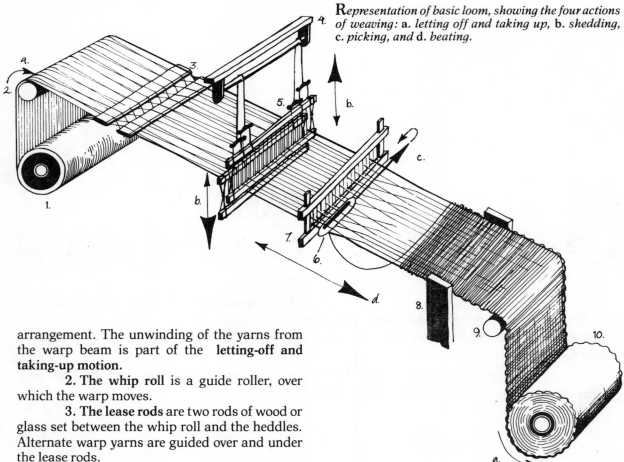

Representation of basic loom, showing the four actions of weaving: a. *letting off and taking up,* b. *shedding,* c. *picking, and* d. *beating.*

arrangement. The unwinding of the yarns from the warp beam is part of the **letting-off and taking-up motion.**

2. **The whip roll** is a guide roller, over which the warp moves.

3. **The lease rods** are two rods of wood or glass set between the whip roll and the heddles. Alternate warp yarns are guided over and under the lease rods.

4, 5. **The heddles** are steel wires secured between the top and bottom bars of a **harness,** which is a moveable wooden frame secured to a roller at the top of the loom and connected to a power source. Each heddle contains a central eye through which one warp yarn is threaded. A minimum of two harnesses are required and yarns are alternated between them. The raising and lowering of each harness with its threaded heddles is **the shedding motion** and creates the shed (triangular space) through which the filling is inserted.

6. **The shuttle and bobbin** is the combination carrier and holder of the filling yarn, or pick. Passage of the shuttle and bobbin through the shed is called **the picking motion,** which deposits the filling between the alternately raised and lowered warp yarns.

7. **The reed** is the comb-like device which serves two purposes—to keep the warp yarns parallel and separated, and to push the filling yarn into place. The mechanical action of the reed is called **the beating motion.** (Also called battening, beating-up or beating-in.)

8. **The temples** are devices at either side of the newly formed cloth which help to maintain the fixed width.

9, 10. **The breast beam** is a bar fixed across the front of the loom over which the new cloth passes before being rolled on **the cloth roller.** This is the companion part of the mechanized **letting-off and taking-up motion,** and is the completion of the weaving process.

This basic loom, and the weaving motions, are sufficient for constructing the basic weaves. Improvements to the loom over the years have focused on three areas: devices for separating the warp for more intricate designs, computers and electronic systems for directing and monitoring the weaving motions, and faster and different methods of placing the filling yarns. Various warp-shedding attachments for weaving specialty fabrics have been devised, and these will be mentioned as the weaves are introduced. Electronics are very much a part of modern weaving in designing, in programming, and in controlling the process. Looms may now operate almost entirely on computer-controlled systems.

Shuttleless looms also have been devised, the **water-jet,** the **air-jet,** and the **rapier-type.** Shuttle action looms were limited to placing the filling at approximately 200 picks per minute. The water-jet loom can place filling yarns at a speed up to 600 picks per minute. In this system, measured lengths of filling yarn are delivered to a water nozzle where a jet of water carries it through the shed. The process produces a 'fringed' selvage, and the cloth must be dried prior to rolling, but the greatly increased speed, and the quietness of the operation, are more important than the necessity to dry the fabric.

The air-jet loom operates on the same principle, with a blast of air carrying the filling through the shed. This method is considerably slower, at 300 picks per minute.

The rapier-type loom weaves at about 300 picks per minute, using two metal arms, called dummy shuttles. The right arm carries the measured filling to the center of the warp where it meets the left arm which takes the filling from the right arm and carries it to the left edge.

Each of the above weaving systems represents a flat machine for producing flat goods. Circular looms have also been devised which weave tubular fabric.

Key Terms

In addition to the terms introduced in the preceding discussion about looms, the following definitions will be of assistance in understanding the discussions of weaving:

WARP AND FILLING YARNS have definite characteristics apart from being the lengthwise and crosswise yarns respectively. Warp yarns (sometimes called ends) are stronger, or of better quality, and usually have higher twist. Filling yarns are weaker and are more apt to be the decorative yarn.

FLOATS are formed when one yarn crosses over more than one other yarn at a time.

GRAIN indicates the warp and filling directions. Lengthwise grain is the direction of the warp, crosswise grain is the direction of the filling yarns. **Off-grain** is a problem of fabric manufacturers and indicates that the weaving has gone off square. Draping will not occur properly, and if a design is printed, it will not be straight. Off-grain may result in **skew cloth** where one side of the fabric gets ahead of the other, or **bow cloth** where the center lags behind the sides. (Off-grain can sometimes be corrected in the finishing procedure. This is discussed in chap. 9.)

TRUE BIAS is the diagonal of a square, that is 45° from either the warp or filling yarns. **Garment**

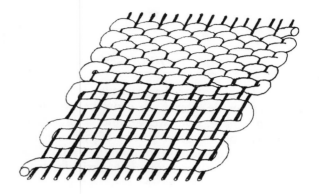

*F*illing-faced, balanced-weave fabric; the warp yarns are strong but fine, filling yarns are thick and appear to hide the warp entirely.

bias is any position between true bias and either the lengthwise or crosswise grain.

THREAD COUNT (or cloth count) is the number of warp and filling yarns per square inch (2.54 cm) of fabric, before finishing. If two numbers are given, the warp count is first. If one number is given, it is usually the total of both warp and filling. The higher the thread count the finer and stronger the fabric. (This thread count should not be confused with the yarn number, which is the measure of yarn size as discussed in chap. 7.)

BALANCE is the ratio of warp yarns to filling yarns. Balanced fabrics have a 1:1 ratio, unbalanced fabrics may have 2:1, 3:1, 1:3, etc. Both balanced and unbalanced fabrics may be of poor or good quality.

SELVAGE is the lengthwise edge of the fabric. A conventional loom makes identical selvages on both sides of the fabric, and the filling yarns can be seen to have reversed direction. **Plain selvages** are similar to the rest of the fabric and do not shrink. **Tape selvages** have larger and/or ply warp yarns to give more strength, and may be basket woven for flatness. **Split selvages** occur when items such as towels are woven side by side and then cut apart, with the cut edges then finished by machine. Shuttleless looms produce either a **fringed selvage**, a **cut and tucked selvage** in which the filling yarn ends are cut and tucked back into the fabric, or a **fused selvage** in which the cut ends are fused by heat.

CREELING is the procedure which winds the warp yarns from their individual spools onto the warp beam in readiness for weaving. Before being affixed to the loom, the warp yarns may be run through a **slash bath** of sizing solution, then dried and rewound. Sizing is often necessary to protect the yarns from the mechanical actions of the loom.

Classification of Weaves

There are three basic weaves, from which all woven textile fabrics are constructed. These are plain weave, twill weave, and satin weave. All other special effect woven fabrics use the basic weaves, alone or in combination, but utilize complex loom attachments and particular techniques to achieve the desired appearance.

BASIC WEAVES

Plain Weave

The simplest plain weave is one in which warp and filling yarns are the same size and are interwoven one-to-one. This is a **balanced plain weave** and may be constructed of light, medium or heavy weight yarns. Both sides of the fabric are identical.

An **unbalanced plain weave** is one in which the warp and filling yarns are unequal in number. The number of warp yarns may be doubled, with the result that only warp yarns show on the top surface, or **face**, of the fabric, or the warp may be increased but not doubled to produce any one of several specific fabrics.

BASKET WEAVE is a plain weave variation in which two or more warps are used as one. If an equal number of filling yarns are used, the result is a balanced basket weave (2x2, 3x3, 4x4).

WAFFLE WEAVE is produced by using two or more warps with one or more filling yarns to produce an unbalanced basket weave, in which the shapes of squares or rectangles vary.

Basket and waffle weaves are flatter in appearance than comparable plain woven fabrics.

Twill Weave

Twill weaves are constructed so that each warp or filling yarn floats across two or more filling or warp yarns, with a progression of one yarn to the right or left to form a distinct diagonal line, or **wale**. Twills have a right and wrong side, and are designated by the direction of the wale. **Right-hand twills** show wales from lower left to upper right; **left-hand twills** show wales from lower right to upper left. The degree of angle is determined by the balance of the cloth. Steep wales indicate a fabric with a high warp count and it is stronger than a fabric with reclining wales, which indicates a higher filling yarn count. Regular wales, on the true diagonal, indicate a balanced

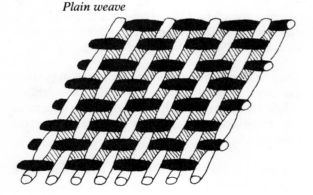

Plain weave

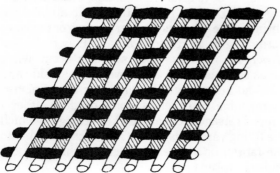

2/2 rib — unbalanced plain weave

2/2 cord — unbalanced plain weave

ratio of warp to filling, and are called **even-sided twills.**

WARP FACE TWILLS have a predominance of warp yarns on the face of the fabric.

FILLING FACE TWILLS have a predominance of filling yarns on the face of the fabric.

HERRINGBONE fabrics are a twill variation having the twill line reversed at regular intervals.

Satin Weave

WARP FACE SATIN WEAVES have each warp yarn floated over four filling yarns (4/1) and interlaced with the fifth, with a progression of interfacings by two to the right or left. The face of the fabric shows a predominance of warp yarns.

FILLING FACE SATIN WEAVES are constructed as a reverse of the above procedure (1/4), with the filling yarns then predominant on the face of the fabric.

Satin weaves have a definite right and wrong side, have a lustrous appearance caused by the long floats of yarns, and are constructed with a high thread count.

SPECIAL EFFECT WEAVES

Crepe Weaves

Crepe was originally a French word meaning crinkle. In English, crepe is used to describe a particular fabric with a pebbly or crinkled effect or texture. Crepes may be obtained by plain weaving high-twist yarns, by the use of textured yarns and by finishing. Woven crepes may be warp crepes, filling crepes, balanced crepes, or other variations.

3/3 twill

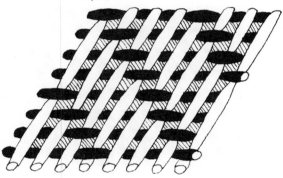

3/1 warp, twill

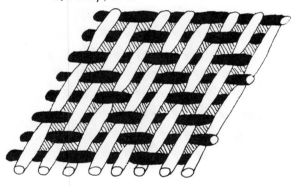

2/1 warp, twill

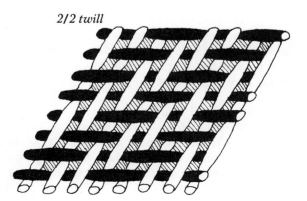

2/2 twill

2/2 twill, herringbone

A cross-sectional view of corduroy production showing the extra filling yarns floated over the basic weave, the float yarns cut, and finally brushed up into the characteristic pile.

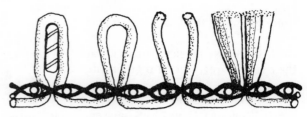

Loop pile fabrics — corduroy, velvets, velveteens, etc. — are formed in a variety of ways. Above, basic steps for the over-wire method: (from left) the loop formed, showing the wire used for catching the yarn; the wire removed forming a looped pile fabric; the loop cut by removal of the cut-wire; and the cut loop's yarn after brushing.

8-thread satin

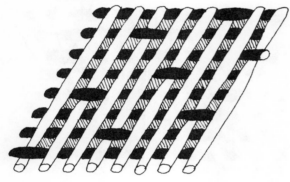

5-thread satin

5-thread sateen

Pile Weaves

Woven pile fabrics are constructed by weaving an extra set of warp or filling yarns into the basic, or ground, yarns to produce a characteristic three dimensional effect.

FILLING PILE FABRICS are made by weaving a second set of filling yarns so that they float over rows of warp, and are cut in a separate operation to form the pile, as in corduroy.

WARP PILE FABRICS are made with two sets of warp yarns and one set of filling yarns.

The **double-cloth method** simultaneously weaves two fabrics with the extra set of warp woven into each. The fabrics are then cut apart and the extra warp forms the pile.

In the **over-wire method**, a single cloth is woven with wires placed across the loom over the ground warp and under the pile warp. The over-wire loops may be cut or uncut.

In the **slack-tension pile method**, a special weaving arrangement forces the pile warp to form loops on either side, or both sides, of the fabric. These may then be cut or left uncut. Terrycloth is made by this method.

Jacquard Weaves

The story of Joseph-Marie Charles Jacquard (1752-1834) and the development of the loom which bears his name is an interesting one, and deserves more attention than can be given in a book of this type. His was one of the last great

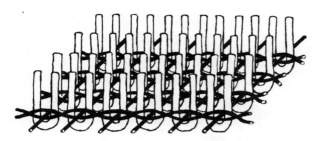

Cut pile fabric

inventions of the Industrial Revolution, and truly revolutionized the weaving of a wide range of fabrics and carpets.

Jacquard weaves are produced on a loom equipped with a special overhead mechanism called the Jacquard head-motion. The whole is called the **Jacquard loom**, a complex two-storey machine, with two or more sets of both warp and filling yarns, in which every warp yarn is individually controlled, and operated by full size punched pattern cards (as devised by Jacquard himself, but resembling a modern computer punched card). A warp yarn to be lifted passes through a hole in the pattern card; lack of a hole prevents a particular yarn from being taken up. This selective formation of each shed before each filling yarn is placed, results in the capacity to duplicate multicolored, intricate designs into fabric. Extremely elaborate patterns, whole scenes, typography, and photographs are possible to reproduce in fabric with the Jacquard loom.

Dobby Weaves

Dobby weaves are fabrics with small figures (dots, geometric shapes or florals) and are produced on a loom with a dobby attachment, usually called a dobby loom. The multiple warp yarns are controlled by up to thirty-two separate harnesses of heddles and the raising and lowering of the warp yarns to create the desired shed are controlled by a hole-punched guide.

Cord weaves are also woven on the dobby loom and produce fabrics with defined cords, wales, or ridges. In **piqué weaves** (after the French word for 'quilted') the cords are crosswise; in Bedford cords, the wales are lengthwise. Cords may also be constructed with stuffer yarns running beneath the wales to give them greater definition.

Leno Weaves

Leno weaves have warp yarns which do not lie parallel, but are in pairs, with one yarn crossed over the other before the filling yarn is inserted. This effect is obtained with a **doup attachment** which may be mounted on a plain or dobby loom. One of the two warp yarns in each pair is threaded through the doup needle attached to each of the two heddles. When one heddle is raised, the doup yarn is drawn across to the left; when the other heddle is raised, the doup yarn is drawn across to the right. The criss-crossed yarn gives greater strength than plain weaves and allows for an open, lace-like fabric. Marquisette and some thermal blankets are leno woven. Leno weaves may be fairly simple, or more complex doup attachments may allow for the weaving of very complex and interesting materials.

Surface Figure Weaves

Extra warp or filling may be used to produce simple or complex patterns on a dobby or Jacquard loom.

In a **lappet weave**, the effect is of hand embroidery over a base fabric. It is constructed with extra warp threads which are threaded on needles mounted on a frame near the reed. Where the design is planned, the frame presses the threaded needles to the bottom of the shed and holds them while the yarns are secured by the filling yarn. The frame is moveable from side to side and is moved to create the overall design. Yarns not used in the right side design are carried as floats on the wrong side of the fabric.

In a **swivel weave**, extra filling yarns are used to weave in a design. Each extra filling yarn is wound on its own shuttle, and enters the shed at predetermined spacings to deposit the yarn. Between pattern repeats, the extra yarn is carried on the wrong side of the fabric.

In **spot (or dot) weaves**, the yarn patterns may be provided by either extra warp or extra filling yarns, and the weaving takes place on a dobby or Jacquard loom. The wrong sides of such fabrics carry the extra yarn floats and these may be cut or uncut. Occasionally, the floats are carried on the face of the fabric and later clipped to form a fringed, or eyelash, effect.

This technique is also used to weave closely spaced designs which are 'right', though different, on both sides of the fabric.

Hand-loomed Weaves

The production of hand-woven textiles is naturally limited, but as a source of individual fabrics they are important both in use and as a source of inspiration for commercial production. Capable of producing the three basic weaves, the powered hand loom requires the expertise and creativity of the individual operator. Knowledge of yarns, and an eye for new color or texture combinations, often results in outstanding environmental textiles which may be used for special applications or as accent hangings in their own right.

Triaxial Weaves

Triaxial weaving is a development of the late 1960's, devised specifically for the space industry's need for a dimensionally stable, lightweight fabric. Construction is based on three yarn directions rather than two. Two warp yarns and one filling yarn meet at 60° angles to form a textile with more stability than traditional weaves or other forms of fabric construction. It is produced only on a special triaxial loom.

Triaxial construction permits lighter yarns to be used, resulting in a lighter fabric, and the choice of three rather than two components increases the performance possibilities. It has excellent resistance to tearing and raveling, and is equally strong in all directions. Application in interiors is mainly for upholstered furniture, where its ability to mold into tight corners and to resist tearing are very attractive features.

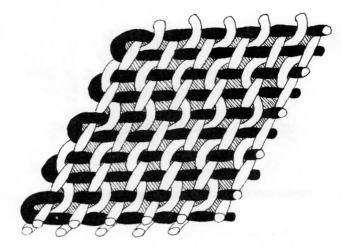

Leno is a complex variation of a plain weave accomplished on a dobby loom with a doup attachment. It effectively secures in place both the warp and filling yarns.

Woven Fabrics

The following listing of fabrics characterized by the type of weave is not all-inclusive, but does indicate the principal fabrics produced in each category.

PLAIN WEAVE: barathea, barkcloth, batiste, butcher rayon, calico, chambray, chintz, cretonne, flannel, gingham, greige (grey goods), homespun, lawn, muslin, ninon, organdy, percale, plaids, sailcloth, sheeting, tweed, worsted.

> *Basket weave:* canvas, duck, hopsacking, monkscloth, oxford cloth, sailcloth.
> *Waffle weave:* honeycomb, waffleweave.

TWILL WEAVE:
> *Even, or balanced twills:* cavalry twill, cheviot, damask, flannel, foulard, houndstooth, serge, surah, tapestry.
> *Warp face twills:* covert, denim, gabardine, herringbone, jean.
> *Filling face twills:* herringbone.
> *Novelty twills:* bird's eye, diaper, gooseeye (reverse herringbone).

SATIN WEAVE:
> *Warp face satin:* satin.
> *Filling face satins:* antique satin, sateen.
> *Warp/filling face satin:* damask.

CREPE WEAVE: Bemberg, chiffon, georgette, granite cloth, moss crepe, sand crepe, voile.

PILE WEAVE:
> *Warp face:* panné, velour, velvet, plush.
> *Filling face:* corduroy, velveteen.
> *Doublecloth:* matelasse.
> *Over-wire:* frieze, grosgrain.
> *Slack-tension:* shagbark gingham, seersucker, terrycloth.

JACQUARD WEAVE: brocade, brocatelle, damask, tapestry.

DOBBY WEAVE: bird's eye, dotted Swiss, huck-a-back, lappet, swivel.

> *Cords:* bengaline, broadcloth, faille, grosgrain, ottoman, poplin, rep, shuntung, taffeta.

LENO WEAVE: chenille yarn, marquisette.

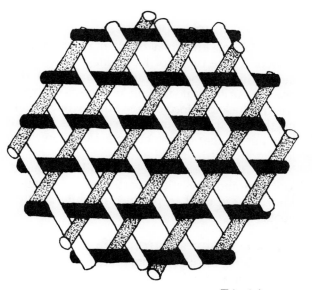

Triaxial weave

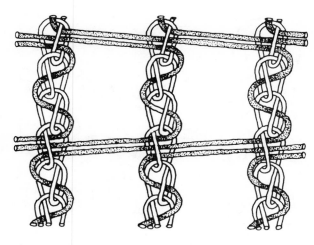

Marquisette

Needle Construction

Knits are the principal fabrics constructed with needles, and they are composed, in their basic form, of one yarn rather than two as in basic weaving. Many improvements in machine knitting have led to knits becoming a real competition to woven fabrics. More knits are being used as textiles for interiors, a field previously occupied almost exclusively by woven goods.

Knitting as a fabrication technique is both faster (about four times faster per square meter [or yard] than weaving) and more efficient than weaving. Because of the inherent stretch capacity of knitted fabrics, they are in great demand for upholstering contoured furniture, where less time and skill is required to obtain a tailored appearance.

Hand knitting as a craft is not as old as weaving; the earliest knit fragments date from around 200 A.D. The type of knitting done by hand is now called **weft knitting**, which means that the structure is formed by horizontal (crosswise) passes of the needles and yarn. **Warp knitting** is an invention of the late 18th century and can only be accomplished by machine. In this type, the loops are formed in a vertical (or lengthwise) direction. The horizontal row of loops is called the **course**. The vertical column of loops is called the **wale**.

In the 1960's, with the possibility of greatly expanded markets, there was a boom in new needle machinery and techniques. Adaptability to a wide range of yarns, combination knit-weave and knit-sew techniques, electronic programming, and original stitch concepts adapted to high production machinery, greatly increased the range of needle constructed fabrics.

WEFT KNITTING

Background

In 1589, an English minister, the Reverend William Lee, M.A., St. John's College, Cambridge, invented and built an original flat-bed machine for knitting hosiery material. It could knit ten times faster than an individual, and used long flexible hooks ending in a sharp needle which, since, have been called 'spring-beard' type. The invention was a great one and was the only type of knitting machine for the next two hundred years. In 1758, Englishman Jedediah Strutt built on the original design, and was able to do rib knitting on a machine he called the Derby Rib Hosiery Frame.

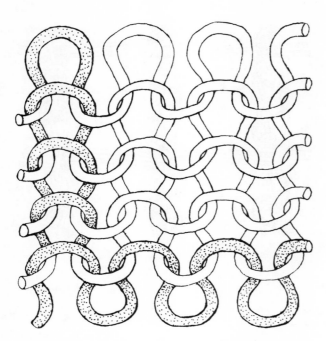

The course (horizontal) and wale (vertical) of a plain knit.

In 1816, Marc Brunel invented the first circular knitting machine, and in 1847, a Matthew Townshend patented a **latch needle**. These two machines, the flat-bed and the circular, and the two needle types, are the basic equipment for modern weft knitting.

Flat-bed Knitting

The machine for knitting flat, open width fabric has its needles arranged in a straight crosswise fashion. The row of needles can knit simultaneously, or knitting can proceed from side to side. The **full-fashioned machine** can also shape materials by automatically increasing and decreasing the number of stitches.

Circular Knitting

This machine has needles arranged around the circumference of a cylinder. As the cylinder revolves, the needles knit courses of loops and fabric produced is in tubular form. Most knitting is now done on a circular machine, and the tubular knits are then slit to form flat fabric.

Rev. Lee's machine knitted at about 600 stitches per minute; modern automatic knitting produces over 4 million stitches per minute.

Machine knit goods are produced as either single knits or double knits.

Single Knits

Single knits may be plain, ribbed or patterned. Three types of loops may be formed, depending on the programmed action of the needles. As illustrated, a knit loop forms the basic stitch, a tuck loop forms a new stitch while retaining the loop from the previous course, and a float loop misses that course but retains the previous loop.

Three basic stitches familiar to hand knitters, and one stitch particular to machine knitting, are used to produce machine knitted goods.

THE STOCKINETTE STITCH (also called flat, or jersey) is the most common, producing a flat face with a characteristic vertical row appearance, and a reverse displaying a horizontal row appearance.

THE PURL STITCH produces fabric that is identical on the face and reverse, and which resembles the reverse side of stockinette stitch.

THE RIB STITCH produces fabric with greater stretch and is machine knit with two sets of needles facing each other so that the stockinette stitch alternates on the face and reverse of the fabric. Rib knits are reversible, and can be even (1 x 1, 2 x 2, etc.) or uneven (1 x 2, 1 x 3, 2 x 3 etc.)

THE INTERLOCK STITCH is a variation of the rib stitch and is formed with two sets of needles which interknit two separate 1 x 1 rib fabrics.

Double Knits

The basis of doubleknit fabrics is the interlock stitch, and it is produced by two sets of needles at right angles. Decorative effects and patterns can be obtained by using a Jacquard attachment for individual needle control. Double knits can also be made by knitting two separate fabrics simultaneously and using periodic binding stitches to hold the two layers together. Besides the basic double knit, the plain interlock, variations such as piqué, pintuck, and double piqué can be manufactured. Production of double knits is very fast, with up to 48 yarns feeding to over 1000 needles, and complex design changes can be accomplished electronically in a matter of minutes.

Knitted Pile Fabrics

Weft knitting machines are used in the production of pile fabrics. The pile is knitted in from an extra set of yarns which is then drawn out in long loops. The loops may be left or cut. Some pile fabrics also use a sliver of fibers rather than a yarn, and this produces a very rich, luxurious pile. 'Fake furs', for instance, are sliver knit fabrics.

Weft Knits in Use

Single knits done in stockinette stitch are the most common knit fabrics and can be manufactured in a wide range of weights and tensions. Besides wide use in apparel, from hosiery and underwear to winter coats, casement and drapery fabrics, either plain or patterned, are frequently made. The possibility of snags and subsequent runs is a drawback of this type of construction, but here the composition of the yarn and the tightness of the knit can be compensating factors. Double knits are much sturdier, with excellent dimensional stability and run resistance. Compared to single knits, they are heavier, firmer, less stretchable, and more resilient. Their apparel use is well known, and they also make very durable upholstery fabric.

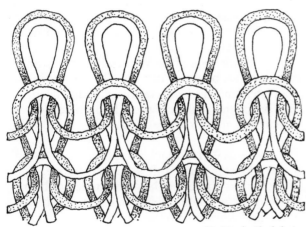

Knitted pile fabric

WARP KNITTING

Warp knitting can only be done by machine. As in weaving, the warp yarns are those which run lengthwise, but in warp knitting there are no crosswise yarns. The warp yarns are each manipulated by one needle, and loops are formed simultaneously across the width by interlocking each yarn with an adjacent, or close warp yarn. Manufacture is very rapid.

Warp knits are classified by the machine used to produce them. There are several, the most important being the **tricot** and the **raschel**.

Tricot Knits

The first tricot (pronounced treeko) machines were designed and made in England in 1775. Their basic operation and the knits they produced were very similar to those of today. Modern tricot machinery is classified as **single guide bar, 2-Bar, 3-Bar,** or more. The single machine produces only basic stockinette stitch; addition of guide bars indicates greater flexibility in pattern as the number of yarns is determined in this manner. The number of stitch variations also increase, depending on number of guide bars.

Plain or decorative tricot fabrics are made on the same machine, making them economical to produce. Lightweight, sheer, or lacelike fabrics are the usual production as the machinery works most efficiently in this area.

Raschel Knits

This versatile machine appeared in the 1960's and is capable of producing fabrics from the finest netting and trimming laces to heavy industrial goods. It uses multiple guide bars (4-56) which makes it possible to lay in a large amount of yarns. Openwork and dense fabrics, stable or elastic, textured or plain, are all possible, as well as plush fabrics and carpeting.

A 'Chaine' raschel machine knits and tucks on the face, and then reverses to create an alternating surface design.

The **Jacquard raschel** uses a Jacquard attachment to produce intricate eyelet stitch patterns.

Other Knits

The machinery listed below is generally used for quite specific fabrics. None are as versatile as either the raschel or the tricot.

MILANESE knits are fairly dense with a fine rib on the face and a diagonal structure on the reverse; used mainly for lingerie and gloves.

MARRATI: This is a variation of the milanese, but produces fabrics on a circular frame.

SIMPLEX: This machine produces double-faced fabrics used mainly for gloves.

CIDEGA: This knits crochet-like or openwork fabrics.

Warp Knits in Use

Tricot knits are generally soft, crease resistant and run resistant, with good drapability. Thickness of the fabric is determined by yarn used, and elongation is affected by the construction. Tight knits have lower elongation, knits of fine **gauge** have greater elongation ('gauge' is stitches per unit of width, 'fine' indicates many stitches.) The strength of tricot is variable; strong yarns, fine gauge and balanced construction all contribute to strength.

Raschel knits combine the characteristics of tricots with their capacity to be produced in virtually any yarn, and in a multitude of patterns and designs.

KNITTING VARIATIONS

Industrial designers and textile specialists have devised many new techniques and machines for manufacturing knit-type fabrics. Included in these recent innovations are:
— inserting weft yarns in warp knits,
— inserting warp yarns in weft knits,
— inserting warp and weft yarns in either warp or weft knits, called 'knit-weave',
— knit-sew techniques which form fabrics by simultaneously forming loops and stitching through.

Weft Insertion

Warp knitting machines can be adapted with attachments to lay in weft yarns. This may be one weft carried across the knitter, or with more complex attachments, a sheet of twenty or more weft yarns can be used as filling. Where warp knits may only be knitted with lengthwise stripes or color variations, weft insertion can produce crosswise variations as well. The finished fabric is more stable across the grain than an ordinary warp knit fabric.

Warp Insertion

This technique involves inserting warp yarns into the crosswise knitted structure of the weft knit. The warps are 'woven' in, that is, interlaced on a 1 x 1 basis with the weft knit yarns. The procedure gives greater dimensional stability in the lengthwise grain.

Knit-Weave

New machines, adapted from both weft and warp knitting machines, are able to insert both warp and weft yarns into the basic structure. The Co-We-Knit machine, an adaptation of the raschel warp knitter, is perhaps the most versatile. Fabrics may be quite fine, but the machine tends to be used most commonly for fairly rigid, coarse fabrics.

Knit-Sew

This procedure is also called 'stitch-through' or 'stitch-bonded', and the principal machines for the production of these fabrics are the European (East German) Mali and the Arachne, and their variations.

MALIMO fabrics are formed with three sets of yarns. Warp yarns are fed from a warp beam. Weft yarns are threaded into a carrier which moves back and forth across the machine, and simultaneously moves forward, placing the filling yarns at an angle to the warp. The sewing yarns are fed from a beam through compound needles which sew between the warp and across the filling, and interlock with the warp yarns in a tricot-like stitch. Variation in the fabric on the basic machine is possible only through variation in the yarns used.

ARACHNE AND MALI machines form fabric in a variety of ways: one uses a web of fibers stitched through with a binding thread carried by a knitting needle; another produces a looped pile fabric; another, warp-knits and simultaneously sews fabric; while still another variation produces fabric by forming interlocking loops in the web without a binder yarn.

Some uses of the Mali and Arachne variations are as backing fabrics, floor coverings, upholstery fabrics, wall coverings, sound deadening and/or thermal insulation, household cloths, packaging, and carpet backing.

THE KRAFTAMATIC machine is a cross between a warp knitter and a tuft sewing machine. The knitter works above and the sewing machine below to produce a double sided pile fabric without grain, and with the tufts securely locked in place. Blankets and carpets can be produced by this method.

Knit-Weaves and Knit-Sewn
Fabrics in Use

The procedures outlined produce fabrics with the best properties of both knitted and woven textiles, and they are economical to construct. Weft or warp insertion in knits produce fabrics that are stronger and have greater dimensional stability than either knits or weaves. They 'cover' better with no greater bulk, and have the comfort and easy draping qualities of knits. Weft and warp insertion in the true 'knit-weaves' have, in addition, great recovery from stress.

The knit-sew fabrics combine the above properties with an absence of grain which allows fabrics to be cut and sewn in any direction.

Production and greater use of these new fabrics, particularly in the environmental field, has potential in North America, but, as a group, they do not command a large share of the market at present.

KNITTING'S 'NEW FRONTIERS'

In the area of machinery, the development of electronic control of all functions is well underway. Increased automation and flexibility of production are astounding. Computer controls with solid state integrated circuit memory can now control all machine functions, including individual needle selection on all needle beds. Memory boards can carry control functions for 64,000 stitches at one time. All other machine operations, such as yarn feed, tension, direction and take-up can be similarly programmed.

The advances in fiber technology go hand-in-hand with machinery development. Textured filaments and new blends mean expanding possibilities in all areas. Knitted vinyl, for instance, is a new fabric with exciting prospects for commercial furniture seating.

The field of upholstery, in general, is open to new knits and their variations. The controlled stretch and good recovery features of knits in the past were limited by a lack of fabric stability, but stability is now a feature of the knit-weaves and knit-sewn fabrics. The resulting better fit and simplified tailoring are important new considerations.

Similarly, the field of draperies, bedspreads and blankets has been opened to knits. Knitted carpets, made on raschel machines, have a distinct advantage over woven carpets in that 100% of the yarn contributes to wear or appearance, whereas 20-30% of the yarn in woven carpets lies on the back and is virtually unused. Knitted carpets, however, do not have the same appearance as tufted woven carpeting, and this is, so far, a drawback to wide consumer acceptance.

Progress in all of these environmental textile areas is constant and will undoubtedly continue.

TUFTED FABRICS

Tufting was first a handcraft, developed in the southeastern United States. Candle wick was used as a tufting yarn to work intricate designs in bedspreads. These 'candlewick' spreads were very popular. Hooked rugs were made by a similar technique.

The handcraft involved working yarns into already woven fabric. The automatic tufting procedure practiced today works on the same principle. The method is flexible in that any weight of backing and tufting yarns may be used.

In the automated system, backing (woven or knit) is secured in a horizontal position, and rows of threaded needles are pushed through the fabric from above. Beneath the fabric, companion hooks catch the yarn and hold it in a predetermined position while the threaded needle is retracted. For cut loop pile, blades are attached to the catching hooks and sever the loops once they are fully made.

When the tufting is completed, the tufts of yarn are untwisted and teased open. This 'blooming' of the yarn helps to hold the tufts in place. As well, the backing fabric is often shrunk in the finishing process which further tightens the tufts in place. Quality tufting is very dense. Knits are the best backing fabric, with more flexibility than weaves. Woven backing sometimes 'grins' through the tufting when the fabric is folded.

Tufting is a very fast process, and less expensive than other methods of producing pile fabrics. Variations in pattern, pile height, and density are matters of simple machine adjustment.

Tufted Fabrics in Use

Carpeting is one of the commonest tufted fabrics, with over 95% of all carpeting made by this method. A tufting machine produces some 700 square meters (yards) of carpeting per hour, has a heavy backing applied, usually with a latex compound which thoroughly locks the tufts in place.

The tufted construction is also used extensively for blankets and bedspreads, as well as apparel and 'fur fabrics'.

BRAIDS, NETS AND LACES

Braids

Braids are primarily a trimming fabric with three or more yarns interlaced diagonally.

Braid

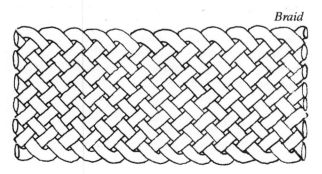

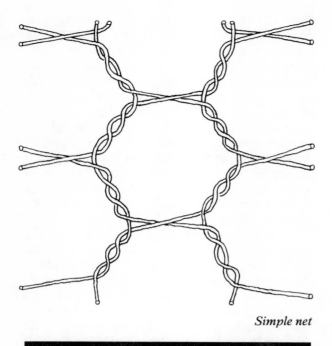

Simple net

They are very strong in the lengthwise direction. (Shoelaces are circular braids.) Flat braids are used as trims in environmental applications. Occasionally braids are made into interesting fabrics by sewing lengths together. Braided rugs are made by braiding various materials and sewing them together in a circular fashion from the center outward.

Nets

Nets are open meshed fabrics made by knotting or knitting. Knotted nets are traditional, with geometric mesh in a range of sizes. Knitted nets are now constructed on tricot or raschel machines, using very fine filament yarns.

Laces

Laces may be knotted, interlaced, twisted or knit. They are fabrics with decorative designs on an open mesh backing.

Making lace by hand is a traditional home craft, using hooks, needles, bobbins or shuttles. Handmade lace is called real lace. From early use as altar cloths and priestly ornaments, handmade lace has had many periods of high fashion. In Elizabethan times, lace cuffs became very popular. The fashion eventually got out of control, with some 'cuffs' up to 61 cm (24") deep, and using some 22 meters (25 yards) of handmade lace.

Lace fabrics may now be constructed by a weaving technique on a complex piece of equipment called the **Leavers Lace Machine.** Utilizing some 40,000 moving parts, and hundreds of miles of threads, the machine duplicates the most complicated handmade lace. The pattern is controlled by a Jacquard attachment.

Lace fabrics have specialty uses as casements or window hangings.

No-element Fabrics

The 'elements' in fabric construction are the yarns and/or threads. 'No-element' is used to denote fabrics constructed without yarns or threads. Felt was the first, and, for centuries, the only no-element fabric. Now it has been joined by a wealth of fabrics produced from fibers bonded or joined in some specific way, and by an equally high number of films, foams, laminates and extrusions.

No-element fabrics came about as a natural progression following vast expansion in the man-made fiber field, and represent a tremendous simplification in textile production. They are manufactured very economically and at high speed, and it is this factor which presents a great challenge to traditional textile methods.

FELTS

The inherent structure of wool fibers gives them the ability to curl, shrink and interlock when subjected to moisture, heat and agitation. This natural tendency undoubtedly inspired the first felts. Now, moisture, agitation, heat and pressure are systematically used to produce felts. The wool fibers used may be short—either new, reprocessed, or reused—and 40-50% of non-felting fibers can be added to the mixture. Alternate applications of warm moisture, agitation, pressure and relaxation are usually sufficient for felting to occur, but sulphuric acid and soap are sometimes added to increase the felting action. The resultant fabric may be less than a millimeter or close to 100 mm (about 1/32" to 3") in thickness. Felts are also formed by felting woven textiles of wool or wool blends.

Felts are inelastic and relatively weak. However, their dense structure contributes to good insulating and sound deadening properties. Thick felts are used as rug pads, and thinner, more flexible felts are useful for wall coverings, pillow and table covers, and, occasionally, draperies.

FIBER WEB FABRICS

Fiber web fabrics are used for a relatively large field of textile products. They are produced in a variety of ways, all of which include the formation of a web of fibers. The fibers may be **oriented** (made parallel) in any one direction; layers of oriented webs may be **crosslaid** in alternate directions; the web may be formed of **crosslaced** fibers; or, the web may consist of a **random** mat. As will be seen, techniques vary, but the following four basic steps are common to manufacture of all fiber web fabrics:

— preparation of the fiber,
— web formation,
— bonding of the web,
— drying and curing of the fabric.

Needle Punched Fabrics

Needle punched fabrics are those made by mechanical bonding of the fiber web; specifically, by the use of a bed of barbed needles which intimately tangle the fibers into a felt-like configuration.

NEEDLE FELTS: Resembling felt in appearance, needle felts are made of fibers other than wool. Fibers are blended and a web formed by automatic means, using forced air or a moving screen. The fiber mat is laid on a moving belt, and it is mechanically bonded by repeated punching of hundreds of barbed needles set in a board which rises and falls on the fiber web up to 2,500 times. The effect of the needle punching is to push and distort the fibers into a thin, tangled mat. Variations of the needle punching technique may also produce fabrics with one surface resembling a loop pile.

Uses of needle felts include carpeting, wall covering, insulation, padding and blankets. One of the most common trade names is Ozite.

Bonded Fabrics

Fiber mats held together by adhesives, fusing, or other chemical or thermal means, are 'bonded fabrics'. The range is large, and takes in disposable and short-lived fabrics as well as durables. Chemical innovations in thermoplastic man-made fibers and in adhesives have made such fabric forming techniques possible.

Adhesive-bonded fabrics had their beginnings in the 1930's as textile companies looked for ways of using cotton waste. After World War II, interest shifted to the man-made fibers when it was realized that the techniques which had been developed could be used to manufacture viable textile products. Since then, the thermoplastic qualities of most man-mades have been exploited, and **thermal bonding** is a common technique. More recent procedures are the **spunbonded** and **spunlaced** methods, with fibers formed and bonded into fabric in one continuous operation. Bonding methods are constantly under review; other processes now in use are **solvent bonding** and **print bonding**. New methods may still be devised.

DRY-LAY WEBBED FABRICS: In this procedure, dry fibers are formed into a web by air dispersion, or a moving screen or belt. Fibers may be random, or oriented in one direction. Pressure compresses the mat, and bonding occurs either with the application of a particular adhesive resin (wet or dry), or by having blended into the fibers a small proportion of fibers with a low melt point (called 'binder fibers'). In either case, the fiber mat is then subjected to heat and/or chemical action which fuses the fibers. Cooling and drying completes the fabric process.

WET-LAY WEBBED FABRICS: This method copies techniques used for paper making. Fibers are suspended in water, then deposited on a surface which drains the water and leaves the fibers in a damp web. Bonding, as in dry-lay, can be by applied adhesives, binder fibers, or by adhesives suspended in the water which join the web and bond it as it dries.

SOLVENT BONDING of fabrics is ingenious. A particular solvent is applied to the web which attacks the fibers and causes them to 'spot weld' at points of contact. Before the solvent can destroy the fibers, it is evaporated off at higher temperatures and leaves the fiber structure bonded. This produces a softer fabric than one in which adhesives are impregnated.

PRINT BONDING is an adaptation of adhesive bonding using a roller, or screen printer, to lay on a design of adhesive, either clear or colored. The print design must be close enough to effect bonding, but the spaces left provide air circulation and greater flexibility in the fabric. J-cloths are print bonded fiber web fabrics.

SPUNBONDS are the product of a four-step integrated polymer-to-fabric process. The fiber is extruded in filament form, drawn to introduce strength, formed into a web on a moving surface, and bonded. Although different bonding techniques are used, the easiest bond is accomplished when two polymers, differing in thermal reactivity, are simultaneously extruded and formed into a common web. Later exposure to heat melts one group of fibers, which serves to bond all of them together.

The spunbonded fabrics are used as tufted carpet backing, reinforcing, interlining, and substrates for various extruded film fabrics. Some trade names are Cerex, Reemay, Typar and Tyvek.

SPUNLACED FABRICS: These are made by a fluid fiber entanglement process. Extruded and drawn fibers are formed into a web on a moving frame (often one with an intricate pattern) and entangled with fluids under high pressure. No adhesive or binding agent is needed. Nexus is a trade name for such a spunlaced fabric.

Fiber Web Fabrics in Use

Most fiber web fabrics are used 'as is', but they are adaptable to coloring and printing finishes. They have wide home and industrial use such as diapers, interfacings, bandages, surgical gowns, and decontamination clothing. There are many environmental uses as well: upholstery and carpet backing, carpeting, blankets, window shades, curtains, placemats and napkins.

FOAMS

Foams are complex cross-linked polymers, formed by a reaction of chemicals which causes the formation of bubbles within a viscose solution. Subsequent drying and curing results in huge, solid blocks or cylinders of dry, flexible, spongy material. The rolls or blocks are then blade cut into the desired thickness, which may be as thin as 0.06 cm (0.024″).

Contents of the solution dictate the size of bubbles (cells) and also the eventual range of physical properties. Foams may be nearly rigid, to very flexible, and may be produced in many colors. Flexible urethane foams are used as cushions, padding, carpet backing, and as an integral part of laminated fabrics.

Some properties of flexible urethane foam are good tensile strength, with excellent abrasion resistance and tear strength, and excellent dimensional stability. There is easy, though limited, elongation, with perfect recovery; it does not sag, mat, or become lumpy. Foam is unharmed by solvents, soaps and detergents, and is unaffected by water, mildew, and microorganisms. It is odorless and hypo-allergenic. It has excellent insulating properties, and remains pliable in extremes of cold or heat. Sunlight causes yellowing but no loss of durability.

Films

Films are polymers formed into continuous flat sheets. Most are made of vinyl or polyurethane, although many of the same chemicals used for fibers are also applicable as films. Films may be plain, expanded, supported or unsupported. They may be clear, colored, translucent, opaque, or clear colored. Films may be as thin as saran wrap or as thick as heavy-duty upholstery.

PLAIN FILMS are dense, firm, smooth and uniform. They have innumerable industrial, agricultural and household uses, from drop sheets to moisture barriers.

EXPANDED FILMS are soft and spongy, with tiny air cells formed through addition of a chemical 'blowing agent' to the solution. They are often used as alternates for leather or suede. They are light and pliable, with a good hand.

SUPPORTED FILMS have a woven, knit or bonded backing and there are many applications: upholstery, wall coverings, automobile seat covers, luggage, etc. Naugahyde is a well-known trade name.

UNSUPPORTED FILMS may have application in any of the areas mentioned above. Colored and/or printed, and with a paper backing, they become wallpaper. Textured, they may be almost anything: rainwear, shower curtains, window blinds, tablecloths, outdoor furniture covers, etc.

Ultrasuede

This popular fabric was devised in Japan and has had wide acceptance for high fashion apparel and as upholstery for quality furniture.

The product is a compound structure using several classified techniques. The final components are polyester and polyurethane. With the feel of genuine suede, it is strong, durable, and easily maintained.

Natural 'Film Fabrics'

While not technically classified as either fabrics or film, leather and tapa are frequently used as textiles and deserve mention here.

LEATHER is manufactured primarily from the hides of animals. (Reptile, fish and bird skins are also used for specialty leathers.) The hides are tanned by either natural or chemical processes, and then split into layers. Depending on thickness, there may be two, four, or more layers. The outer layer is called **top grain**, subsequent layers are 'first split', 'second split,' etc. The bottom layer is called slab. Only the top layer has the characteristic animal grain. Splits require finishing and embossing to resemble top grain leather. Suede is produced by napping the underside of a layer.

TAPA is one of the earliest fabrics created from a solid layer. The source of tapa is the inner bark of the paper mulberry tree in the South Sea Islands, or the fig tree in the Mediterranean and Central American areas. Cloth is made by soaking the bark, then beating it with wooden mallets into a smooth, paper-thin sheet. The natural color of tapa is a light tan, and it was traditionally block printed in shades of brown and black.

EXTRUDED FABRICS

This is a new field. Extruded fabrics are a variation of films. They are produced from polymer solutions in a sheet, like films, but they are neither continuous nor flat.

First application of the technique was for practical vegetable wraps, and these may still be seen (around heads of lettuce, for instance). The fabrics are formed by piercing, slitting and/or punching out shapes in a just-produced film, then stretching, and sometimes embossing. The resulting fabric is a lace-like structure with durability, airiness and texture. Design potential is unlimited, and this new fabric form will no doubt be further exploited.

Compound Fabrics

Many fabrics, both ancient and modern, are composed of more than one component. The category includes:

— embroidery: yarns stitched on a fabric ground;
— applique and patchwork: small pieces of fabric used to decorate, or to form, large pieces;
— quilting: fabrics and filling stitched together;
— laminated (or bonded) fabrics: layers of fabrics, films, or fabrics and films stuck together.

EMBROIDERY

Embellishing a fabric with yarn, feathers, quills, bangles, or sequins is, in many cultures, as old as cloth making itself. It is one of the most popular of handcrafts. Dominant in furnishings are Kashmir crewel embroideries, in which wool yarns are chain-stitched onto homespun cotton. The paisleylike motifs are as traditional as the technique.

Most domestic embroidery today is machine embroidery, made on a Schiffli machine, and called **Schiffli embroidery**. Characteristic of this embroidery is the technique used, in which the decorative yarn does not penetrate the cloth but is held in place with binding threads stitched through from the back. Thousands of needles stitch simultaneously, working from a hole punched guide which directs the placement of each stitch and the number of repeats in an overall pattern. Embroidered goods are produced in relatively short lengths, as the machinery works from selvage to selvage.

A variation is Schiffli lace, achieved by embroidering a grill-like pattern with very compact stitches, and then burning away the ground fabric with acid so that only the 'lace' remains.

APPLIQUE, PATCHWORK AND QUILTING

In the recent past, there has been an astonishing growth of interest in handcrafts, folk arts and quilting. Quilt-making was an accepted and necessary function of every North American household from the earliest days, and was a craft with a soul, engaging not only the eyes and hands, but also imagination and a sense of history. The art declined as improved heating made layers of bedding less essential, and as machine-made blankets became available. Making things by hand lost favor for several generations, and it is only recently that we have come to revalue the work of human hands (and domestic sewing machines!).

Home quilting, appliqué and patchwork, made easier with new materials, are once again becoming treasured textiles for the interior. With a 'trend' underway, the textile industry found ways to mass produce such goods. While they cannot duplicate the emotional attachment and significance of genuine handwork, the appearance may be similar and certainly adds a comfortable ambience to home interiors and institutional settings.

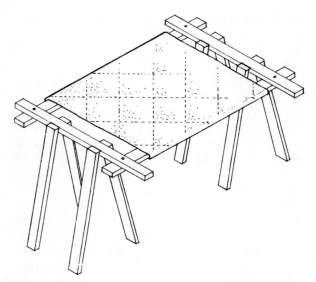

Hand-quilting frames are simple structures usually at table height or lower which hold the layers together for final stitching.

Appliqué

Appliqué is the process of sewing small pieces of fabric onto a larger piece to create interesting patterns or designs.

Patchwork

Patchwork is the sewing together of different pieces of fabric to make a large piece. It was once the art of making whole cloth from bits and pieces of scraps, or clothing that was worn. It was born of necessity, where money and material goods were scarce, but time and labor could be given to such a task.

Home patchwork is now done, either by hand or on home sewing machines, using new materials. The appeal of modern patchwork fabrics is in the originality of the design, pattern, or the combination of colors and textures.

APPLIQUE AND PATCHWORK have not been adapted to mass production using original techniques. Occasionally, cloth is printed to resemble either fabric.

Quilting

Quilting is the stitching together of two or more layers of fabric and filling. In earlier times, the filling was layers of wool or cotton, usually well worn. The top side was given a decorative treatment with designs in patchwork of scraps or 'hardly worn' fabrics. The underside was simply a presentable backing, most often cotton. It also enjoyed periods of high fashion;

quilting for formal attire was *de riqueur* during the Spanish Bombast period in Europe (1545-1620), when it was the fashion to adorn clothing so heavily with ornaments, a single layer of fabric could not support them. It is said that England's Queen Elizabeth I wore skirts so heavy with jewels they had to be equipped with little wheels to allow her to walk. Furnishings in comfortable 17th and 18th century homes often included complete sets of matching quilts, quilted canopies, and side curtains.

Today, home quilt makers use any long-lasting fabric as both top and underside, synthetic batting of polyester, and sew them together with cotton-polyester, polyester, twistless nylon, or silicone coated thread. Machine-made quilted fabrics use similar components and several methods of joining the layers together.

Machine Quilting

Machine quilting is done by several methods, effectively joining the layers of fabric and filling, and varying in their appearance from authentic to modern.

HAND-GUIDED QUILTING is the most versatile and by far the most costly. It is done with industrial sized single-needle sewing machines by individual operators. The three most popular types are **outline quilting**, in which the quilting stitches follow the motif of a printed fabric; **trapunto quilting**, in which only portions of the cloth are quilted and stuffed (often in a centered design); and **vermicelli**, an all-over, noodle-like quilting pattern.

AUTOMATED QUILTING is a procedure in which a whole width of cloth is passed through a multiple-needle machine, producing a variety of simple geometric patterns.

STITCHLESS QUILTING is a relatively recent technique, in which the layers are fused or bonded in a quilted pattern, using adhesives or heat. The Pinsonic Thermal Joining Machine welds layers together by heat from ultrasonic vibrations.

Quilting Materials

Any relatively stable fabric can be used for the coverings. Depending on the end use, the top may be a quality upholstery fabric, a fashion fabric, or white goods. If a reversible fabric is required, the underside is also a show fabric. If the quilted fabric is intended for bedspreads, a non-slip backing is often used. If it is intended as upholstery, the back is often black or white cheesecloth. Batting may be cotton, foam, or fiber-fill of acetate or polyester.

Embroidery and Quilted Fabrics in Use

The beauty and distinction of hand-done embroidery and quilting should not be overlooked. Innovative design and workmanship of the highest quality is available throughout North America, and, for both conventional and unconventional applications in interiors, they are worth seeking out.

Machine embroidered and quilted fabrics find many uses as environmental textiles. Care must be taken to assure that threads and sewing techniques are durable, as broken threads are both unsightly and allow the layers to shift.

Crewel embroidered fabrics make outstanding upholstery, and plain or patterned fabrics, quality quilted, add interest, texture, and durability to furnishings.

LAMINATED FABRICS

Modern laminating had its beginnings in the late 1950's as a means of using up inventories of lightweight fabrics. Operations were often marginal, and, as a result, early bonded fabrics were of dubious quality. Public acceptance of the concept was excellent, however, and quality controls were soon instituted.

Today, laminates, or bonded fabrics as they are sometimes called, are made with a multitude of materials in both good and poor quality. These compound fabrics must be assessed carefully to determine that:

— the layers are securely bonded,
— adhesives have not penetrated the surface or backing,
— the grain lines (if applicable) of the two fabrics are compatible,
— there is no stiffness, off-color, or unusual odor,
— adequate care instructions are available.

Fabrics are intimately bonded together in two basic ways: the wet adhesive method, or with foam-flame bonding.

Wet-adhesive Method

In the wet-adhesive method, rollers apply a carefully controlled quantity of adhesive to the underside of the face fabric, which is then pressed to the underside of the backing fabric. Two types of adhesive are used:

WATER-BASED ACRYLICS require a cure temperature of 148°C (300°F). It is the lower cost method, but applicable only to fabrics or films that can stand the temperature.

SOLVENT-BASED URETHANES cure without heat, but the moment of contact between the tacky adhesive surface of one fabric and the fabric being bonded to it is crucial, and the bonding process must be done in smaller batches. A good bond, however, has excellent durability and fabrics bonded with this adhesive may be washed or dry-cleaned.

Foam-flame Bonding

In foam-flame bonding, one surface of a layer of foam is flame melted as it is brought into contact with the underside of the face fabric; further along the automated line, the alternate surface of the foam layer is melted as it is brought into contact with the underside of the backing fabric.

Common Laminations

FABRIC-TO-FOAM AND FILM-TO-FOAM LAMINATES are also known as 'foambacks'. A layer of foam is bonded to the underside of a layer of fabric, or film, by either of the two methods.

FABRIC-TO-FABRIC BONDS are composed of any two fabrics (e.g., wool blend face and nylon tricot backing) bonded by either of the two methods. Fabric may also be bonded in this manner to a layer of fibers, to produce fabric for special end uses.

FABRIC-TO-FOAM-TO-FABRIC BONDS: In this combination, the intention is to retain a foam layer. Thicker foam, and the foam-flame bonding technique is used.

OTHER COMPONENTS combined by lamination techniques are: metallic polyester film bonded to clear film (Mylar is the trade name); fiberfill batting bonded to a face fabric; open-net backing bonded to open lace type fabric; open-faced fabrics bonded to metallic films; sheer lace type fabrics bonded to clear vinyl.

Laminated Fabrics in Use

Use of laminates is highest in the apparel field, where the insulating, self-lining, and reversible characteristics are very attractive. In environmental use, laminates have very wide acceptance: shower curtains, wall coverings, tablecloths, furniture coverings, draperies and casement cloths.

82

9 FINISHING

In the modern textile industry, finishing is a term which encompasses a vast array of activities and materials. Unfinished textiles are virtually nonexistent. In fact, one could almost use the synonymous term 'not completed' to describe a textile product which had not received at least half a dozen finishes.

The exceptions to this broad generalization are some of the fiber web fabrics and films manufactured for specific uses. They are often used 'as is', but it must be remembered that curing or heat setting are part of the manufacturing process in these cases, whereas they would normally be considered finishes.

The bulk of woven and knitted fabrics are produced as *greige*, or grey goods. They are not literally grey, but may be any degree of off-white, or even colored, with impurities and blemishes, and totally devoid of character. Finishing transforms them into fabrics we can identify.

There are roughly five hundred trade-marked fabric finishes, and more appear each year. As these finishes relate to environmental textiles, labels are an important aspect. Usually, they are informative about the finish, explicit about maintenance, and a guarantee of effectiveness and/or permanence.

Finishes fall into various categories. In usual chronological order they are: basic (routine, general, preliminary) finishes, surface treatment, functional enhancement, coloring and printing.

If the grey goods have not been produced in an integrated operation, where finishing follows manufacture, then the unfinished goods are sent or sold to a *converter*, a firm which 'converts' or finishes textiles.

Basic Finishes

Before fabric can undergo treatments and finishes to modify its appearance or change its quality, it must be made ready, or pre-treated. These preliminary finishes depend on the fiber and construction method used to produce the fabric. Those made of natural fibers require more pre-treatment than man-made fabrics.

On a fiber content basis, the following are considered as basic finishes:

COTTON AND LINEN: boiling, singeing, desizing,

bleaching, optional mercerizing, preshrinking, stabilizing, tenter drying.

WOOL: perching, burling, specking, mending, sewing, carbonizing, fulling, scouring, crabbing, preshrinking, stabilizing.

SILK: boiling off, bleaching, drying, optional weighting.

RAYON, ACETATE, TRIACETATE: singeing, scouring.

SYNTHESIZED FABRICS: desizing, scouring, dry heat setting.

Blends pose particular problems for finishers. A natural/man-made blend usually considers the requirements of the natural fiber, but equal attention must be given to the synthetic component to assure that it is not adversely affected.

There is not one set order to the following pre-treatments. The progression of basic finishes varies with both the fiber content and the planned eventual finishes. Finishes may be mechanical, chemical, or a combination of the two. Most fabric converters have sophisticated machinery which combines several finishes in one continuous automated line.

Boiling
Cotton, linen and silk are boiled in water to remove the natural gums, pectins and waxes.

Bleaching
Bleaching is usually done with chemicals such as chlorine or peroxide. Bleaching serves the dual purpose of making grey goods pure white and also increasing the fiber's capacity to absorb dye at a later stage.

Desizing
Sizing is often added to the warp yarns in the weaving process. These products may be starch, wax, gelatin, oil, or chemical polymers. In the desizing treatment special enzymes are applied to convert the sizing to compounds which will easily wash out.

Brushing
This is a mechanical process to remove short fine fibers from the surface, carried out by passing the fabric over a revolving drum equipped with fine bristles. The procedure is sometimes used in conjunction with singeing or shearing.

Singeing
In this procedure, the fabric is literally singed with gas jets or white hot metal to burn off the fuzz of fibers on the surface. Immediately after singeing, the cloth is immersed in water. The water bath often contains enzymes which break down any remaining starches into soluble sugars, which are easily washed out in subsequent wet steps.

Sizing
Sizing fills the fabric with specific compounds (such as starch or glue) to give it weight and strength.

Tenter Drying
This procedure follows various wet treatments which leave the fabric damp and pulled out of shape. The tenter frame holds the fabric by the selvages and exerts tension, if needed, while carrying the cloth over a heat source to set it to its proper width. If the cloth has gone off-grain in the manufacturing process, cloth straighteners on the tenter frame will automatically sense it, and adjustments may be made to pull the cloth into square.

Pre-shrinking
This procedure varies for fabrics of different fibers.

COTTON: Basically, in the case of cotton, preshrinking simply gets the fabric back to its original size after many wet treatments have stretched it out of shape. This is done with compression and heat, and sometimes the addition of ammonia, which penetrates the fiber and changes the molecular structure. The ammonia swells and relaxes the fibers. When it is removed, the cotton will not shrink.

RAYON: The pre-shrink process for rayon involves saturating the fabric with caustic soda which swells the fibers permanently, and sets them in the weave position.

WOOL: Controlling shrinkage in wool is a complicated problem, and no one process is practiced by all converters. Methods include mechanical compacting and cold water baths. Chemical treatments may be applied, such as the wet-chlorination process, which is designed to change the fiber surface so that the frictional properties are altered, thus preventing felting shrinkage. Additives, such as resins, rubber derivatives and polymers, are also used to impregnate and/or coat the wool fibers.

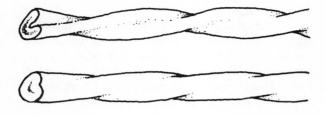

Cotton fiber, greatly enlarged, showing the natural fiber (top) and a mercerized fiber (bottom).

Stabilizing

This is a process for setting the woven or knit fabric in a particular size configuration. It is sometimes considered synonymous with shrinkage control. Dry heat is used at temperatures up to 204°C (400°F) to lock the construction dimensions in place. Application of synthetic resins is an alternate method of stabilizing.

Mercerizing

Mercerization is a patented process first developed by English chemist John Mercer in 1844. The object is to improve strength, luster, and dyeability of cotton. The procedure saturates the cotton fibers with caustic soda while the fabric is held under tension. The fibers so treated are changed from somewhat irregular and crinkly to round and straight. Mercerizing 'in the piece' (fabric as opposed to yarns or threads) reduces differences between various kinds of cotton, and alters and makes uniform both immature and 'dead' fibers which normally react differently to dyes.

Perching

This is an early examination procedure. Cloth is passed over a frame (called a perch) of frosted glass lighted from below as well as above. Visual inspection is carried out by individuals, and flaws, stains, knots, etc., are marked.

Fixing

After perching, imperfections are fixed in the following ways:

BURLING entails removing loose threads and knots

with tweezers, called burling irons.

SPECKING is also done with burling irons, and removes specks, burrs and motes.

MENDING is repairing small defects by hand.

SEWING is repairing larger defects by sewing, darning or hand weaving.

Carbonizing

Carbonizing is a chemical finish. A solution of sulphuric acid is used to saturate the wool fabric, with the object of 'burning out' any vegetable matter. The fabric is heated for a brief time and the acid converts the vegetation to carbon, which can then be brushed out.

Fulling

Fulling is an old mechanical technique to soften and compact woven wool fabrics. In the procedure the fabric is agitated or twisted in warm soapy water and rinsed thoroughly in cold water. The fabric yarns shrink together and the fabric itself softens.

Scouring

This is washing with soap, alkalis, or detergents in water, or alternately, chemical solvents may be used.

Crabbing

Crabbing is a mechanical finish applied to wool to set the weave. The fabric is immersed in hot, then cold, water and fed into pressing rollers with the warp and filling yarns carefully set at 90° to each other. Improper crabbing can set an off-grain.

Weighting

Weighting is a sizing technique applied to silk. After boiling off the natural gums, silk fabric is very soft and light. Because the fibers are very absorbent, weighting with metallic salts, such as stannous chloride, is possible, and is done to make the silk fabric heavier. However, if overdone, the silk fabric tends to crack and split. Additionally, weighted silks are less durable and more sensitive to sunlight, air and perspiration. The amount of weighting is controlled by law and is usually less than 10-15%.

Sericin, or other organic gums, may be used legally to weight silk, but fabrics must then be dry-cleaned as washing will remove the gums. In addition, sericin or gum weighted silk is subject to spotting with water.

Dry Heat Setting

This process is used on synthetics to set the fabric in a particular configuration. The purpose is usually to introduce or increase dimensional stability in a smooth, flat shape, but heat setting is also used to set desired creases. The temperatures are carefully controlled, and the degree necessary is that at which the interior of the individual fiber polymer develops 'flow' or melt. The physical characteristics of the polymer are changed, set occurs, and the fabric is not degraded in any way.

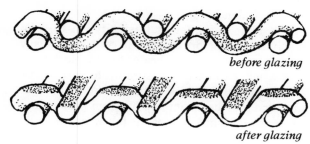

before glazing

after glazing

Application of resin, heat and pressure cause permanent flattening, forming a durable glazed fabric.

Surface Treatments

Surface treatments are those which affect the appearance and/or hand of the fabric. Many are traditional mechanical treatments, others are durable resin finishes, and some are a combination of chemical and mechanical processes to effect a particular appearance or touch.

MECHANICAL TREATMENTS

Sueding

This procedure involves 'sanding' of the surface with abrasive rollers to produce a characteristic very low pile.

Napping

Also called brushing, gigging, raising, or teaseling, the procedure results in formation of a nap (or pile) by subjecting the surface to a vigorous brushing action with wire bristles mounted on rollers. Fabrics may be napped on one or both surfaces.

Polishing

Polishing is applied to pile fabrics to straighten the fibers and impart luster. A felt blanket is used as a base, and the surface to be polished is brought into contact with a heated cylinder set with serrated fluted blades which comb the pile fibers into alignment.

Plissé

This wrinkled effect is obtained by printing cotton with concentrated caustic soda applied with a roller. The parts of the fabric so printed shrink, and cause the whole piece to assume a crinkled configuration.

Shearing

Shearing is a mechanical process which involves shearing (or cutting off) surface fibers, or, making a pile or nap even. The machine is similar to a reel type lawnmower—a spiral cylinder fitted with blades.

Decating

This is a mechanical process used on wool, silk, rayon or their blends and can be performed wet or dry. The object is to set a luster on wool, to soften the hand and reduce the shine of silks or rayons, and to increase stability of all. The wet process forces hot, then cold, water through the fabric, followed by pressing. In dry decating, first steam and then cold air are forced through, followed by pressing. The intensity of the heating-cooling cycles, and the degree of pressure in the pressing step, are variable. The most intense procedure is called full decating. This is followed by semi-decating, and, least severe, continuous decating. Proposed end use of the fabric determines which method is used.

Corduroy

The long filling floats woven into the fabric are not always cut as part of the manufacturing step. This process cuts the floats, and the resulting pile is repeatedly brushed and treated with oils and waxes to set the corduroy luster.

Calendering

The calender is basically an ironing machine. The factory equipment consists of heavy steel rollers which can be heated to variable degrees and which can exert pressure up to 140 kg per square centimeter (2000 lbs/square inch). The machine may use from two to seven rollers, and the type of roll determines the fabric finish.

EMBOSSED effects are achieved by using one steel roller with an engraved design, and hard fiber-covered rollers in the balance.

MOIRÉ effects are achieved in the same manner, using a moiré engraved roller.

SCHREINER calendering uses a roller on which very fine lines have been engraved. This gives the fabric extremely fine ridges which reflect light and simulate mercerized cotton.

PALMER calendering is used on satins, taffetas and twills to give them a mellow hand. Steam-heated rollers covered in felt give the fabric a smooth, attractive finish.

FRICTION calendering produces a glazed effect. Steel rollers moving quickly alternate with slower moving cloth-covered rollers to impart a surface glaze. This finish is not as permanent as newer methods using a durable resin finish.

FLOCKING

This mechanical treatment produces designs on fabrics by glueing cut fibers onto the surface. Conversely, the entire surface may be flocked. A permanent adhesive is printed on the cloth with a roller, the flocking fiber is sprayed or blown on, sticks to the adhesive treated areas, and the fabric is then cured.

Electrostatic Flocking

This is an extremely fast and efficient system, and flexible to changes in fabric and flocking. The fibers to be used for flocking are chopped less than 6 mm in length and treated to make them electrostatically responsive. The machinery carrying the base fabric is electrically charged and the flocking fibers adhere in an upright position.

The process is used to produce upholstery fabric, draperies, carpets, blankets, pool and game table covers, wall coverings, and outdoor surface coverings for putting greens, swimming pool surrounds and tennis courts.

DURABLE FINISHES

Durable finishes have been widespread since the Everglaze process for making durable glazed chintz was introduced by Jos. Bancroft and Sons in 1938. Many of the traditional methods are used, but the addition of chemical substances to the fabric before or during treatment render the achieved finish as durable as the life of the cloth.

Synthetic Resins

This was the first material used to produce durable finishes. Resin is an adhesive synthetic substance, and, properly cured, is insoluble. It is applied to cloth in a water solution which also contains a chemical catalyst to stimulate the resin to polymerize when exposed to heat. This polymerization locks the resin into chains and cross chains on and between the individual fibers and makes the finish durable.

Durable Pressing

This is the method used to produce durable finishes, and is identical to calendering except that the addition of resins to the fabric before calendering makes the finish permanent. Virtually all fabrics, natural and man-made, can be given durable finishes with selected resins.

EMBOSSING of durable textural effects is practically limitless. Plain cotton, for instance, can be made to look like linen, leather, satin, piqué, seersucker, heavy cord, crepe, moiré, or almost anything else. Double calenders have been devised with male and female rolls, the projections on one roll fitting into the indentations in the other.

DURABLE GLAZING is done with friction calendering of resin treated fabrics.

DIMENSIONAL STABILITY, CRISPNESS and RESISTANCE TO WRINKLES are also added to fabrics given durable resin finishes.

Effect of Resins on Fabrics

Resins generally have a beneficial effect on fabrics. However, it is dependent to a large degree on the quality of the cloth, the quality of the chemicals, and the care taken with the mechanical finish. Resins weaken the fibers slightly, and the stiffening of the fabric with resin contributes to a decrease in abrasion resistance. Resin may also make a fabric brittle, and less absorbent.

CHEMICAL FINISHES

Besides the traditional and durable finishes already noted, the following treatments are designed specifically to modify the appearance or hand of fabrics.

Acid Finishes

An acid finish is used on cotton sheers to produce a transparent or parchment-like effect. Sulphuric acid is used as a very brief bath, followed immediately by neutralizing. The whole cloth may be treated, or acid may be used to 'burn out' designs which appear more transparent than the balance. Conversely, designs may be left and the background made sheer.

The technique is also used with blends of fabrics, in which case the acid completely destroys one fiber, leaving intricate designs of the other.

Caustics or Phenol

These may be used to produce irregular texture effects on specific fabrics. Use must be carefully controlled to avoid destroying the fabric.

Stiffening Finishes

In addition to the sizing of fabrics, various thermosetting resins, cellulose and plastic compounds are used to produce fabrics with durable stiffness.

Softening Finishes

Many products are used as softening agents. Oil, fat, wax, soap, detergents, substituted ammonium, and silicone compounds are used to improve hand and drape of fabrics. The silicone finishes are relatively durable.

Delusterants

Normally, natural luster-free, or solution delustered fibers, are used to produce fabrics with little or no luster. However, the effect can also be obtained by immersing a fabric in any of the following: barium sulphate, china clay, aluminum oxide, zinc oxide and methylene urea. These external delusterants are deposited on the fibers and effectively hide their shine.

Optical Brighteners

These are various substances which attach themselves to the fabric and, when exposed to sunlight, absorb ultraviolet light and reflect it as visible blue light. It is a fluorescent effect, which helps white or bright fabrics maintain a new appearance.

Functional Enhancement

Finishes classified as functional are more concerned with a fabric's performance than its appearance or hand. They add such features as water resistance, mothproofing, soil release, etc. The range of these finishes is large and most are relatively recent.

Water Repellent Finishes

These finishes coat or seal a fabric so that water cannot pass through. Early coatings included rubber, oxidized oil and varnish. Today, a wide range of coatings are in use: silicone finishes — with the trademarked names Hydro-Pruf, Sylmer, Cravenette 330, Ranedare S, Aquagard, and Impregnole; pyridium finishes — Norane and Ranedare; methylol stearamide — Tanpel S; quaternary ammonium compounds — Zelan and Carvenette.

A most effective water, oil, soil and stain repellent finish is supplied by fluorochemical finishes, as in the trademarked products Zepel and Scotchgard. These can be applied directly with other finishing agents, and require no special equipment or handling. Scotchgard is available in aerosol spray cans and is equally effective applied in this manner.

Flame Retardants

Some fabrics are inherently flame retardant: aramids, asbestos, glass, novoloid and modacrylics. Most textile fibers will burn, and the presence of flame near a flammable fabric of open or airy construction has in the past been sufficient to start tragic fires. As a result, governments have enacted legislation to restrict the use of flammable textiles in public places and for apparel, and most manufacturers have willingly researched flame retardance and developed appropriate finishes.

There are two types of flame retardant finishes. One group is water soluble and a new finish must be applied after washing, or, in some cases, dry-cleaning. The other group is classed as durable and will withstand washing, dry-cleaning and the weather. The labels of such durable flame retardant fabrics should be examined carefully, however, to understand what the finish will withstand and its approximate lifespan. Care of the treated fabric should also be carefully outlined by the manufacturer, and, of course, followed by the user in order to retain the effect of the finish. Fabric softeners, soaps and chlorine bleach may destroy the finish.

WATER SOLUBLE COMPOUNDS include borax, boric acid, ammonium phosphate, ammonium sulfate, and some mixtures of these.

INSOLUBLE SALTS include metal oxides such as ferric oxide, stannic oxide and manganese dioxide.

OILS, WAXES, OR RESINS with incorporated chlorinated substances, phosphorous compounds, or antimony compounds are used, as well as substances that react with the fibers to produce molecular changes in cellulosic fabrics.

Finishes must be carefully matched to fabrics, and the selection of appropriate chemicals is a particular textile science. Cellulosic fibers, natural and man-made, and acetates are among the most flammable, and there are numerous specific compounds for these fabrics.

There are many problems in making fabrics flame retardant; one that is yet to be successfully resolved is the matter of blends. In some cases, the two fibers in a blend cannot be treated the same, and do not accept different finishes. Additionally, fire retardant finished fabrics may give off toxic fumes when exposed to fire, or the smoke produced may be excessive.

Some trade names which may be encountered are as follows: Banfire, CM Flame Retardant, Fi-Retard, Firegard, Firemaster, Firemaster 200, Firestop, Fyrol 76, Proban, Pyropel, Pyrovatex CP, THPC, X-12.

In the area of flame retardance, the designer must proceed with caution. Textile chemists, for their part, are turning attention to designing molecular changes in fibers in order to have inherent flame retardance, rather than finish controlled flame retardance.

Antistatic Finishes

Static build-up in fibers and fabrics is a very real problem for manufacturers and consumers alike. In the factory, humidity, lubricants, and various antistatic finishes are used to control the buildup of electrons during the manufacturing process. Dependable, long-lasting antistatic finishes have yet to be devised for fabrics which must undergo frequent laundering or dry-cleaning. For these, commercial fabric softeners are effective in reducing static. They coat the fibers,

preventing electron build-up and increasing conduction.

Effective finishes have been developed for incorporation into the fiber. Fybrite is used on polyester, and a particular nylon—Nylon 22N— is static free. Other finishes classed as durable are based on polyethylene glycol or polyalkylene glycol ethers. Trade names for these include Aston, Nopcostat, Permastat, Stanax and Valstat.

Mothproofing

Various finishes are in use which make protein fibers unfit as moth larvae food.

Wool is the most susceptible fiber, and the most frequently damaged. Products toxic to the mature, egg-laying moth and the larvae (which actually eats the fiber) have been developed and may be added to the fiber during fulling or dyeing. Trade names include Crestocide, Hartocide, Mitin, Neocide, and Repel-O-Tac, and the effects of these products are considered durable.

Proper care of untreated wool or wool blends is essential. Carpets and upholstery must be kept clean; soiled wool is particularly subject to attack. Napthalene in the form of crystals or mothballs repels the mature moth and prevents the deposit of eggs. However, the somewhat offensive odor of napthalene is a deterrent to its use.

Damage to wool products by moth larvae and carpet beetles costs hundreds of millions each year. As a result, research is ongoing to develop new, effective mothproofing systems. Studies are underway to find ways to make wool's keratin protein unpalatable, and to find substances which might be added to the sheeps' diet to make their wool inherently mothproof.

Bacteriostats

Mildew, mold and rot are caused by microorganisms—bacteria, fungi and microbes. All develop and spread on fibers exposed to moisture. They lead to the destruction of a wide range of materials (fibers, wool, etc.), the spread of disease, infections and unpleasant odors. It is speculated that the heavy use of spices and herbs in the ancient Mediterranean world was to protect items (even mummy wraps) from rot.

Antimicrobial and bacteriostatic finishes have been around since 1900. Some are soluble, others durable. Some durable finishes remain on the yarns during care, while others become part of the fiber structure itself. Bacteriostats (the general term for microorganism repellents) are often included with other finishes. Renewable finishes are widely used on apparel and household materials by dry-cleaners, and as commercial and home laundry products. Some trade names are Borateem, Dowicide, Sanitized and Sanitone.

Durable finishes are composed of amines, acids, metallic salts (zirconium, copper, mercury, silver) and other active ingredients. Some trade names in this category are: Guardsan, Hyamine, Marcocide, Nuodex, Permacide and Vancide. Labelling is important. If a textile product is to be laundered or dry-cleaned frequently, and the climate in the area of use tends to be warm and moist, then total dependence should not be put on a durable bacteriostat. Use of one of the renewables will guarantee protection.

Fabrics routinely treated with bacteriostats are sheeting, mattress fabrics and paddings, carpet padding, carpeting, blankets, tents, tarpaulins, upholstery fabrics, fabrics for hospital, institutional, or commercial use, and a huge range of apparel and footwear.

Insulating Finishes

Finishes have been developed which add an insulating layer to fabrics. These were originally conceived for apparel use in jackets and coats, but were found to be less effective than anticipated.

Use in closely constructed drapery linings, however, is very effective. The finish may be an aluminum adhesive coating, or a plastic coating. Both are effective for retaining interior heat in winter and reflecting the sun's heat in summer. Trade names are Milium, Temp-Resisto, and Therm-O-Ray. Fabrics so treated lose some effectiveness with laundering, but, if so labelled, are unaffected by dry-cleaning.

Soil and Stain Resistant Finishes

In general, water resistant finishes such as Scotchgard and Zepel are the most effective repellent to dry soiling and water or oil borne stains. All soil and stains should be removed as soon as possible, as the finishes do not claim to resist soil or stains indefinitely.

Soil Release Finishes

These finishes are similar to soil resistant finishes except that their function is to facilitate the release of stains or soils during laundering. They operate in one of two ways: provision of a hydrophilic surface which attracts water, allowing it to lift out the stain or soil; or, coating of the fibers so that soil does not penetrate. The finishes are most often included in durable press finishes, but are also available for untreated, and/or synthetic, fabrics. Chemicals used are fluorocarbons, acrylates, and hydrophilic copolymers. Trade

names are Dual-Action Scotchgard, Fybrite, Visa, Cirrasol and X-it. They often provide side benefits to a fabric such as introduction of antistatic qualities, some prevention of pilling and fuzz, prevention of soil redeposition, and a softer hand. Because soil is a fabric destroyer when it remains in the fabric, soil release finishes may be said to make fabrics more durable.

Minimum Care Finishes

For this area, some definitions are in order:

WRINKLE RECOVERY, or CREASE RESISTANCE indicates the ability of a fabric to recover from deformation while the fabric is dry.

WASH AND WEAR was a breakthrough of the fifties and generally was a result of the new thermoplastic fibers which could be heat set to build in optimum appearance and superior recovery from laundering.

PERMANENT PRESS or durable press was introduced in 1964 and referred to a fabric's ability to retain presses and creases, otherwise a smooth original appearance through repeated laundering. Both finishing processes and fiber choice is involved.

The ability of certain man-made fibers to totally resist deformation has been noted. The following discussion is limited to finishes applied to fabrics which are inherently wrinkle prone.

Wrinkle recovery and durable press are closely related. Both properties are built in to cellulosic fabrics with finishing resins. These react chemically with cellulose molecules to form a system of cross-linking which holds the fabric in a particular configuration. Wrinkling is inevitable in cotton and linen fabrics. In the 1920's, research started in earnest to find ways to alleviate the problem, and the resin finish was developed at that time. The early finishes had a serious drawback in that they drastically reduced strength and abrasion resistance in treated fabrics. Linen, with strength to spare, continued to be given the new finish, but manufacturers felt that cotton would not give satisfactory performance. Research continued on finishes and, by the sixties, 100% cotton fabrics could be treated for crease resistance with 'acceptable' (about 40%) loss of strength.

Durable press finishes, which entail use of the same cross-linking techniques, are now most often applied to fabrics (or ready-made apparel) of cotton blended with polyester. The polyester adds the strength lost by the treated cotton. Durable press is done in four ways:

PRE-CURE indicates fabric impregnation with the cross-linking finish and heat-curing flat.

POST-CURE indicates fabric impregnation, drying at low temperatures, cutting and sewing into garments, pressing into shape and then curing at high temperatures.

VAPOR PHASE is a treatment of made-up garments using formaldehyde and sulphur dioxide.

NO-CURE is simply a heat setting process of made-up thermoplastic fiber garments. No finish is involved.

As the last three systems refer only to permanent press of apparel, it is the pre-cure method that is of interest for environmental textiles.

Durable press finishing today uses a variety of cross-linking resins, plus a catalyst, softening agents, a fulling agent, and a wetting agent. The cross-linking still results in loss of strength, but the minimization of care is considered paramount. The fabrics, natural or modified cellulosic, or blends of cellulosic and man-made, are saturated in a wet bath or with steam, and then cured by flat calendering.

Trade names are numerous and well known, but consumers are so accustomed to durable press that the use of trademarks is infrequent.

Coloring

The appeal of color is universal. And color we have—an abundance in nature and, some say, an over-abundance in virtually every man-made article from toothpicks to airplanes.

Fabric has been colored for centuries. Some colors, like purple, were so rare and costly that they were the domain of kings. Until the mid-nineteenth century, all dye was obtained from natural sources: reds, such as madder, from a Mediterranean plant root, or cochineal from a Mexican insect; blue from indigo leaves; yellow from the stigmata of the saffron plant; brown from the logwood tree; and many variations from other sources.

In 1856, Sir William Perkins (England) accidentally produced the first synthetic dyestuff —mauve, made from a coal tar derivative. Development since has been rapid and steady. Now, thousands of dyes are available, and the field is still viable and expanding.

CLASSIFICATION OF DYES

Dye is any compound which can be fixed on another substance to evoke the visual sensation of color. Fabric dyes are of many types, and can be classified by color, chemical type, method of application, or fibers to which they apply. The textile industry tends to group dyes by the latter method—fiber type. New synthesized fibers usually require new dyestuffs, and these are often created as part of the fiber development. Dyes may be **reactive**, in that they form a chemical bond with the fiber, or they may be held on by mutual **chemical attraction.**

The following types of dyes relate to specific fibers, or groups of fibers:

Direct Dyes

Direct, or substantive, dyes form the largest and most commercially important group. They are water soluble, and are used primarily on cellulosic fibers and, to a lesser degree, on protein fibers and polyamides. There are two types, benzidine (and its substituents and amines) and polyazo.

Direct dyes are dissolved in water and a salt is added to control absorption rate. They are relatively colorfast to sunlight, but colorfastness to washing may be poor unless resin finishes (such as for crease resistance) are also used. Resin finished, direct dyed fabrics are colorfast to washing. The dye adheres by chemical attraction. Direct dyes can also be 'developed' by the later applications of chemical developers, which may change the hue slightly but ensures superior washfastness. However, they are then less colorfast to light.

Direct dyes produce bright colors, and are generally used for fabrics in the medium to low price range.

Azoic, or Napthol Dyes

These are used in cellulosic fibers and, to some extent, on acrylics, nylon, polyester and polypropylene.

Color is produced in the fiber by applying a colorless diazo compound, followed by napthol. (Sometimes the two are used simultaneously.) Reaction on the fiber produces the dyed effect. These compounds are applied cold, and the fabric is then given a hot detergent bath to attain the desired result.

Brilliant colors are produced at low cost. They have good colorfastness to light, washing, bleaching and alkalis. A problem is a tendency for the dyes to **crock**, or rub off onto other fabrics.

Vat Dyes

Vat dyes are one of the older types of dye, developed in Europe in 1910. They are colorfast and wear well, although the dyeing procedure must be carefully controlled. They are used on cellulosic fibers, and some man-made fibers, but never on wool or silk. Because of their dependable colorfastness, they are often called **fast dyes**—fast meaning lasting in this case.

Sulphur Dyes

Sulphur dyes produce fair to good color-fast dark shades on cellulosic fibers. If not properly applied, they may break down on the fabric, causing it to weaken or disintegrate. They are relatively low cost.

Reactive Dyes

These dyes were introduced in 1956 and are used on cellulosic fibers, nylon, wool, silk, acrylics and blends. They combine with the fiber molecule in a complex system using a reactive molecule. Reactive dyes produce bright colors with excellent colorfastness to washing and light. A drawback is their susceptibility to damage from chlorine. Colorfastness to dry-cleaning, fume fading, crocking and perspiration is good to excellent.

Acid Dyes

Acid dyes are mainly organic acids produced as salts. They are used in solutions of sulphuric, formic or acetic acids. The dyes are used on protein, acrylic, nylon, some modified polyesters, and selected polypropylene (olefins). They are ineffective on cellulosic fibers or those sensitive to acids.

These dyes are flexible, with varying degrees of colorfastness to light, laundering and dry-cleaning. Fiber, end use of product, and anticipated maintenance, should all be known before an acid dye is chosen.

Metallized Acid Dyes

These are acid dyes with metal added. The effective fiber range is the same, and the added metal, mostly chromium, sometimes cobalt, aluminum, nickel, or copper, results in an insoluble dye with improved colorfastness to light, launder-

ing and dry-cleaning. The dry-cleaning colorfastness factor is important for metallized dyes used on wools and silks.

Disperse Dyes

This group of dyestuffs was formerly called acetate dyes, as they were originally developed for that fiber. In addition to acetate, they are now used on polyester, acrylic and nylon. The dye particles in solution attach to the fiber and then dissolve into it, producing good colorfastness to light, laundering and dry-cleaning. These dyes require fixing with heat (205°C/400°F) and this is done by hot air, infrared heat zones or hot surfaces.

Affinities of Dyes to Fibers

DYES	*FIBERS*
DIRECT	cotton, linen, rayon, wool, silk, polyamides
AZOIC (naphthol)	cotton, linen, rayon, acrylic, nylon polyester, polypropylene
VAT	cotton, rayon, linen, some man-made fibers
SULPHUR	cotton, rayon
REACTIVE	cotton, linen, rayon, nylon, wool, silk, acrylic, and blends
ACID	wool, silk, modified rayon, modified acrylic, nylon, modified polyester, some olefin
METALLIZED ACID	wool, silk
DISPERSE	acetate, nylon, polyester, modified polyester, acrylic
BASIC (cationic)	acrylic, modified nylon, modified polyester

FUME-FADING-RESISTANT FINISHES: Disperse dyes on acetate, nylon or polyester are subject to change or color loss in the presence of atmospheric fumes, particularly gaseous oxides of nitrogen. For this reason, particular fabric finishes have been devised to counteract the fading. The finishes are produced by various tertiary amines and are comparably durable.

Basic (Cationic) Dyes

These dyes, which include the original synthetic dyestuffs, are salts of colored organic bases. They are exceptionally effective on acrylic fibers, producing a chemical reaction, and therefore have excellent colorfastness. Basic dyes are also used on modified nylon and modified polyester, and occasionally as 'topping colors' to increase the brilliance of other dyes.

METHODS OF DYEING

Color may be applied to textiles at almost any stage of manufacture, from fiber to finished goods. The methods outlined below relate to the stage of production at which the application of coloring takes place.

Solution Dyeing

This method uses pigment colors added to the polymer solution before extrusion into fibers. While they are not technically dyes because they are insoluble in water and have no affinity for fibers, pigments are used to color fabrics through solution dyeing. In the procedure, the pigment colors are added to the fiber solution or molten polymer, and the fiber is extruded in a colored state. They have good colorfastness to laundering, dry-cleaning, light, perspiration and crocking.

Pigment colors are used in solution dyeing of acetate, rayon, nylon, polyester, and other man-made polymer solutions which will accept the pigments. Glass fibers may be dyed in this manner.

Fiber Dyeing

This dyeing process takes place at the raw fiber stage, and provides excellent color penetration and a tendency to colorfastness. It is also called **stock dyeing**, or, in the case of wool fibers in the sliver stage, **top dyeing.**

Yarn Dyeing

Coloring the yarns which are to make up a textile is one of the oldest methods, and incorporates several systems.

SKEIN DYEING subjects loosely gathered ropes of yarn (skeins) to a dye bath. Skeins are gently agitated and automatically moved through the bath.

PACKAGE DYEING involves having the yarn wound on tubes (called packages) and then dyed by immersion.

BEAM DYEING takes place after yarns are creeled onto a warp beam.

SPACE DYEING occurs when different areas of the skein, package, or beam are dyed different colors.

Yarn dyeing gives good color, and is used for fabrics with various colored yarns, such as plaids, checks, stripes, muted color arrangements, etc.

Piece Dyeing

This method refers to dyeing manufactured fabric, and is the easiest and least expensive way to produce solid color fabric, and occurs when the fabric is composed of one fiber. Variations occur when fabrics are composed of two or more fibers.

BECK DYEING passes the fabric in a loose rope form through the dye vat, and repeats, as necessary, for correct color intensity.

JIG DYEING has the fabric wound from one roll through the dye bath and onto a second roll. The number of passes back and forth determines the intensity of the color.

PADDING is another method of dyeing full width goods. The fabric is run through a dye box, then through squeeze rollers which force in the color and remove excess liquid. Padding is the system used for all continuous dyeing procedures.

PRESSURE JET DYEING is a system specifically for man-made fabrics which require a higher temperature to set the dye. A special, high pressure, high temperature dyeing machine is used.

UNION DYEING applies to carefully balancing dyestuffs so that one dyeing of a fabric composed of two or more fibers results in one even color. Usually, dyes can be combined in one dye bath. The appropriate dye is then picked up by the fiber for which it is intended, and other dyes in the same bath simultaneously 'meet up with' their target fiber. This is called the **one-bath process.**

If separate dye baths are required to union dye a fabric of multiple fibers, a **two-bath** process is used.

CROSS DYEING takes advantage of the fiber differences to produce different colors on one fabric with one dye bath. Many interesting effects may be obtained by this method. It is particularly effective with acrylic and polyester fabrics.

Polychromatic Dyeing

This is a flexible technique for dyeing in random patterns. Two methods are used:

DYE-WEAVE: In this method, dye is forced through jets onto the top edge of a metal plate set at a 45° angle to the fabric. The dye runs down at irregular speeds and hits the moving fabric in a random manner. The pattern formed has sharp and blurred areas.

FLOW-FORM: This procedure has a pierced roller filled with dye. The dye is rolled on which gives a marbleized effect.

In either method, the dye applicator (jets or roller) can be moved sideways to add diagonal or horizontal pattern to the finished fabric. Speed of application, speed of the cloth, and amount of color are all variables.

Tufted carpeting takes this method very well, as dye penetration is excellent. Interesting furnishing fabrics are also polychromatic dyed.

Printing

Printed fabrics are those with a design, pattern or motif applied to the finished fabric. Some techniques are very old—fragments of printed cloth have been discovered at locations all over the world. Modern methods use liquid dye baths, others use pigment dispersions in paste, and the newest technique uses paper or photographic transfers.

Dyebath printing is commonly known as resist, because the pattern is formed by making that portion of the fabric resist the dye. Pigments in paste or other medium are utilized for direct printing, which may be by block or roller, and for stencil and screen printing. A reverse procedure removes dye from a colored fabric in a pattern, and is called discharge printing.

RESIST PRINTS

The methods employed in resist printing are similar, and evolved in separate areas in the far east.

Tie-Dye

This method, which has had a recent revival as a modern craft, utilizes various means to shield parts of the fabric from the dye.

PLANGI TIE-DYE uses waxed thread to tie circles of fabric in bunches, or to secure bunched folds. The fabric is immersed in the dye bath where loose fabric receives color, but the areas where dye cannot penetrate remain white, or uncolored by that particular dye bath.

TRITIK is a similar technique, except hand stitching is used to gather the fabric together in intricate designs.

IKAT, or KASURI: This is a Japanese and Indonesian method of resist dyeing in which warp yarns are tie dyed in the loom. When the cloth is woven a pattern appears at fixed intervals.

Batik

This method uses wax as the dye resist substance. The craft originated and was perfected by the Javanese and makes possible intricate designs executed in many colors. It is not amenable to automatic production.

Intricate batik dyeing uses a *tjanting,* a copper cup affixed to a wood or reed handle, with a small spout in the cup for measured application of the wax. The cup is heated in a flame to melt the wax. The design is drawn in wax on the fabric and it is then piece dyed, which colors the exposed material and leaves the areas penetrated by wax. After thorough rinsing, the wax may be removed with heat, either by hot water or by hot ironing between absorbent surfaces. The process is repeated many times, blocking (by wax penetration) different or additional portions of the fabric to produce a variety of colors and patterns.

A method to speed up fine design printing was devised by the Javanese women, using a *tjap.* This is a block with the design worked in copper wires affixed to the surface. The block is dipped in hot wax to coat the wires which are then pressed to the fabric, transferring the design in wax to the surface of the material.

Intricate batik is a lengthy process, up to two months for a 1.8 meter (2 yard) length using tjanting, up to fifteen days using the tjap.

Simple batik is done by painting on larger sections of wax with a brush. Sometimes the cooled waxed portion is deliberately cracked so that fine lines of color appear in the uncolored portions.

COLOR PRINTS

Several methods of printing color on fabric have been devised and these systems represent the bulk of color-printing fabric.

Key Terms

The following key terms are common to all color-printing methods:

BLOTCH is a term signifying a printed solid color background. It sometimes presents problems with dye penetration.

COVERAGE is the percentage of printed area on a given cloth. It may be as little as 10% or overprinted with colors to obtain up to 140% coverage.

DYE AFFINITY is the compatability between specific fibers and specific dyestuffs.

GRINS are slices of ground fabric showing through a printed cloth. It usually signifies off-registration.

HALFTONES are subtle shadings from one color to another. These are possible with roller and transfer printing, but not with screen printing.

MOTIF is the single pattern element, such as one flower or simple geometric shape, or a whole bouquet of flowers.

OVERLAYS (or fall-ons) are areas that are printed more than once. They may darken an existing color or produce a new one. (Blue overlaid on red will produce purple, for instance.)

PATTERN REPEAT is a complete pattern unit. This may be one row of polka dots, or a complete floral design.

PENETRATION is the degree of absorption of the color in the fabric. Poor penetration results in incomplete coverage in some cases, or it may be the cause of later color abrasion as the dye wears off the surface allowing the fabric color to show through.

PIGMENTS are alternates to dyestuffs. They are

cured on the fabric with heat, so do not require the washing and rinsing of dyed fabrics.

REGISTRATION is the alignment of successive color printing. Failures in alignment are called off-registration, and may show either unintentional overlays, or grins, or both.

SELVAGE LEGEND is the information printed on the fabric edge. It may include the pattern designer's name, copyright, manufacturer, and blocks of the colors used in printing.

STRIKE-OFF is a trial printing of one or more pattern repeats. It is a factory procedure used to establish color lines, check pattern, and to test cloth/dye affinity and finish.

Stencil Prints

This method was developed in Japan and can be considered the forerunner of screen printing. It is a handcraft. To stencil print, designs are cut into a film of oil-coated paper or thin metal. The stencil is then secured to the cloth surface and color is applied with a brush or spray gun. Additional color is applied using separate stencils. A multicolored design requires careful fitting of each stencil so that the design registers properly.

Screen Prints

Screen printing is a stencil-like process adapted to a fine screen rather than a solid plate. When the method was devised, the design was cut in a solid film and this film was laid over the fine mesh. Dye was then forced through the mesh into the fabric, and prevented from reaching the fabric where the film had been left intact. Nowadays, handcraft screen printing utilizes a chemical blocking substance on the screen itself to cover areas where color is not wanted.

In automatic screen printing, the mesh screens are prepared by engraving techniques, chemical substance blocking, or photochemical processes. To screen print, the prepared screen is fitted to the fabric and the dye forced through the open mesh areas with a rubber blade device called a *squeegee*. Multicolor prints are made with several screens, and there must be careful registration of each screen.

FLAT-BED SCREEN PRINTING is a semi-automatic technique using two operators. At present fabrics may be printed at about 6.4 meters (7 yards) per minute. The cloth is automatically moved, intermittently, across the print table, and the screens are fixed and colors applied with the help of electronic devices. The system is widely used for printing extremely large pattern repeats.

ROTARY SCREEN PRINTING is a much faster method, capable of printing roughly 100 meters (110 yards) per minute. Screens are adapted to rollers, where the circumference of each roll determines the lengthwise size of the pattern repeat, and the number of rollers in the machine determines the number of colors. Color is contained within the roller, and an automated squeegee device forces a controlled amount of dye through the screen as it comes in contact with the fabric. The fabric is carried on a backing belt which minimizes distortion—an important factor with knitted fabrics.

Rotary screen printing is a competitor with direct roller printing, and results are identical. Screens are easier and cheaper to make than the engraved rolls used for roller printing. Rotary screens may be very wide, up to 5.1 meters (200"), and they can be arranged in pairs to simultaneously print both sides of a fabric.

Direct Prints

This is the commonest method of color printing, and ranges from handcrafts to full automation.

Representation of a roller printing machine: Thousands of meters (yards) of fabric per day may be continuously printed in this manner. At the center (1) is the main powered cylinder. Material to be printed (2) is delivered over guide rollers (3) into contact with the cylinder. A backing cloth (4) cushions the contact. As the cylinder moves the fabric, it is brought into contact with the engraved printing rolls (5), each of which is coated with dye solution from individual color baths (6). 'Doctor blades' (not shown) remove excess dye from each printing roll so that only the recessed, engraved details carry dye for deposit on the moving fabric. The printed fabric

(7) then proceeds to drying, steaming, pressing, or other final finishing steps. In actual production, there may be sixteen or more print rolls operating on a single machine.

BLOCK PRINTING dates back to around 2500 B.C. It is a method of stamping colored patterns on fabrics by means of carved blocks of wood, or other solid material. The blocks are usually small, the largest for handcrafting being around 30x45 cm. (12 x 18″). Each block stamps one color at a time on the flat fabric; the dye paste may be used as a block dip, or be applied to the block surface with a rubber roller.

FLAT BED PRINTING was an outgrowth of block printing. In the 13th and 14th centuries, block printing was an established craft in some European centers. By the 17th century, textile centers in Germany, Holland, Switzerland, Spain, France and England featured intricate block printed designs on linen and cotton. As demand for the prints grew, the technique expanded in size until it utilized a flat table and a flat-bed press engraved with a design. The system reached a pinnacle with Christophe Phillippe Oberkampf, who originated the Toiles de Jouy prints in Jouy, France, in 1760. The prints were notable for their well-drawn, attractive designs, which depended on events of national interest for their fashionable patterns.

Oberkampf's death, and the Napoleonic Wars, caused the eventual dissolution of the Juoy factory in 1830. It had enjoyed a very successful seventy years, and left a distinctive textile legacy.

ROLLER PRINTING was the result of the invention of a roller print machine by Thomas Bell, in Scotland, in 1783. It combined metal engraving techniques with color printing, and is the basis of modern roller printing.

Today, the design to be printed is etched into metal with acid or photoengraving techniques, and the engraved metal is affixed to rollers. A large main cylinder rolls the fabric into contact with the smaller printing rollers which are arranged around it. Each printing roller has an individual dye bath which applies color to the deeper engraved area, and scrapes dye from the smooth metal areas. (This is in reverse to block printing, where dye adheres to the high areas.) As the padded cylinder rolls the fabric past each printing roller, the dye is transferred from the engraved sections to the fabric. Roller machines can print up to sixteen colors at one time at a rate of about 182 meters (200 yards) per minute. Automation assures accurate printing. As in rotary screen printing, the size of the pattern repeat is limited to the size of the printing roller.

Duplex prints are a modification of direct roller printing, producing an identical print on both sides. Duplex prints may resemble fabrics usually made from dyed fiber or yarn.

Photographic Prints

These are produced on fabrics by a technique similar to printing photographs on paper. The fabric is treated with a light-reactive dye. When the photographic negative (black and white or full-color) is placed on it, and light transmitted through it, the photograph is printed on the cloth, and needs only stabilization and washing to make it permanent.

Transfer Prints

This is a variation of decal decoration. The fabric dye is fixed on a special paper, which is then laid on the fabric and subjected to heat and pressure, which transfers the color pattern from the paper to the fabric. It uses only disperse dyes, so fabrics amenable to this process must have this dye affinity. It is also called **sublistatic printing**, as the transfer process sublimes the dye from solid to gaseous form and back to solid on the fabric surface. The technique is widely used for printing polyester knit T-shirts, but has interesting possibilities for future development.

DISCHARGE PRINTS

Rather than apply color, discharge printing removes color from an already dyed fabric. It is done with a rotary screen printing device and applies a bleach or chemical dye remover to the fabric in a designed pattern. Small white designs, such as polka dots or tiny florals, on dark fabrics, are usually discharge printed.

The method may also be combined with color printing to remove color and print simultaneously.

ETCHING, OR BURN-OUT PRINTING is an interesting variation of discharge printing, in which an acid is used to burn out sections of cellulosic fiber in a fabric composed of polyester and cotton. The technique is very effective on a basic polyester sheer woven with a heavier cotton or rayon filling yarn. Burning out the heavy yarns in a design leaves interesting sheer sections on a textured background.

Fabric designers are almost without restriction in having their original designs committed to fabric. All of the automated printing processes are flexible and accurate. The range of colors is large and the intricacy of design almost unlimited.

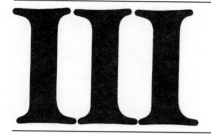

III

TEXTILES IN INTERIOR DESIGN

Choice is a precious commodity. Where textiles for interiors are concerned, the range, as we have seen, is truly staggering. The wealth of materials from which to choose makes the work of interior designers both exciting and frustrating.

As short a time as fifty years ago, the choice was perhaps one tenth of what it is today. Textile scientists have provided fabrics to meet virtually all functional needs, and have added to aesthetic qualities and cost effectiveness as well. At the same time, users of textiles have become accustomed to the recent features and look for more innovations. Requirements of application have also grown; where once a cushion was simply a soft seat, now it must keep its shape, withstand chemical and mechanical maintenance, and look like new.

The designer's task in this scenario of broad choice and big expectations is not a simple one. The most important quality for a designer is flexibility; the best possession is knowledge.

10 CHOOSING TEXTILES

The range of consumer goods based on textiles is increasing rapidly, and expenditure on furnishings, as well as clothing and industrial goods, continues to grow. Increasing consumption of fiber is certainly not new. The textile industry, historically, is one which has exhibited steady growth for its entire life.

With such trends, and because the textile manufacturers are constantly innovating and increasing production, it is essential for those in a position to specify textiles to have a wide knowledge of the selection available, and to know the bases for a wise choice.

Factors in Selection

With every planned textile application there are questions: what fiber? which yarn construction? what method of manufacture? what finish? The interior designer's awareness of the choices will determine the answers and, ultimately, the suitability of the chosen textile.

Some relatively new factors affect the choice of textiles in this late twentieth century era and, to meet these needs, textile products are becoming more and more versatile.

One of the most noteworthy recent changes in consumerism is the necessity to conserve energy. Textiles are recognized as providing important thermal insulation, and the increased call for carpeting and insulating draperies in both public spaces and the home environment reflects this new awareness. It has resulted in an upsurge of production in these areas.

Along with energy conservation, consumers are more environmentally aware. The desire for less noise, less glare, less 'artificiality' in the built environment, adds points to the choice of textiles, especially for areas traditionally treated with hard-surface finishes. Carpeted areas combat noise pollution, provide insulation and contribute visually to a feeling of warmth, and, to meet this need, the manufacturers have been able to engineer 'hard wear and easy care' factors into their products to make them equal to (or better than) hard-surface floorings. Solid walls may be replaced in some applications with fabric-covered moveable screens. Draperies no longer simply frame a window but may attempt to insulate against cold or heat, filter the sun's rays, or block light entirely.

Textiles for interiors exhibit strong fashion trends, and this traditional reason for their choice will continue to be significant. The range of available color is only matched by paint, and the combination of color and texture is almost exclusively the field of textiles. They are relatively easy to change, a factor important to commercial or institutional clients who desire to exhibit a continually new, fresh, up-to-date image. Fortunately, textiles are also relatively easy to handle, so this change is feasible, not prohibitively expensive, yet monumental in effect.

Lastly, economic factors are, as always,

of importance. High capital and financing costs cause clients to insist on value, and to look hard at the investment/life span ratio. Manufacturers of specific textiles, however, are confident that their particular products are price competitive with other finishes and that, wisely chosen, textiles can deliver the right texture, color, pattern, performance, safety, durability, comfort and ease of maintenance to meet an increasing range of applications.

These factors, combined with consumer preference, dictate that the designer be a knowledgeable intermediary, capable of judicious assessment and wise choice.

The requirements for a particular textile must be defined in terms of the user's needs. These needs are, briefly, the psychological, physical and economic needs of the user as they relate to the textile choice at hand. Appearance, performance and maintenance factors merit different degrees of emphasis, depending on the proposed end use. Deciding which textile meets the criteria of a specific design problem is the challenge which the ensuing discussion addresses.

Market Flow Chart

Designers play a multi-faceted role in the specification of fabrics and carpeting.

Fabric/Carpet Mills		Fabric/Carpet Importers
DESIGNERS, SPECIFIERS, BUYERS		
Direct to Job	Distributors	Retailers
DESIGNERS, SPECIFIERS, BUYERS		
Commercial		Residential
DESIGNERS, SPECIFIERS, BUYERS		**DESIGNERS, SPECIFIERS, BUYERS**
Offices, Commercial	Lodging, Food Services, Transportation	Health Care Facilities	Education, Recreation
Detached Dwellings	Apartments, Condominiums	Mobile Homes

Aesthetics

Needs in this area include the user's perception of beauty, and the psychological needs which deal with 'feelings'. To some extent, these needs are subliminal, and relate to a perception of harmony and balance as expressed in color, line, texture, pattern, etc. They are sense-perceived —the eye sees and the hand automatically reaches out to touch—and answer the user's need for a sense of well-being. The verbalization of these needs should be solicited and encouraged at an early stage, as they will be a determining factor in the client's final approval of the designer's choice.

COLOR

Color offers enormous design potential, and textiles are a major vehicle for its introduction to an interior. Differences in tone and hue are as unlimited as the full color spectrum. Colored, fiber-based materials have become more dependable, and almost all textiles can be colorfast. Protective finishes, while not completely foolproof, have greatly reduced the problems of soiling and fading.

Color in textiles need not appear flat or dull. Nature's colors are composed of minute color particles, and textiles can have similar depth and interest by 'fracturing' color. The breakup may be achieved in many ways: manufacturing cloth in yarns of different colors, cross dyeing, space dyeing, etc.

The designer must remember the importance of light — artificial, natural and reflected—when determining the use of color in interiors.

The perception of color is a highly complex human faculty. Not yet fully understood, it is 'explained' in terms of electromagnetic waves of light measured in millimicrons striking the retina of the eye. This stimulates the optic nerve to transmit an electric impulse to the brain where it is interpreted as a particular color. Perception of color is a changeable sensation, dependent on light and the juxtaposition of other hues. Even the intensity with which an individual looks at a color can alter his perception of the shade.

As everyone is aware, colors engender psychological or emotional responses, often universal reactions indelibly stamped on the collective unconscious—feelings of warmth if the color resembles the sun, or coolness if it stirs memories of water.

Color in nature is seasonable, and must have been viewed with wonder by our primitive ancestors. Their search for a bit of the magic of color began with the dawn of civilization, when flowers, berries, bark, nuts and roots provided the first dyes. As we have seen (chap. 9), the history and development of dyes is an interesting one. Today, the U.S. domestic market alone is valued at roughly seven hundred million dollars. The industry is still one of the most difficult and technically complex processes, some dyes taking up to ten months to produce. Our wonderland of cheap, effective color—everywhere around us— should not be taken for granted.

TEXTURE

All material has texture. It is, in essence, a pattern of lights and shadows caused by elevated portions of the surface. It is most apparent in a coarse fabric, but texture may be described as smooth or rough, soft or hard, level or uneven, shiny or dull, in any combination and degree. All of this is determined by the fiber content, the elements of construction, and how the textile is produced. A manufactured fabric may also be finished to provide additional texture, either by embossing, pressing, or the application of a substance to the surface.

Texture does not need a direct tactile connection to be effective; it also may visually impart an imagined sensation of touch which is both pleasing and appropriate to the use.

PATTERN

Pattern, like color, can reflect many moods. It can become an integral part of the textile as it is constructed, or be applied to a finished surface. Pattern is a specific arrangement of shapes and colors that distinguishes it from all others. It may be immediately eye-catching—a bold floral or geometric—or so subtle as to be almost missed—a tone-on-tone chevron. A **motif** is a pattern unit, which may be a polka dot or an entire scene. Repeated over and over, it forms the **pattern repeat,** which may be as small as a centimeter or as large

as one and a half meters (½″-5′).

Stripes, checks and dots are ancient, common patterns, yet are as effective and popular today as ever, lending themselves to a myriad of interpretations in scale and mood, from subtle to psychedelic. Geometrics, florals, scenics, paisleys, brocades—the range of patterns is practically limitless, and all may be utilized on textiles for the interior.

These aesthetic considerations help in the selection process. Based on user reactions, visual perceptions and tactile connections, they are factors which make any selection unique.

A Rainbow of Symbolism

To primitive people color was an 'elemental experience'; today, it's 'psychologically meaningful'!

RED	**health and vitality**
Bright red	*passion*
Dark greyed red	*evil*
Pure pink	*delicacy, festivity*
Warm medium pink	*innocence, calm*

ORANGE	**enthusiasm, zeal**
Light orange	*intensity*
Dark orange	*ambition*

YELLOW	**inspiration**
Medium yellow	*goodness, wisdom*
Strong light yellow	*stimulation*
Dark medium yellow	*love of humanity*
Gold	*luxury, glory, distinction*

GREEN	**sociability**
Yellow-green	*youth, freshness*
Medium green	*honesty, practicality*

BLUE	**idealism**
Strong blue-green	*restlessness, nostalgia*
Greyed blue-green	*placidity, repose*
Dark greyed blue	*kindness, sincerity*
Light medium blue	*peacefulness*

PURPLE	**magnificence**
Strong blue-purple	*sternness*
Light purple	*fragility, softness*
Medium purple	*poise*

Functional Needs

A textile's ability to adequately serve a particular need is its **function.** Selection is based on particular requirements, and the chosen product is then expected to perform well in whatever situation it has been placed.

A textile's performance rating is based on two main assessments: **durability** and **maintenance**. These assessments must be based, in turn, on the properties—inherent characteristics, chemical reactivities, and environmental sensitivities—of the particular fiber or textile. There are no clear-cut 'good' and 'bad' properties for the simple reason that requirements differ.

Functional selection must always be based on the specific end use and placement of the textile. Whether drapery, carpet or other use, particular and definite circumstances will apply which will translate into specific criteria. A drapery treatment may call for visual impact, or glare control, or insulation, or a combination of all of these. Upholstery may have to be particularly abrasion resistant; an institutional carpet may require resistance to certain stains.

Overall needs of the space must also be considered. Whether the requirements call for sound deadening, insulating, brightening, low cost, luxury, bacteria control or minimal maintenance, careful research of the specific needs will give the designer sound parameters with which to focus on the solution.

Durability

Durability is the capacity to last or endure without deterioration or destruction, and with minimal loss of appearance for a reasonable length of time.

Maintenance

Maintenance, specifically, refers to the ongoing treatment necessary to keep a textile clean. Cleaning refers to periodic efforts to renew abused or soiled textiles. The two are collectively known as 'maintenance'.

Maintenance is measured in ease or difficulty, in required frequency of attention, and by what continual and/or periodic methods care is undertaken.

Durability and Maintenance

Durability and maintenance are linked, and are considered together as the performance aspect of any textile. They must be assessed, based on the performance data available, that body of information, either known or provided by manufacturers, about fibers, yarns and textile goods. These form the reference points for textile selection.

Interpreting the performance data, balancing the pros and cons, weighing the alternatives, and choosing the textiles for specific use is a satisfying aspect of the designer's expertise. Assessment starts with the fiber and progresses through all the subsequent processes to build the necessary composite picture of the finished textile's attributes. Each of the following areas may be assessed relative to the performance data provided:

COMPONENT FIBER(S): The composition of the textile, its fiber or fibers, may be assessed on the basis of its properties, as outlined in chaps. 4 and 5.

YARN CONSTRUCTION: How the yarn was made from fibers, or how it was mechanically treated. Simple yarns with medium twist generally contribute to longer wear than complex yarns with loops which may be easily snagged. Tightly twisted yarns may relax when subjected to moisture.

FABRIC CONSTRUCTION: The method of construction has a direct bearing on durability and maintenance. Abrasion, loss of strength, shrinkage, stretching, etc., can all occur because of construction.

FINISHES: These may be applied at the fiber, yarn or finished textile level, and may change or alter an original characteristic. Finishes may radically affect durability, sometimes weakening a fiber 'plus' in order to obtain a particular missing property.

APPLICATION OF COLOR AND PATTERN: Dyestuffs or other substances often affect maintenance, and may also alter the durability of a textile.

INSTRUCTIONS AND MAINTENANCE: Care and cleaning procedures are determined by the textile producer, and instructions should be clear and concise. When in doubt, in the absence of clear instructions or before making up fabrics into draperies or upholstery, a wise precaution is to have a test piece cleaned by the method(s) to be recommended.

All textile performance is, of course, relative to use. Exposure, climate and levels of abuse and maintenance, must be taken into consideration. In some cases, the safest possible solution will not prevent deterioration; in other applications, discreet use and tender care can assure long life to a textile of questionable choice. As a general rule, institutional settings require a higher level of caution in the durability and mainten-

ance areas; residential, ceremonial, and occasional public use areas may allow for more flexible choice regarding performance in order to arrive at an innovative or especially decorative solution. Good communication between the designer and client is the essential ingredient for best selection.

Economic Considerations

Matching the textile to the budget can be a real challenge, and the price of the goods per meter or yard is not the only factor to consider in estimating cost. Square meter or yard cost, make-up and/or installation, ancillary materials, maintenance and life span must all be taken into account. In addition, an individual or exclusive textile may be desired, which will undoubtedly add to the cost.

The price of a textile is not always determined by quality. The price of staple, mass-produced fabrics (such as sheetings) is determined by fiber content, fineness of yarn, closeness of weave, colorfastness and pattern, and here, price generally does reflect quality. Other textiles, however, whether limited production, specialty, handcrafted or imported, reflect higher costs of low volume manufacturing and marketing, so the price does not necessarily infer quality.

It must not be assumed that an expensive textile product will pay for itself with long wear. It may or may not, but often luxury fabrics are not durable. The designer need not refrain from specifying such textiles—for drama, special effect, uniqueness, or sheer luxury—but should make the client aware of any serious limitations in maintenance or life span.

Costing
ACCURATE COST: The cost per meter or yard of fabric cannot be used to estimate true cost until it has been converted to cost per square unit. The conversion to square measure is necessary because of the varying widths of goods. As an example, 1 meter (yard) of 90 cm. (36″) fabric at $20.00 is twice the price of 1 meter (yard) of 180 cm. (72″) material at $20.00.

Fabrics with large pattern repeats must also be costed carefully. Pattern match sometimes entails a 25% increase in length of cut.

MAKE-UP AND/OR INSTALLATION COSTS: These refer to costs of having casements or draperies made up, of having furnishings upholstered, etc. Where there is custom work, costs usually escalate sharply. Even with stock items, there will be make-up and installation costs.

ANCILLARY MATERIALS include such items as backing material, underpadding, linings and interlinings, tapes, tracks, etc.

MAINTENANCE varies widely. It may be minimum in terms of frequency and cost of treatment, or maximum if a textile requires frequent dry-cleaning or special treatment.

LIFE SPAN of the specified textile will have a direct bearing on cost. Averaging the initial cost over the number of years of expected satisfactory appearance and use, gives a clear picture of annual cost.

Cost Effectiveness
Specification decisions should not be finalized before considering cost effectiveness of textile components, based on requirements and performance criteria.

LIFE-CYCLE COSTING is a method used to estimate costs over the life of purchased items and is used to obtain the optimum price of components. The idea of trying to predict cost effectiveness is not new; any wise consumer uses the process automatically, without putting a 'method' tag on the thought processes. Basically, the method assesses projected special costs—installation, labor, ancillary materials—and maintenance costs—regular preventative care and corrective treatments—and adds these to the actual acquisition price to obtain the total estimated cost over the expected life span of the item. **Service life** is a term to describe the effective life span. It is based on test results from the manufacturer or actual experience with long-term use.

Accuracy with life-cycle costing depends on reliable information regarding service life. If possible, it is advisable to obtain written warranties from the manufacturer on life span of the goods along with detailed care instructions. Care costs are difficult to estimate accurately and it would be wise to add a percentage for inflation in the life-cycle cost estimate.

Factors such as insurance, carrying costs of financing and professional services, must be included in accurate life-cycle costing.

PEOPLE COSTING is a concept based on the knowledge that environment affects human performance. If a designer can indicate, and authenticate with past studies, that a particular solution to an environment will improve efficiency or productivity the client may be in a position to see an actual return on the investment.

11 TODAY'S TEXTILES

Today's built environment differs sharply with that of fifty years ago. It displays a certain anonymity in contrast to the earlier eras of custom building when construction materials, structure and joinings were evidence of the human touch. Moldings, cornices, paneling and multi-paned windows contributed to a feeling of individuality and human scale. Today's textiles may be effectively used to fill that void. Undifferentiated, glass-walled interiors now depend on furnishings to provide the essential humanizing treatment, and fabrics are the major contributor.

It is wise to keep this primary function in mind. Aesthetic and psychic considerations help the occupants or users of interior spaces feel more related and secure. While specifying textiles for window treatments or upholstery, the designer is first and foremost specifying textiles for people. It is to best fulfill this dual requirement that designers need knowledge of textiles. Suitability and function are essential criteria for textile selection; aesthetics are precious; intelligent and thoughtful combination is the challenge.

Performance Criteria

Appropriate use of a textile is based on its individual characteristics and its intended placement and use. These may be assessed based on a number of particular performance criteria. The designer must decide, based on the user's needs, which of the criteria are essential for each particular textile choice.

CRITERIA FOR AESTHETIC PERFORMANCE

The factors which influence aesthetic choice are appearance and touch. In this area is found visual pleasure or displeasure, comfort or discomfort, and the user's consequent feeling of being either comfortable or uncomfortable with the fabric. Color and pattern are essential ingredients in aesthetic choice, of course, but these do not relate to performance criteria.

Appearance and touch are related to a fabric's texture, luster and how it maintains its original look. Texture is such a variable factor that it cannot be tied directly to performance. It depends on the fabric's cumulative fiber surface. This, in turn, depends on how the constituent yarns have been formed, whether tightly twisted or loose and fuzzy, and how the fabric has been constructed, i.e., closely set, very open or irregular. The following factors related to a textile's performance influence appearance.

Luster

Luster is a visual property and refers to the sheen of a fiber. It is caused by light rays breaking and reflecting from the fabric surface, and is more subdued than shine. (Mylar has shine; satin has sheen.) Silk has a high luster; cotton, linen and wool are classed as low luster. Man-made fibers have variable degrees of luster. Both fabric construction and finish have a great effect on luster, and can reverse the above fiber-based distinctions.

Fuzzing and Pilling

Fuzzing is the result of fibers working out of the fabric surface. Pilling occurs when this fuzz is tangled and rolled into tight balls. Both are unsightly. When hydrophilic (absorbent) fibers fuzz and pill, it is generally temporary and the pills are easily removed; when hydrophobic (non-absorbent) fibers pill, they are persistent and difficult to remove. Fabrics made from short fibers will form pills more easily than fabrics of longer fibers. Filament fibers are inherently fuzz and pill resistant.

Electrical Attraction

Electrical attraction is a factor in appearance inasmuch as the same static which contributes to safety hazards (discussed later) also tends to attract dust, thread, hair and lint to a fabric's surface. If a static-prone fabric is used where these elements are present, it will be difficult to maintain a good appearance. Such particles cling tenaciously, sometimes they are difficult to vacuum and must be physically picked off the surface.

In addition to appearance, physical comfort is affected by electrical attraction. A static-prone fabric used as upholstery will cause a user's clothing to cling to its surface; when the user leaves the seat, often his clothes, if made of hydrophobic materials, will carry static and cling together or to other clothing layers.

Color Changes

It is expected that the color of a textile will last and retain its original shade, whether pure white, subtle, vibrant or very dark. Any factors which may affect this dependability must be given careful consideration.

FADING may be a problem if a textile's fibers are affected by sunlight or atmospheric conditions, or if the dyes used to color the textile are not fast to sun exposure, strong light, air pollutants or required cleansing solutions. The degree of consideration must be based on the methods of maintenance. Acetates colored with disperse dyes, for instance, are subject to gas-fume fading, unless treated to resist such fumes.

CROCKING is the rubbing off of excess dyestuff from a fiber's surface. It is the result of too much dye being used, sometimes to obtain a very dark shade, or, in some cases, of using a dye with imperfect affinity to the fiber. It may occur when the fabric is dry or wet. Apart from the very real problem of having color rub on to other fabrics — particularly clothing — or bleeding into uncolored or other colored portions of a pattern, the fabric's appearance will change by a lessening of the color intensity and, in extreme cases, with the fabric's ground or natural color showing through.

COLOR LOSS at time of laundering or dry-cleaning is an occasional problem if the manufacturer has treated the fabric with an inappropriate dye. If the colorfastness is neither known nor guaranteed by the manufacturer, fabric samples must be tested before assembly to assure colorfastness to the method of cleaning to be recommended.

Hand

Hand denotes the way a fabric feels when stroked or handled. Terms such as soft, crisp, silky, waxy, rough, are used to describe the hand of a textile. It is affected by fiber shape, yarn and fabric construction and some finishes and dyes. In fabrics that will hang, it is a factor in drapability. In fabrics which will be in contact with the body, it is a factor in comfort.

CRITERIA FOR FUNCTIONAL PERFORMANCE

The function of a textile is to behave in a planned, predetermined way. How well this may be depended upon is related to the many functional attributes which each fabric component — fiber, yarn, construction, finish — contributes to the eventual cloth or carpeting. A further requirement is that the product be amenable to maintenance activity geared to keeping it in, or near, its original state for a reasonable time period.

Durability

Durability is the ability of a textile to last, or to continue in a given state without deterioration for a **reasonable** length of time.

FIBER CONTENT is a strong influence in this area. It may be chosen for its ability to resist abrasion and hard use, or to maintain a soft hand and good drapability. Depending on the intended end use, the factors to consider in the fabric's fiber component are strength and flexibility.

YARN STRUCTURE contributes to durability. Simple ply yarns or multifilaments give good wear; complex yarns are less resistant to abrasion.

FABRIC CONSTRUCTION is an important factor. Generally the plainer, firmer and smoother the surface, the better the durability to physical use. Decorative fabrics which may snag or run may be durable or completely unsuitable; it depends on the application. With suitable placement and proper handling such fabrics may last perfectly well.

Abrasion Resistance

Abrasion resistance is the ability to resist wear from flat rubbing, flexing, or edge abrasion. It contributes to textile durability and resistance to splitting. Damage from abrasion may be the result of certain inherent fiber properties, or problems with textile construction. Fabrics made from fibers that possess both high breaking strength and abrasion resistance can be used for a long period of time without showing signs of wear. Also, textiles with flat compact yarn structure and optimum interlacings are less subject to damage than those with irregular surfaces.

Absorbency

Absorbency is the ability to take in moisture. In general, all textile fibers have a certain amount of moisture as part of their structure. The absorbency of a fabric is determined by the fiber components, influenced by modifications or finishes, and to a certain degree by the fabric structure. Fibers which absorb moisture easily are called hydrophilic fibers. Those fibers which have difficulty absorbing moisture or are able to hold very little, are called hydrophobic fibers.

The relation of fiber strength to moisture content is an important consideration in evaluating fabric behavior. Some fibers are stronger when wet than dry, others are weaker when wet, some show no change; these factors influence care and maintenance. Fabrics with no moisture regain, such as fiberglass casements, wash and dry easily and quickly. Absorbency is related to static build-up, stain removal and spotting, and dimensional stability when wet.

Elasticity, Elongation and Recovery

Elasticity is the ability of a fabric to increase in length when under tension and then return to the original length when released. Good elasticity tends to increase the breaking strength of a fabric.

Elongation is the amount of stretch or extension that a fabric will accept before it breaks. Excessive elongation may cause sagging in hung fabrics. It is important that elasticity and elongation be considered together in fiber evaluation.

Recovery is a term used to indicate the degree of return to shape after elongation, and is closely related to elasticity. Good recovery will prevent 'bagginess' from occurring in upholstery fabric after many hours of use.

Resiliency

Resiliency is the ability of a fiber to return to shape following compression, bending or other deformation. It is evaluated on a comparative basis from excellent to poor. Recovery is a significant factor in the resiliency of a fiber, and usually good elastic recovery indicates good resiliency. This property plays an important role in the rapidity with which flattened carpet pile will regain its shape and restore its appearance.

Dimensional Stability

Dimensional stability is the capacity to retain shape. It is an important element for all textiles, but particularly those fabrics that are hung or used as coverings. It is dependent upon absorbency, elasticity, elongation, recovery, and the construction of the fabric. Freely hanging fabric may sag, shrink or hike (alternately sag and shrink) when exposed to changes in humidity. Elongation (sagging) should not be greater than 2%. A loosely constructed fabric, particularly one of heavy yarns, will sag more than a tightly woven one. Casements or draperies of hydrophilic fibers absorbing moist warm air from the exterior may shrink, sag and hike with disastrous results when suddenly subjected to dry, cool, mechanically conditioned air. Fabrics used for upholstery, wall coverings or carpeting need dimensional stability to prevent them from stretching, which results in loose or buckled surfaces. Shrinking may result in pulled seams or excessive tension. Especially in variable climates, cautious fiber content choice is recommended, and testing for dimensional stability is advisable.

Cover Efficiency

This is the ability of a fabric to occupy space or to conceal with a minimum of fibers and weight. It is dependent on the density of the fiber and the structure of the cloth.

FIBERS with high density (weight per unit volume), such as fiberglass, are compact and heavy as compared to fibers of low density, such as wool, or crimped synthetics. Low density fibers are lighter, with more loft or bulk, and cover more efficiently with less fiber content and weight.

FABRIC STRUCTURES of closely set yarns with high thread count offer more cover than open construction.

Sunlight Susceptibility

Sun may discolor, fade or rot fabrics. It is dependent on the fiber content, the dyes used, any sun resistant finishes applied, and the type of exposure to which the fabric is to be subjected. Sun rot is a serious matter; casements or draperies so susceptible may totally disintegrate in the first laundering or dry-cleaning after a period of exposure to the sun.

CRITERIA FOR HEALTH/SAFETY PERFORMANCE

The factors mentioned under this general category are also of importance as aesthetic and functional considerations. However, where health or safety is a requirement, they are of prime importance.

Fire Resistance

This factor is dependent on the fiber content of the fabric, but to some degree, is also influenced by the fabric structure. Fibers have various reactions to heat and flame, and these must be carefully noted. An open, loose construction is more apt to burn freely than a tightly set fabric, depending, of course, on fiber content. Fire retardant finishes applied to the fabric must be considered. Their efficacy and life span should be closely noted. Written guarantees are the best

protection for both the client/user and the designer.

Microorganism and Insect Resistance

Some fibers are inherently resistant to mildew, fungus and bacteria. Others are very vulnerable to such attack in the presence of moisture and warmth. Accumulated soil on resistant fibers may also foster microorganic growth. Protection for fabrics composed of vulnerable fibers may be obtained through use of bacteriostatic finishes. The problem of mildew, fungi and bacteria growth is most severe in the sub-tropics, or during seasons of sustained warmth and high humidity anywhere. The health factor is important in fabrics specified for hospitals or other care institutions, where the use of fabrics which support bacterial growth could contribute to the spread of disease.

Insects such as moths, carpet beetles and weevils may be attracted to fabrics, dependent on their fiber component. Cellulosic and protein fibers are natural food sources for these insects and they must be protected. Moth-proofing for wools is essential, and specific insect inhibitors must be considered if these are anticipated in the vicinity of the fabrics specified.

Static Resistance

Resistance to static is the capacity of a fabric to act as an effective conductor of electricity. Static accumulates most on non-conductors, and only in the absence of adequate humidity. It is fiber dependent. Static resistant finishes on normally static-prone fibers, or the addition of conducting fibers to finished fabrics, are relatively effective. Static accumulation is a safety factor where flammable materials or sensitive machinery is to be used.

Summary of Components

A textile is the sum of its component parts: the constituent fiber or fibers, either as produced or modified; the yarn or yarns; the fabric's construction; and applied finishes. Preceding chapters have dealt with all of these areas. Because each and every factor is of importance in making a textile selection, all must be assessed and considered. The following summaries represent an amalgamation of these factors.

FIBER PROPERTIES SUMMARY

Each fiber has a set of properties, which apply **in the fiber state.** These include inherent characteristics, chemical reactivities and environ-

mental sensitivities. They were discussed in chapters 3, 4 and 5.

Inherent Characteristics

DESCRIPTION of the fiber includes its size, shape, uniformity, natural color and luster.

STRENGTH of the fiber rates its tenacity in grams per denier, from weak (1.5 gpd) to exceptionally strong (8 gpd), and refers as well to the fiber's flexibility, or ability to be repeatedly flexed without breaking.

DIMENSIONAL STABILITY notes several factors: the elongation, or tendency to stretch; the recovery, or percentage of return after a 2% elongation; and the degree of elasticity, which rates recovery from poor (75%) to excellent (100%). The resiliency is the capacity to return to shape after compression.

DENSITY is the weight per unit volume and is expressed in grams per cubic centimeter. The higher the density, the heavier the fiber. Density ranges from exceptionally low (0.9 gpcc) to high (2.5 gpcc).

ABSORBENCY in fibers is measured with two factors: the moisture regain, or amount of moisture contained in a fiber at standard conditions — 21.1°C (70°F) at 65% relative humidity, and the moisture absorption, or the water holding capacity at 100% humidity. Both are expressed as percentages of the weight of the bone dry specimen.

Chemical Reactivities
These refer to each fiber's reaction to alkalis, acids, and solvents or other chemicals, and affect the maintenance of a finished fabric.

Environmental Sensitivities
Each fiber is either unaffected by, or sensitive to, conditions in the environment. If a fiber has a particular sensitivity to sun, heat, fire, water, moisture, microorganisms, insects or aging, this must be taken into consideration when planning placement of the textile within a space.

The inherent characteristics and the chemical reactivities of a fiber are the least adaptable to change by later construction or finishing. The environmental sensitivities are the most adaptable to change, whether it augments or inserts a positive effect, or lessens or deletes a negative effect.

YARN SUMMARY
Yarns are composed of fibers, so that all of the above properties apply. In addition, the type of yarn and its eventual weight and texture, are factors which influence the textile it forms.

Yarn Types
SPUN YARNS are composed of staple fibers, and may be either **singles** or **plys**. Singles are inherently weaker than plied yarns, and are more easily abraded.
Staple yarns are spun of relatively short staple cotton, and have a fuzzy surface.
Carded yarns are spun with the shortest cotton staple fibers removed, and are

somewhat smoother.
Combed yarns are spun exclusively of long staple cotton fibers, and are the finest, or smoothest yarns.
Woolen and worsted yarns are similar to carded and combed cotton yarns.
Tow and line yarns are of linen, and relate to staple and combed cotton yarns.

FILAMENT YARNS may be monofilament, or thrown strands of continuous multifilaments. They reflect the strength of their constituent fibers, and are not easily abraded.

TAPE YARNS are formed of slit films and are very similar in performance to filament yarns.

TWISTLESS, SELF-TWIST, FASCIATED AND SHEATH YARNS refer to yarns which are held together by adhesives or mechanical processes other than spinning or twisting.

CORD AND CREPE YARNS are variations of ply yarns where a firm twist is applied.

TEXTURED YARNS may be spun or filament and have been given mechanized treatment to form yarns with greater bulk, usually through some form of crimping and heat-setting of the man-made fibers.

COMPLEX YARNS, or specialty yarns, may be singles or plys, and are manufactured for appearance. They have a variety of deliberate irregularities which give them interesting texture.

METALLIC YARNS use metals as part of their composition and have a decorative metallic appearance.

STRETCH YARNS are usually filament yarns textured by the false twist method to produce reliable stretch and recovery.

Yarn Twist and Yarn Count
These terms describe the finished yarn. The twist may be S or Z — clockwise or counterclockwise — and the yarns may be balanced or unbalanced. The twist in balanced yarns does not exceed the optimum level for holding; an unbalanced yarn, hung in a loop, will twist on itself because it has greater twist than is necessary to hold the fibers together.
Yarn count is a method of stating the weight of a measured amount of yarn. The yarn number reflects this weight.

FABRIC CONSTRUCTION SUMMARY

Today's fabrics are formed in a variety of ways.

Woven Fabric

All woven fabric is based on three basic weaves, or combinations of them.

PLAIN WEAVES have yarns interwoven on a one-to-one basis, or in balanced or unbalanced variations, such as 2x2, 2x3, 4x4, etc.

TWILL WEAVES form a diagonal pattern on the cloth by moving the weaving pattern one yarn crosswise with each row.

SATIN WEAVES have yarns in one direction floated over a number of other direction yarns to form a smooth, lustrous surface.

SPECIAL EFFECT WEAVES use one or more of the above basic weaves to form a cut or loop pile, a pebbly surface, a multicolored design, or special texture.

TRIAXIAL WEAVES are made on a special loom with three, rather than two, yarn directions.

Needle Construction

Knits, and several variations, are formed with needles.

WEFT KNITTING is based on hand knitting techniques, and the fabric is formed by crosswise progressions of the yarn. It produces flat or tubular goods as single knits, double knits or pile fabrics.

WARP KNITTING is a very fast machine technique producing plain or decorative tricot knit fabrics in a variety of weights. Raschel knits are made on a very flexible machine which produces fabrics ranging from fine netting to industrial goods.

Knitting Variations

These variations include knit-weave, knit-sew and malimo, and are produced on specially adapted knitting machines. They have particular characteristics to meet specific functional needs.

Tufted Fabrics

The technique for producing tufted fabrics started with handcrafted items, and involved inserting yarns into a woven or knit backing with yarn threaded needles. They are produced in a wide range of weights; the most important production is carpeting.

No-element Fabrics

This is the term used to denote that no yarns or threads are used in construction. They are produced directly from fibers, or directly from polymer solutions.

FELTS of wool are probably our oldest fabric. Felts today may be wool, animal fibers, other textile fibers, or combinations, and they are often mechanically produced by the needlepunching technique, which tangles and compresses the fibers into a flat, somewhat inflexible fabric.

BONDED FABRICS are fibers held together with adhesives, heat, or a combination of both.

FOAMS are produced from polymer solutions that incorporate sponge-like air bubbles before the liquid mix is cooled or cured.

FILMS are also produced from polymer solutions, extruded into thin flat sheets which may be very thin or relatively heavy. Expanded films have a slight cellular structure introduced in the solution stage. Supported films have a fine fabric backing. Films may be textured, colored or printed.

EXTRUDED FABRICS are variations of films. They are produced in the same manner but are immediately subjected to other processes which may pierce, cut, expand, emboss, or otherwise add interest and texture.

Compound Fabrics

These fabrics are composed of more than one component, joined by various means.

EMBROIDERY is any fabric overlaid with decorative yarns.

QUILTING is an old technique and originally used patchwork in intricate patterns as a top layer. This was arranged on a filling and a backing, and the layers stitched through. **Machine quilting** may be hand-guided, outline, trapunto or vermicelli and is done on a special industrial sewing machine by an individual operator. **Automated quilting** is done in a multi-needle machine which stitches in a set pattern. **Stitchless quilting** fuses layers of fabric and filling together with adhesive stitch bonding or ultrasonic vibration.

LAMINATED FABRICS are made from a variety of materials. Layers made of fabric, foam, or film are bonded together with adhesives or heat.

SUMMARY OF FINISHES

Finishes fall into several categories, and they make appreciable differences to the properties of fabric.

Basic Finishes

These finishes may be characterized as preliminary to other finishes. They are basically steps to clean the cloth and stabilize the size and shape.

Surface Treatments

These affect the appearance and/or hand of fabrics.

MECHANICAL TREATMENTS are used to produce a nap, to smooth or polish the surface, or to produce texture.

FLOCKING is a technique for adhesive bonding miniscule lengths of fiber on a fabric surface. Flocking may be applied in a pattern or to cover the entire surface.

DURABLE FINISHES add chemical substances to traditional mechanical treatments to produce fabrics with permanent press, crease retention, durable glazing or embossed designs.

CHEMICAL FINISHES are used on fabrics to stiffen, soften, deluster or optically brighten.

Functional Enhancement

This is the area which most affects the performance criteria of fabrics.

WATER REPELLENCY treatments seal a fabric so that water cannot pass through. Water based stains are held on the surface for a considerable period of time.

FLAME RETARDANTS are applied to cellulosic fabrics, acetates and triacetates which normally ignite and burn freely, and to any other fabrics which will burn in the presence of flame. The area of flame retardance is one in which to proceed with caution, and to be sure of knowledge regarding efficacy of finish, maintenance recommended, and expected life span of the finish.

ANTI-STATIC FINISHES are not yet dependably durable for fabrics that will be frequently laundered or dry-cleaned. It is more effective to have static inhibitors built into man-made fibers, which are the most liable to static build-up.

MOTH-PROOFING is an effective finish for protein fabrics to make them unpalatable as moth larvae food.

BACTERIOSTATS protect fabrics made of fibers which are adversely affected by microorganisms. The various finishes are effective and durable, and prevent the growth and/or spread of fungi and bacteria.

INSULATING FINISHES are applied to fabrics to add to their thermal insulation value. They are usually aluminum in adhesive, or plastic.

SOIL AND STAIN RESISTANT FINISHES are identical to water repellent finishes.

SOIL RELEASE FINISHES are used to facilitate the removal of soil or stains. They may coat the fiber so that soil does not penetrate, or provide a water attracting quality to the fiber which allows cleansers in water to lift out the soil.

MINIMUM CARE FINISHES are identical to durable finishes, and are used to make wrinkle-prone fabrics, such as cotton and rayon, nearly wrinkle resistant.

Coloring

Fabric dyeing matches fibers to particular dyes to produce relatively fast colors. Dyeing may be done at the polymer solution stage, or the fiber, yarn or fabric stage.

FIBERS may be solution dyed by adding pigments to the polymer solution before extrusion of the fibers, or they may be immersion dyed.

YARNS are immersion dyed one color, or may be space dyed to produce variations of color or more than one color in the same length of yarn.

FABRICS may be piece dyed which involves several methods for immersing the fabric or otherwise exposing it to the coloring solution. Union dyeing carefully balances dyes to produce one color in a fabric of two or more fibers. Cross dyeing takes advantage of the fiber differences to produce different colors in one fabric in one dyebath. Polychromatic dyeing applies color in random patterns on finished fabric.

Printing

Printing applies colored design or pattern on fabric. There are many techniques. Colors applied to the surface of a fabric may not be as durable as immersion dyed fabrics.

Coloring and printing do not radically alter the performance of a fabric, although they may be slightly weakened, stiffened, or made more susceptible to light and chemical damage.

Textile Geometry

Most fabrics are formed of fibers or yarns geometrically arranged into a finished fabric shape. The geometry of a textile contributes to its eventual performance as a finished drapery, upholstery fabric or carpeting. The various fabric construction methods have been reviewed; how this textile geometry relates to certain of the specific performance criteria follows.

Geometric factors influence the transmission of air and moisture through fabric. They affect the dimensional stability, abrasion resistance, hand and drape, and the tendency to retain soil. These factors may, in turn, be affected by certain fabric finishes, either positively or negatively.

Airflow

Air passage through fabric is desirable in situations where the textile will be in contact with the body, such as upholstered seating. Fabric that is impermeable causes body heat to be trapped. If the interior is in a warm climate, or tends to be overheated, or, in some cases if the persons using the seating are overheated (in sports club lounges, for instance) an uncomfortable stickiness will result. Materials that are good airflow conductors have the following geometric features: fibers that combine into yarns in such a way as to leave airspaces, producing thick fluffy yarns, and fabrics with irregular or rough surfaces.

If airflow is not desired, which might be the case for fabrics used as casement over a window which radiates hot or cold air, then fabric with smooth yarns densely set to leave minimal spaces in the fabric interstices should be considered.

Moisture Permeability

The same geometric characteristics which permit or prevent airflow also operate for water vapor or moisture. In addition, the absorption capability of the fiber(s) will play a significant part. Terrycloth is a prime example of a moisture transmission fabric; both the fiber content (usually cotton) and the loop structure of the fabric contribute to the wicking action which absorbs and holds moisture.

Water repellency may also be determined by a tight geometric configuration with only miniscule interstices where moisture can accumulate. A finely constructed cloth of a hydrophobic fiber, such as nylon, will prevent water from penetrating.

Dimensional Stability

Geometric factors are extremely important on the dimensional stability of a fabric. Compact materials with firm yarns and a high thread count are less subject to dimensional change, while the same yarns constructed in an open fashion with low thread count will be subject to shrinking or elongation.

Abrasion Resistance

Where flat rubbing, flexing or edge abrasion is concerned, the geometric arrangement of the yarns should produce a smooth, firm surface. An irregular configuration or low yarn count with minimal interlacings will allow the fabric to be roughened or snagged by abrasion. The size of the yarn is also important, thick yarns being much more resistant to damage than fine yarns.

Hand and Drape

The hand of fabrics is influenced by flexibility, resilience, elasticity, density of the fibers and surface contour of the fabric. The geometric factors involved include the shape of the constituent fibers, the length of the fibers, and the arrangement of the yarns in the fabric.

Drapability is influenced by the same factors as hand, and the capacity to drape easily is found in fabrics that are soft rather than firm, limp rather than rigid, and pliable rather than stiff.

Fabric Soiling and Maintenance

These are affected by geometric factors as follows: firmly constructed fabrics with smooth surfaces tend to resist soiling simply by not providing spaces for dirt to settle. The same fabric however, if permeated with an oily substance or staining solution, will be harder to clean.

Loosely structured fabrics permit penetration of soil, but accumulated soil will not be so evident as in smooth fabrics. They are more difficult to clean completely because soil may lodge tightly in the yarns.

A Mini-glossary of Common Fiber Trademarks

Acrilan
  acrylic, modacrylic
Anso
  nylon
Antron
  nylon
Arnel
  triacetate
Avlin
  polyester
Avril
  high wet
  modulus rayon
Beaunit
  nylon
Bi-Loft
  acrylic
Blue "C"
  nylon, polyester
Cantrece
  nylon
Caprolan
  nylon, polyester
Celanese
  nylon, acetate
Chromspun
  acetate
Coloray
  rayon
Cordura
  nylon
Crepeset
  nylon
Creslan
  acrylic
Cumuloft
  nylon
Dacron
  polyester
Elura
  modacrylic
Encron
  polyester
Enkaloft
  nylon
Enkalure
  nylon
Enkasheer
  nylon
Enkrome
  rayon
Estron
  acetate
Fibro
  rayon
Fortrel
  polyester

Herculon
  olefin
Hollofil
  polyester
Kevlar
  aramid
Kodel
  polyester
Lanese
  acetate, polyester
Loftura
  acetate
Lurex
  metallic
Lycra
  spandex
Monvelle
  biconstituent
  nylon/spandex
Multisheer
  nylon
Nomex
  aramid
Orlon
  acrylic
Qiana
  nylon
Quintess
  polyester
SEF
  modacrylic
Shareen
  nylon
Spectran
  polyester
Teflon
  fluorocarbon
Trevira
  polyester
Twisloc
  polyester
Ulstron
  nylon
Ultron
  nylon
Vectra
  olefin
Verel
  modacrylic
Zeflon
  nylon
Zefran
  acrylic, nylon,
  polyester

TEXTILE
SELECTION
CHARTS

The series of charts which follows is a composite of information found throughout the book. The necessarily abbreviated facts have been compiled in short form to serve as a ready reference and as a jog to memory of more detailed knowledge.

No single chart tells the whole story about a fiber or cloth. Each of the first four charts contributes particular information pertinent to fabric; the remaining two are intended as general information checklists helpful in the selection of today's textiles.

Accurate assessment of the properties and characteristics of blends is difficult because a given percentage of fiber does not necessarily add that exact percentage of its properties to the blend. Laboratory tests are required for exact readings of details such as tenacity and absorbency. If such tests have been conducted by specific manufacturers the results are generally available on request. However, rough but reliable estimates of combined properties can be attained using the fabric manufacturer's stated fiber proportions.

Properties of Unmodified Fibers used in Environmental Textiles

FIBER	STRENGTH	FLEXIBILITY	ELONGATION	RECOVERY	ELASTICITY	RESILIENCE	DENSITY	ABSORBENCY
COTTON	high	good	low	poor	low	low	high	high
FLAX	very high	poor	low	poor	low	low	high	high
HEMP	very high	poor	low	poor	low	low	high	high
JUTE	very high	poor	low	poor	low	low	high	high
SISAL	high	poor	low	poor	low	medium	high	low
COIR	high	poor	low	poor	low	medium	medium	low
WOOL	low	excellent	high	good	high	high	low	high
SILK	high	very good	medium	good	high	medium	medium	high
MOHAIR	medium	excellent	high	good	high	high	low	high
RAYON	*	good	low	poor	low	low	medium	high
ACETATE	low	fair	low	poor	low	low	medium	low
TRIACETATE	low	good	low	good	medium	high	medium	low
ACRYLIC	medium	good	high	fair	medium	medium	low	low
MODACRYLIC	medium	good	high	good	medium	very high	medium	low
NYLON	high	good	high	excellent	high	very high	low	low
OLEFIN	*	very good	*	good	medium	very high	low	low
POLYESTER	*	very good	high	excellent	high	medium	medium	very low
SARAN	medium	excellent	high	good	high	medium	high	low
GLASS	high	good	low	good	medium	high	high	nil
METALLIC	low	poor	low	poor	low	medium	high	low
VINYON	*	fair	*	*	low	medium	high	low

* indicates a variable property determined by polymer content and/or production method.

RESISTANCE TO: †								
ALKALIS	ACIDS	SOLVENTS	SUN	MICROORGANISMS AND INSECTS	HAND	LUSTER		*FIBER*
high	low	high	good	poor	soft, cool	low		COTTON
high	medium	high	excellent	fair	crisp or soft, cool	low		FLAX
low	low	medium	good	poor	stiff	low		HEMP
high	low	high	good	fair	stiff	low		JUTE
high	low	high	good	fair	stiff	low		SISAL
medium	medium	medium	excellent	fair	stiff	low		COIR
low	medium	high	poor	poor	soft, warm	low		WOOL
low	low	high	poor	good	very soft, warm	high		SILK
low	medium	high	fair	poor	soft, warm	high		MOHAIR
medium	medium	high	poor	poor	limp, cool	low		RAYON
medium	low	high	poor	fair	soft, warm	*		ACETATE
medium	low	high	good	fair	soft or crisp	*		TRIACETATE
medium	medium	high	excellent	excellent	soft, warm	*		ACRYLIC
high	high	high	excellent	excellent	*	*		MODACRYLIC
high	low	high	poor	excellent	*	*		NYLON
high	high	low	poor	excellent	waxy or soft	*		OLEFIN
medium	high	high	good	excellent	*	*		POLYESTER
high	high	high	good	excellent	*	high		SARAN
low	high	high	excellent	excellent	crisp, cool	medium		GLASS
high	high	high	excellent	excellent	crisp	high		METALLIC
high	high	high	good	excellent	*	medium		VINYON

† see separate chart for resistance to heat and flame.

Reactions of Unmodified Fibers to Heat and Flame

FIBER	HEAT RESISTANCE	NEAR FLAME	IN FLAME	REMOVED FROM FLAME	ODOR AND RESIDUE
COTTON	150°C 300°F	no shrinkage, ignites on contact	burns quickly	continues burning	burning paper odor; light, fluffy ash
FLAX	260°C 500°F	no shrinkage, ignites on contact	burns quickly	continues burning	burning paper odor; light, fluffy ash
WOOL	132°C 275°F	curls away from flame	burns slowly	self-extinguishing	burning hair; small brittle bead
SILK	135°C 275°F	curls away from flame	burns slowly, sputters	usually self-extinguishing	burning hair; crushable bead-like residue
RAYON	177°C 350°F	no shrinkage, ignites on contact	burns quickly	continues burning	burning paper odor; very little ash
ACETATE	177°C 350°F	fuses and melts away from flame, ignites quickly	burns quickly	continues rapid burning	acrid odor; irregular hard, black bead
TRIACETATE *(heat treated)*	232°C 450°F	as acetate	as acetate	as acetate	as acetate
ACRYLIC	150°C 300°F	fuses away from flame, melts, ignites quickly	burns rapidly with hot flame, sputters, melts	continues burning and molten polymer drops off	acrid odor; irregular hard, black bead
MOD-ACRYLIC	150°C 300°F	fuses away from flame, melts	burns slowly if at all; melts	self-extinguishing	acrid odor; irregular black bead
NYLON	150°C 300°F	melts away from flame, shrinks, fuses	burns slowly with melting	self-extinguishing	celery-like odor; hard, tough grey or brown bead
OLEFIN	75°C 165°F	fuses, shrinks from flame	melts and burns	continues burning and melting with sooty smoke	paraffin wax odor; tough brownish bead
POLYESTER	120°C 250°F	fuses, melts and shrinks from flame	burns slowly with melting	self-extinguishing	chemical odor; dark, tough bead
SARAN	115°C 240°F	fuses, melts, shrinks from flame	melts, yellow flame	self-extinguishing	chemical odor; crisp black bead
GLASS	315°C 600°F	will not burn	softens, glows red	hardens, may change shape	no odor; hard white bead
METALLIC	variable, dependent on coating, if any	*pure* metal: no reaction *coated* metal: melts, fuses and shrinks	glows red burns as coating	hardens as coating	no odor; skeleton outline as coating
VINYON	65°C 150°F	fuses and melts from flame	burns, melts	self-extinguishing	acrid odor; hard, black irregular bead

Advantages and Disadvantages to Environmental Textiles based on Construction Method

	ADVANTAGES	DISADVANTAGES
WEAVE		
CLOSE-SET WITH HIGH THREAD COUNT	Excellent durability, strength, abrasion resistance and dimensional stability. Covers well and provides a degree of water repellancy and some fire retardance, depending on fiber.	Depending on yarn count, may be very firm and inflexible, may not 'breathe'.
LOOSE-SET WITH LOW THREAD COUNT	Flexible, good draping qualities, more porosity.	Poor dimensional stability, abrasion resistance and cover capacity.
JACQUARD AND DOBBY	'Built-in' pattern, texture and/or color. Good resilience and durability.	May have a tendency to snag or ravel if there are floats, poor abrasion resistance.
LENO	Excellent dimensional stability, draping quality.	
KNIT		
WARP KNIT, WEFT KNIT	Elasticity, stretch and resilience	Poor dimensional stability, may be subject to snagging.
KNIT-WEAVE, KNIT-SEW MALIMO, TRICOT, DOUBLE-KNIT, RASCHEL KNIT	Good dimensional stability and covering capacity.	Knits in heavy yarns may be inflexible or stiff, subject to snagging.
NO-ELEMENT		
FELT, BONDED FABRIC	Solid and inflexible, excellent resilience	Does not drape or recover from stretch; poor tear strength.
FILM	Water repellant, easy cleaning, good strength if supported.	Does not breathe; unsupported film has poor strength, does not drape well.
FOAM	Good thermal and acoustical insulating properties, used as a backing.	Strength depends on density. High density foams do not drape or hang well.
EXTRUDED	Interesting new appearance.	Unproven by time.
COMPOUND CLOTHS		
EMBROIDERED, QUILTED FABRIC	Warmth, good stability. Has interest as art form.	Threads may snag; does not drape well.
LAMINATE	Insulating qualities. Metallic laminates of visual interest.	Layers may separate.

Common Property-modifying Chemical Finishes

	PURPOSE	DISADVANTAGES
ANTI-SLIP	Urea and formaldehyde resin for carpet backing and some upholstery fabrics.	Some individuals sensitive to formaldehyde.
ANTI-STATIC	Various fabric coating chemicals to absorb atmospheric moisture, thereby reducing dryness which attracts static.	Not durable for cleaning processes.
BACTERIOSTATIC	Chemical agents to inhibit bacterial growth and fungi. Durable.	None.
CREASE-RESISTANT	Resin finishes heat-set on cotton, linen, rayon to give crease resistance.	Decreases absorbency; stiffens fabric slightly; temporary unpleasant fishy odor; soil retention increased.
DURABLE PRESS	Same as crease-resistant except greater quantity of resin used. Used to set creases or permanent texture.	Same as crease-resistant.
FLAME RETARDANT	Various chemicals to add resistance to flame to normally flammable fabrics.	Stiffens fabric slightly; decreases strength. In presence of fire, may give off toxic fumes, increased smoke; some not durable to bleach.
MOTH/INSECT-RESISTANT	Chemical added to the dye bath of wools or other natural fibers to make the material indigestible. Permanent, low in cost.	None.
STAIN AND WATER REPELLANT	Chemicals to coat the yarns in fabrics to make them resistant to water, while retaining air permeability of fabric. Most commonly used fluorocarbons also resist oily stains.	Most effective on tightly constructed fabrics.
SOIL RELEASE	Chemical wetting agents used on washable fabrics to permit better water absorbency. Water based cleaning methods are thus better able to lift out soil. Good durability.	None.
THERMAL INSULATION	Thick foam and/or resin finish used on drapery fabrics to prevent heat/cold transfer.	Reduces drapability. Loses some effectiveness with each cleaning.

Performance Requirements of Textiles in Environmental Applications

PERFORMANCE REQUIREMENTS

ENVIRONMENTAL TEXTILE APPLICATION	FIRE RESISTANCE	STRENGTH	ABRASION RESISTANCE	DIMENSIONAL STABILITY	RESILIENCE	COLOR STABILITY	CROCKFASTNESS	LIGHTFASTNESS	GLARE RESISTANCE	PRIVACY	CLEANABILITY	STATIC RESISTANCE	INSECT RESISTANCE	ACOUSTICAL CONTROL	THERMAL CONTROL	HAND
CARPET	*	*	*	*	*	*	*	*			*	*	*	*	*	*
CASEMENTS	*	*		*			*	*	*	*					*	
DRAPERY	*	*		*		*	*	*	*	*			*	*	*	
UPHOLSTERY	*	*	*	*	*	*	*	*			*	*	*			*
WALL COVERINGS	*			*		*					*	*		*	*	

Environmental Use of Textiles, by Fiber

	COTTON	LINEN	JUTE	SISAL	WOOL	SILK	ACETATE	TRIACETATE	ACRYLIC	MODACRYLIC	GLASS	NYLON	OLEFIN	POLYESTER	RAYON	SARAN	METAL
CLOTH CASEMENT CLOTH	*	*			*	*				*	*	*		*	*		
DRAPERIES	*	*			*	*	*	*	*	*		*		*	*	*	*
UPHOLSTERY FABRIC	*	*			*	*	*		*			*	*	*	*		*
WALL COVERINGS	*	*	*		*	*											
BEDSPREADS	*	*			*	*	*	*				*		*	*		
BLANKETS	*				*				*	*		*					
SHEETING	*					*								*	*		
SLIPCOVERS	*	*			*	*						*	*	*	*		*
TABLE LINENS	*	*										*		*	*		*
TOWELS	*	*															
CARPETING CARPET FACE				*	*	*			*	*		*	*	*			
CARPET BACKING			*										*				
AREA RUGS	*			*	*	*											
MATS	*			*	*				*	*		*	*	*			
OTHER INSULATION											*						
PADDING							*		*					*			

12 PROFESSIONAL PRACTICE

Designer liability is becoming an increasingly important issue. Aesthetic and functional planning of living and work spaces is now only a part of interior design, and designers are being held responsible for the performance of the products they specify in the areas of function and safety. This new accountability requires a sound basis of information.

Reading labels and fact sheets, and asking questions, are invaluable aids to keeping knowledge current, and the designer must never assume that what was known yesterday applies today.

Quality Safeguards

The best safeguard against errors with textile specification is a good understanding of the elementary facts and relationships. The specification process is based, first of all, on overall economic consideration which includes the stability and durability of the textiles being considered and the maintenance factors related to product life span; and, secondly, on evaluation of the materials being considered.

ECONOMIC FEASABILITY

Working within a client's budget, to specify textiles requires the designer to consider the following:

Stability and Durability

The proposed cloth or carpeting must be assessed as appropriate for the function. While this may seem elementary, it sometimes occurs that a client has unrealistic expectations of a textile product's capacity to endure hard use. The designer must feel confident of the material's ability to fulfil the expected function for a reasonable period of time, and should be able to give the client an intelligent appraisal as to its stability and a good approximation of its durability.

User Interface

The specified textiles should meet the aesthetic needs of the users and provide the expected degree of safety, comfort and/or privacy, while meeting the visual needs of compatible interfacing with other components through color and geometric coordination. They should be able to maintain color stability and resist abrasion, fading or crocking. Acoustic and thermal insulating factors should be provided through accurate appraisal of expected heat/cold problems, and knowledge of impact and airborne sound within the space.

Maintenance

Daily and periodic care requirements must be known for materials being specified, and this maintenance data should be given to the client. Textile components should not require costly maintenance or frequent replacement, but should be relatively easy to maintain over the expected life span. Flexibility should be carefully considered if relocation of the components is a possibility.

EVALUATING TEXTILES

Evaluating textiles may be fast or time consuming, free or costly, approximate or conclusive. It may be a normal part of production or to meet a specific code. Testing of textiles to meet particular performance criteria is increasing on all levels.

Free and immediate results are available through the senses—hand testing and observation. Simple burn tests will identify cellulose and protein fibers. Professionals in fabrics may taste silk, crush a fabric in the palm, check for fuzzing and pilling with a rotary finger rub, pull threads to check raveling and rub a fabric with a handkerchief to check for color crocking. These methods establish some basics and provide fast evaluation of certain performance requirements. They are not to be taken lightly, but for the most

---

The Terminology of Flaws and Faults

A FLAW   is an individual inconsistency in a fabric. It may be amenable to repair when discovered during factory inspection, or it may be tagged and an allowance in quantity offered at time of sale.

A FAULT   is inconsistency in an entire piece or lot of fabric which changes it from the intended standard.

FLAWS

A BAR, BARRÉ, or BAR MARK is the most common apparent flaw. It is a horizontal band varying in size from a single pick (either too heavy or too light) or, if a whole bobbin of flawed yarn is involved, the bar may be 5-15 cm. (2-6″) in depth, or occasionally greater.

BROKEN WARP ENDS are a frequent occurrence, but are usually mended before the fabric is shipped. If the broken warp causes a complex of mispicks and warp floats, the material is tagged.

BURR is a common term for any vegetable matter, cottonseed, silk larva bit, or other natural material inadvertently left in a natural fabric.

DIRT or GREASE is usually removed in scouring, but occasionally is encountered at the end of a piece.

FLOAT flaws may be horizontal or vertical. A horizontal float is generally termed a *mispick;* a vertical float is a *warp float.* Very short floats are usually harmless and acceptable. Longer floats may be mended with a needle.

FLY is yarn contamination by other fiber or lint. If it is slight, it is usually picked out with a needle.

A HOLE is a major flaw, either the result of a *smash*—the beater falling on a shuttle trapped in the warp during the weaving process—or a broken end in warp-knit goods. Depending on size, it may be successfully mended.

KNOTS, if they are small, may be pushed to the reverse of the fabric. If they are large, they must be untied and darned into the fabric.

A REED MARK is a vertical streak caused by a distorted wire in the reed, or comb.

A SKIP PICK is a horizontal flaw caused by a missed shot of filling yarn. In a plain weave, it results in two filling yarns running as one.

A SLUB is an overly heavy area in a yarn; it may be vertical or horizontal.

A SLUG is a loose filling yarn. The slack may be pulled to the selvage, or it may be darned into place.

FAULTS

COLOR VARIATION is any off-standard color in the cloth. It may or may not be acceptable, but usually cannot be matched.

OFF-GRAIN is a finishing fault in which the horizontal yarns run at an angle. Striped fabrics are the least tolerant of this fault; in plain goods, it may be acceptable.

MISPRINT is a finishing flaw of printed goods and is generally not acceptable.

PILE LOSS may occur during dyeing, printing or finishing. It may be slight, or extreme. End use will determine whether it is an acceptable fault.

SELVAGE PROBLEMS, if they are extensive, are usually not acceptable as they affect the hang and shaping quality of the fabric. Selvages may be too tight (short) or too loose (long). If the problem is slight, or intermittent, it is considered a flaw.

SLIPPAGE of warp yarns during finishing may distort the fabric.

TENDER GOODS is a term used to designate fabric which has lost strength because of improper use of heat or chemicals. It is an uncommon problem, but serious.

part, designers need to supplement this type of hands-on experience with more specific and exacting tests.

On particular materials, these methods may include hang tests—hanging a substantial length of fabric to check for draping quality, transparency/opacity, shrinkage and elongation; cleaning tests, fading tests, wear tests, bacteria and insect resistance tests and fire retardance tests.

Performance Test Methods

Performance testing methods are usually grouped in three categories:

PHYSICAL TESTS are used where compliance with specified requirements can best be established with tests which simulate the intended use condition.

CALCULATION METHOD is used where compliance with requirements can be established by means of graphic and/or numerical calculations, using accepted engineering practice and applicable codes.

OBSERVATION is used where compliance with performance requirements can only be established by observing the textiles under specified conditions. Visual evaluation should be based on unanimous agreement of a panel of at least three independent observers.

Verifying Test Results

Designers should be aware that performance testing presents many problems. Predicting a material's performance under various use conditions is sometimes impossible to determine in a laboratory setting. Often, several test methods are used in order to fully understand how a material will function in a particular situation. When requesting technical data from a manufacturer, the designer should outline the intended use of the material, specifying exactly how and where a textile product will interface with other components. It is important to obtain test information in written form.

To verify the claims made by manufacturers, millions of dollars are spent yearly, evaluating performance test methods. To assure that tests provide valid results, the following criteria have been established:

— Test methods should simulate, as far as possible, conditions typical of actual use.
— The test should provide reliable and quantitative results.

— It should be possible to repeat and reproduce test results. Tests conducted on a given material in the same laboratory, under the same conditions, should reveal continuity of results.
— The test method should be economic. The size and cost of testing equipment, the time required for the test, and the sample size or quantity required for testing must be considered.
— Test results should be reported in terms that are understandable by the people who will read them. Interior designers, architects and code officials must be able to apply test findings in their practices.

PERFORMANCE TESTS

Virtually every functional aspect of a textile may be tested by one or more of the methods outlined. Producers of brand name products often make available documented test results. Except in unusual circumstances, where the slightest deviation may be a hazard to health or safety, these guarantees of performance should be acceptable to both the designer and client. Written warranties cover such aspects as breaking strength of carpet, static resistance, flame retardance, guaranteed durable finishes, etc. For specific textiles, such as carpeting, tests are available to determine sound transfer, resistance to forces, pill resistance, adhesive strengths, static load resistance, surface flame spread, smoke density, colorfastness, shrinkage and most effective cleaning method. Tests to ascertain shading co-efficients, shrink/sag tendencies, insulating values and heat transfer, may be available from casement and drapery fabric manufacturers or independent testing laboratories. Abrasion and exposure tests for upholstery fabrics may also be undertaken to meet specific performance criteria.

Two areas which are often questioned and may need independent tests are colorfastness and maintenance methods. (Fire regulations are dealt with in the following section.)

Colorfastness

Textiles may change color because of various conditions. Environmental factors, such as sunlight, and wear factors, such as abrasion, may result in color alteration. Laundering or drycleaning may also cause fading or color change. **Colorfastness** refers to fastness to fading forces such as light or wear; **colorfastness to cleaning or washing** refers to fastness after laundering or dry-cleaning. Both are more of a problem with strong or dark colors than with pastels or lighter shades. In a patterned or various colored fabric, one color may be less fast than others. Resistance to staining is a further consideration of colorfastness if the textile is to be subject to contact with chemical fumes, oily substances or other specific materials.

When assessing color change of any kind, the light source used in the examination process is very important. The originals and tested samples should be observed in daylight, fluorescent and incandescent light.

CROCKING is the transfer of color from one fabric to another by rubbing. Dark colors and printed textiles are most liable to color loss through crocking. A simple test on a device known as a **crockmeter** subjects the fabric sample to a measured amount of abrasion with a white testing cloth, both dry and damp. The degree of color pick-up is matched to a chart and a rating is determined. Class 1 indicates a high degree of crocking; Class 5 indicates negligible or no crocking.

FROSTING is similar to crocking, but shows color loss only in areas subject to relatively severe localized flat abrasion, such as the welt on the top front edge of an upholstered cushion. Union dyed fabrics or printed materials are most susceptible. A test for frosting may be conducted on a surface **abrader** which subjects the sample to a multi-dimensional rubbing action, and then compares the color of the abraded sample to the original.

COLORFASTNESS TO LIGHT is tested on a **Fade-Ometer** which accelerates the light exposure effect to approximate weeks or months of exposure to sunlight or other strong light. Fabrics may be exposed for 10-200 hours, depending on the expected real life exposure. Drapery fabric is usually tested for 80 hours and a fade rating given.

COLORFASTNESS TO WASHING is tested in a variety of ways because of the wide differences in acceptable laundering procedures. In testing fabrics the following variables must be taken into consideration:

— Pre-soak or no pre-soak
— Washing temperature — cold to hot
— Cleansing additives — soap, detergents, bleaches; all of various strengths and types
— Proportions of cleansing agent to water
— Mechanical action
— Washing time

From these laundering tests, a recommended method, as well as methods or products to be avoided, can be determined.

COLORFASTNESS TO DRY-CLEANING is tested with perclorethylene for three reasons: it is the most common comercial dry-cleaning solution; it is more severe in solvent action than Stoddard solvent (petroleum base); and color that is unaffected by perclorethylene will also be unaffected by Stoddard, while the reverse is not the case.

COLORFASTNESS TO FUME FADING is a concern with fabrics which will be exposed to the oxides of nitrogen contained in heating or illuminating gases. The most susceptive is acetate dyed with disperse dye. Finishes to prevent fume fading may be applied but these are generally not permanent and will be removed with the first cleaning. Samples of new, and cleaned, fabric may be tested in a **gas fading chamber** and the results assessed visually.

Maintenance

The same laundering, dry-cleaning and spotting tests used to test colorfastness are also used for checking other factors such as shrinkage, stretching and change in hand or texture. Repeated treatments are necessary to accumulate a true picture of the long-term effects of maintenance.

LAWS AND REGULATIONS

Textile laws and regulations, and the industry's quality programs, are stringent and are a dependable source of information for the designer. Identification and marketing are controlled by government trade or commerce departments; industry guarantee programs are self-imposed and regulated for the benefit of both manufacturer and consumer.

Identification

The most important law for textile specifiers and buyers is the **Textile Fiber Products Identification Act** (TFPIA) which was first adopted in the United States in 1960. It is the standard for all American textile producers. Similar regulations are in force in most countries which require identification of fibers in foreign textiles being offered for sale.

The main purpose of the Act is to protect consumers and manufacturers from misbranding and false advertising of the fiber content of textiles. Labeling of the fabric or textile product is required to contain the following information: the generic name(s) of the fiber(s) present in the fabric (Trademark names may or may not be included); the **percent fiber content by weight;** the **country of origin** of a fabric imported into the United States; and the **manufacturer's name or registered identification number.** Labeling of wool products forms part of the TFPIA, and the various designations were discussed in chap. 4.

Marketing

Marketing of fibers as commodities, as brand name fibers, or as controlled brand name fibers was discussed in chap. 2. Many of the licensed brand names have been noted throughout the book.

Product Guarantees

Manufacturers' guarantee programs often offer restitution to the purchaser if the textile fails to meet stated performance criteria. Labeling, hang tags, or selvage legends refer to specific textile warranties, and also may refer to guaranteed finishes. Examples are the **Coin** trademark program guaranteeing the bonded fabrics from Coin Sales Corporation, and the **Zefstat** 5-year free replacement anti-shock guarantee program for anti-static carpets offered by the Dow Badische Company. The designer should ensure that the client is aware of any such programs.

Care Instructions

Governments require that instructions for care be attached; permanently on apparel, or as hang tags and handouts for roll goods. They have left to the textile industry the responsibility for accuracy of the care instructions. The manufacturer, by attaching a care label, is indicating that these instructions are correct and, when followed, will not substantially affect the use of the textile. Designers have the responsibility of ensuring that the goals of the regulation will be met. They must instruct clients/users to follow the care instructions given to them with the textile product, and to let any legitimate dissatisfaction be known to the source where the textile was purchased, and/or the manufacturer.

Fire Regulations

In order to understand flammability and fire regulations and testing, it is important to know the stages in the development of a fire.

STAGE 1 refers to the time of ignition and the initial fire growth. If the fire remains in the area of ignition (say, a wastepaper basket) it is considered a stage 1 fire. At this stage, material characteristics that may contribute to the further development of fire are very important; the ease of ignition, flame-spread qualities, and the amount of heat and smoke released by a material will play a large part in determining either the eradication or spread of the fire.

STAGE 2 is considered the growth stage when an entire compartment or room becomes involved in the fire. During this stage, the heat generated by the burning of combustible materials may cause the fire to **flashover** to an adjoining room or corridor. Flames spread, oxygen is depleted, smoke, toxic and volatile gases are created.

STAGE 3 is a fully developed fire. Flashover has occurred and the fire continues to spread rapidly throughout the building. Lateral spread may occur through doors, ceilings and horizontal ducts. Vertical spread occurs through stairs, elevators, open windows and building ducts and shafts.

HAZARDOUS MATERIALS

The degree of combustibility, flame-spread rate, smoke release and fume toxicity are all facets of hazardous materials. Potential fire hazards are numerous. Natural and man-made cellulosic fabrics and underpaddings, if not treated with flame retardants, ignite on contact with flame and burn freely. Perhaps the greatest interior fire hazard is the abundance of plastic in interior finishes and furnishings, and synthetic fibers which are chemically related to plastic.

Plastics

Plastics are everywhere in the built environment, and it is useful to consider their potential danger. They present three major areas of fire hazard.

COMBUSTION SPEED: Plastics burn much more rapidly than natural products, causing a faster flame spread.

HEAT: Burning plastics produce intense heat, causing greater fire severity and spread of ignition. One pound of polystyrene releases 10,000 more BTUs (British Thermal Units) than one pound of pine.

SMOKE: Plastics produce great quantities of dense black smoke. Toxic and/or flammable gases are released throughout the combustion period.

FIRE CODES

Fire departments, fire protection associations and consumer safety agencies are united in the goal of educating and regulating to prevent fatalities from fire and smoke inhalation. Regulations are numerous, and standards now exist in most developed countries for carpets and mattresses, as well as apparel. Although many local or regional flammability standards have been formulated for upholstered furniture and upholstery fabrics, no universal standards are, at this time, in force.

Application of Code Standards

It is essential that designers become familiar with codes in their area of practice. When referring to codes and standards, designers should be aware that index ratings are confusing, and vary according to test method. In some tests, a high index rating indicates greater hazard; in others it represents a lower hazard. Fire code officials are faced with extremely difficult decisions, and it is important that designers realize that their decision-making process is not a simple one. Test methods evaluate flame-spread factors, ease of ignition, heat production rate and heat potential. All of these separate factors must be assessed, and combined with knowledge of how materials interface within the space.

The safety decisions of designers are equally complex, because of the additional concerns about function, costs and aesthetics. Evaluating alternatives and probabilities related to a particular specification may sometimes result in a combination of factors to achieve a level of fire safety equivalent to component approval strictly by code.

FLAMMABILITY TESTING

Fire tests are invaluable in determining the potential hazard of materials. The long lists of flammability performance tests shown on many interior products may be confusing. However, each test serves a particular purpose. The following is a outline of some current test methods.

Methenamine Pill Test

This test was developed by the National Bureau of Standards and adopted by the U.S. Department of Commerce in 1970. All carpeting produced in the United States must pass this test. It evaluates the ease of surface ignition and surface flammability. Some regulatory agencies require tests on the back as well as the top surface, and occasionally on carpet underpadding as well.

TEST PROCEDURE: A carpet sample 22.9 cm (9″) square is placed on the bottom of a 30.5 cm (1 ft.) draft-protected square box, open at the top. The sample is held in place by a 22.9 cm (9″) square metal plate, with an 20.3 cm (8″) diameter hole in the center. A highly flammable, timed Methenamine pill is placed in the center of the carpet and ignited. Surface flame should not show considerable spread. If the sample burns to within 2.5 cm (1″) of the metal plate, it fails the test. The test is repeated 8 times and 7 out of 8 samples must pass to qualify for test approval. Rating is straight forward: pass or fail.

Steiner Tunnel Test

This test was developed by A. J. Steiner for the Underwriters Laboratories Inc. in the U.S. The test was originally devised to test the comparative surface burning characteristics of building materials and interior finishes. It is designed to simulate a fully developed fire, and provides data on flame-spread, fuel contribution and smoke density. It is currently required by many regulatory agencies.

The carpet industry opposes the test method for carpet for the following reasons: Primarily designed for wall and ceiling finish materials, the tunnel test requires carpet to be tested upside down which causes many fibers to melt and drip at an early stage in the test procedure. Research has proven that temperatures during a fire are much higher at the ceiling level than at the floor level. Also, testing carpets with this method is inconclusive as it has been difficult to establish repeatable data.

TEST PROCEDURE: A sample of the material to be tested, 50.8 cm. x 7.5 m. (20″ x 24′), is secured to the ceiling of a 7.6 m. (25′) tunnel. A double jet gas burner at one end is lit and burns for ten minutes. Air is induced into the tunnel to pull the gas flame up-stream for about 122 cm. (4′). The distance of the burn along the test sample is measured to determine the flame-spread rating. Materials are rated according to flame-spread range, 0 indicates no burn, and 100 is a moderate burn rate.

The Chamber Test

This method was developed as an alternative to the Steiner Tunnel Test to determine the flame spread and flame propagation of carpet. It is used by some regulatory agencies.

TEST PROCEDURE: A carpet sample 0.6 x 2.4 m. (2 x 8′) is installed on the floor of a chamber. A gas flame is then applied to the carpet for 12 minutes along with a controlled air draft. Calculations for rating are based on the length of the flame spread and time of flame travel. The rating index has not been accepted as relevant as it divides material into two groups and continuous classification is difficult.

Flooring Radiant Panel Test

This test is highly recommended for testing floor covering systems; it measures radiant exposures which are very important in full scale corridors. The flooring system is tested, as used, on a horizontal plane. The test procedure is simple and the apparatus simple and compact, utilizing a small test sample. Reproducibility and repeatability are excellent. The test specifically simulates and measures the flame spread in a corridor or exit which is under the influence of a fully developed fire in an adjacent room. In actual situations, a fully developed fire transmits heat and radiant energy to the ceilings and walls of an adjacent corridor which ignites the carpet and blocks the only means of escape. Most major regulatory agencies have adopted this test.

TEST PROCEDURE: A sample, 20.3 cm x 99.1 cm (8 x 39″), is mounted horizontally and receives radiant energy from an air gas-fueled radiant panel mounted above the sample at an angle of 30°. After the sample is preheated, a gas-fired pilot burner ignites the flooring sample. The distance burned is measured and converted into a flux number which becomes the flame-spread index, expressed in watts per square centimeter (watts/cm^2). The higher the number, the more resistant the material is to flame propagation. A critical radiant flux rating is the minimum energy necessary to sustain flame in the flooring system, and the recommended limits at present are 0.22 watts/cm^2 for corridors and exits of commercial buildings, and 0.45 watts/cm^2 for corridors and exits of hospitals and nursing homes.

Smoke Density Chamber

This test was devised to measure the smoke potential of solid materials.

TEST PROCEDURE: The chamber is an enclosed cabinet 61 x 91.4 x 91.4 cm (2 x 3 x 3′). A 7.6 cm (3″) square sample of material is secured vertically in a holder while exposed to heat under flaming or nonflaming conditions. A photometric meter measures light density in the resulting smoke. The rating is from 0-800, with most regulatory agencies who use this test method requiring a smoke density of 450 or less (flaming).

In the United States, the Federal Government, the industry and designers are trying to develop upholstery flammability testing methods. A basic controversy exists between the manufacturers of upholstered furniture and cigarette manufacturers. In current unofficial upholstery flammability tests, lighted cigarettes are used as the realistic fire source.

Some regulators and fire standards agencies request full scale burning tests of furnishing components before approval for specific applications. This method is expensive and is not widely required. A mandatory test method will undoubtedly be devised in the not too distant future.

Responsibilities

Designers have a responsibility to see that various regulations aimed at consumer safety are followed. Risk management is concerned mostly with fire regulations and the decisions which designers, as well as code officials, have to make regarding product specification. The following is a basic fire risk management checklist which should be reviewed frequently:

— Obtain up-to-date, pertinent fire code standards for your area of practice;
— Know who to contact for specific and detailed information;
— Attend fire safety seminars provided for designers;
— Keep informed on new test methods as they are developed;
— Early in any design process, determine the potential fire hazard of the project;
— Determine the performance test method that will provide the level of fire protection information required for the project;
— Use concise fire terminology in specifications.

GUIDELINES FOR THE SPECIFICATION OF UPHOLSTERED FURNITURE

Designers specifying upholstered furniture for commercial and institutional use should be aware of particular installations that may present special fire hazards. These include areas where smoking is permitted, areas which accommodate seating for extended periods of time such as planes, buses, rapid transit systems, transportation terminals, cocktail lounges, restaurants and lounge areas in public buildings. Areas where the lighting level is low, and live-in accommodations that include bedding as well as seating, are particularly vulnerable to fire hazard.

For any of the commercial or institutional situations just mentioned, and particularly where there is a combination of all four factors (smoking, extended periods of seating, low light levels and live-in situations) special upholstery flammability considerations are in order.

— Fabric with a high thermoplastic content or a form of flame-retardant or heat barrier should be specified;
— Areas where a cigarette may lodge and burn should be minimized. These include tufting or other decorative surface treatment used on horizontal seats and arms, welt cording, which should be composed of a treated material or PVC and used only where necessary, and the crevice where back and seat areas join;
— Seams used across the seat area should be avoided, because they tend to pull loose under heavy use, which exposes the inner filling material to possible ignition from a cigarette.

As mentioned previously, designers should not use inappropriate terminology in dealing with fire-related terms. Descriptive expressions such as 'non-burning' and 'non combustible' are not part of the accepted terminology and tend to be confused with phrases which have definite and precise meaning.

In the United States, the Federal Trade Commission has warned that certain cellular plastic products present serious hazards in case of fire. They produce significantly higher flame spread in actual fire conditions. Designers should be cautious about specifying these materials as furniture components: polyurethane foam, polystyrene foam, polyvinyl chloride foam, ABS foam, cellulose acetate foam, epoxy foam, phenolic foam, polyethylene foam, urea foam, polypropylene foam, silicone foam and foamed latex.

Reaction of Fibers to Fire

CELLULOSIC FIBER	Cotton, linen and rayon burn readily unless treated to make them flame-resistant.
ACETATES	Acetate and triacetate are slower burning than cellulosic fibers, but ignite readily, and melt before burning.
ACRYLICS	These synthetic fibers melt and burn at a slower rate than cellulosic fibers or acetates.
POLYESTERS	Polyesters will burn as long as ignition source is present, but self-extinguish when removed. Blended with a more flammable fiber, they continue to burn.
OLEFINS	These do not resist flames, but burn slowly when directly exposed to ignition source. Melting and burning continue when flame is removed.
NYLON	Nylon melts before burning, and the construction method strongly influences the burning rate. Some forms of nylon are flame-resistant. All are self-extinguishing.
SARAN	These synthetics soften and char when exposed to flame, but will not support combustion.
MOD-ACRYLICS	These fibers burn only when in direct contact with flame, self-extinguish when source of burning is removed.
SILK	Silk burns slowly in flame, and sputters. When the flame is removed it usually self-extinguishes.
WOOL	The least flammable of the natural fibers, wool is slow to ignite and is naturally somewhat flame-resistant. Burns slowly, if at all, and chars. When flame is removed, it self-extinguishes.
GLASS	This fiber is noncombustible, and will only react to fire if blended with a more flammable fiber.

One of the designer's responsibilities is to know the susceptibility of fibers to fire. For more details, see the chart in chap. 11.

SPECIFYING FLAME RESISTANT MATERIALS

When specifying a flame-resistant textile, the following information should be requested from the manufacturer: the fiber content and the type of flame retardant chemical used if the fabric is labeled 'flame resistant'. The designer will then have to establish whether or not the flame-retardant chemical meets the required standard of the local authorities. The same checklist of information will be necessary for all textiles being specified, whether linings or face fabrics.

When specifying flame-resistant upholstered furniture, the following is a checklist of information to be obtained from the manufacturer:

— The fiber content of the upholstery covering;
— If the fabric is labeled 'flame resistant', the type of flame retardant used;
— If welt cording is used, its material content;

— If fabric is to be specified 'customer's own material', whether the fabric will accept a chemical retardant treatment, whether the treatment will adversely affect the soil resistance of the fabric, and whether any shrinkage will occur;
— The filling materials used in the horizontal areas, vertical areas, deck areas and loose cushions;
— Whether any of the above filling materials are to be treated with flame retardant;
— If a heat barrier is to be used, the type, and how it will be applied — as a liner, backcoating or encased around the filling;
— Whether the flame retardant chemical used or proposed meets the required standards of the authority with jurisdiction;
— If flame retardants are added to upholstery fabric, filling material or welt cording, the cost for each component.

Documentation

It is strongly advised that efforts to acquire information about material performance be transacted in writing. Warranties are often made available through the manufacturer or the supplier, but usually have to be specifically requested. Each warranty stipulates certain installation, operational and maintenance requirements which, if neglected, invalidates the warranty agreement. The designer should pass on this information to the client, in writing, and keep a copy on file.

If specific warranty agreements are not available, the designer should note and record all pertinent information written on carpet backs, hang tags, etc., and keep a complete file on the project, and, in particular, informative correspondence to manufacturers and the client.

The designer's own checklists and matrix forms (if used) can also illustrate a conscientious effort to investigate a product's reliability. Success in establishing compliance with standards governing professional liability will be, in most cases, in direct proportion to the quantity and quality of the documentation of professional concern.

The development of a performance checklist is very useful in summarizing all the information accumulated through the performance evaluation process. Items such as carpet, drapery, wall covering, seating, and space dividers can be listed with the necessary fire safety requirements and test methods. Requirements determined by prescribed federal or local codes should be matched to the test methods acceptable to codes, regulations, and/or local standards along with the designer's own special tests, and all results recorded. Designers should realize that the installation location of some components is important because many code requirements vary with the proposed use or location of the material. This should also be noted and recorded.

Other checklists may be devised to measure individual components against all the performance requirements: health and safety, maintenance, durability and functional effectiveness.

These forms provide an accurate record of performance requirements for each design project, and as the project proceeds, could prevent oversights in compliance with various code requirements. Most important, the written record documents the designer's professionalism and accountability.

IV TEXTILES IN THE BUILT ENVIRONMENT

The built environment is a term that encompasses all human construction, and serves to differentiate that area from the natural environment. Our concern is with buildings designed for habitation, work, ceremony, education, entertainment, and care, and our focus is on their interiors. In North America, these interior spaces serve a population of two hundred and fifty million—hardly a narrow field!

Textile use in interiors has increased incredibly since the end of the Second World War. New materials and new methods of maintenance have made it possible to install carpeting and cloth in totally new areas, such as factories, hospitals and schools.

Some forms of textiles are finding use as building components in new construction, and as retrofitting elements in older structures. The thermal and acoustical insulating properties of textile products have been accepted by architects, conservationists and consumers.

Our review of textiles in the built environment will focus on the traditional uses—casements, draperies, upholstery, wall coverings and carpeting.

13 CLOTH

Cloth, in the context of fabrics for environmental use, can no longer be simply defined, as one contemporary dictionary does, as "a fabric formed by weaving, felting, etc., from wool, hair, silk, flax, cotton, or other fiber…" In our terms, cloth may be knitted, knotted, or woven. It may be no-element or compound, and it is of virtually any fiber, yarn, or element. The distinction we have chosen to make is between 'cloth' and 'carpeting'. Cloth, then, is any material used for casements and draperies, for applying to walls or ceilings, as hangings, or as coverings for furnishings of any description.

Casements and Draperies

There are many ways in which interior designers treat windows. There are no longer hard and fast rules, and shutters, blinds, screens, or no covering at all, are as viable for particular applications as coverings of cloth. Casements and draperies, though, are so universally functional, attractive, economical and flexible, that they deserve first consideration.

Casement is the term for a window covering cloth that is sheer or semi-sheer. Draperies are opaque. Either may be hung as panels or gathered. Both serve the function of curtaining a window, wall or area.

HISTORY

Curtains used to be cloths hung to cover cold walls, or to fill open doorways. The main purpose was to keep the heat in. Windows as we know them were non-existent, openings in the walls were covered with wooden shutters or oiled linen. When glass for windows came on the scene, it was thick, bubbly and small. In the for- tress-like castles of the middle ages, windows were hardly more than slits in the thick walls. With increased stability in society, the homes of the wealthy began to open up and soon multi-paned windows of great height and graciousness appeared. They were largely left uncovered, but gradually simple curtains were devised—cloths hung by metal rings on ornate iron rods—which extended beyond the opening so that the fabric could be drawn from the window by day and ornament the wall on either side. And ornament they did! The fabrics were as ornate as the style was simple, with heavy damasks, brocades, velvets, intricate embroidery on heavy linen, satins and silks, and all trimmed with braids and tassels.

In the Victorian era, which influenced not only England but also Europe and North America, everyone who could afford it followed the trend of lavish fabrics for window hangings. Greater density of population then dictated that something cover the windows by day, for privacy, as well as at night, and lace curtains were added.

The opulence—or pseudo opulence—

came to an end in the 1920's and a sparse modern look came into vogue, with plain fabrics and pinch pleats for every application.

Today, it is the best of all worlds: a wonderful range of fabrics, options in style, and, best of all, the freedom to break all the old rules. Windows can, and should, reflect location, lifestyle, and individual likes and needs. The designer, planning window treatments for others, is similarly freed of past restrictions, and can now specify casements and draperies for the client, as well as the window.

USER REQUIREMENTS

Windows are a sharp visual transition from solid wall to light-filled void. The user, or occupant of the space, has particular needs. These are, primarily, to control the light, then, in no particular order, to control the view (from outside as well as from inside), to provide privacy, to ventilate, to insulate, and to protect furnishings from the sun.

Light Control

During the day, light changes. At some time, whatever the exposure of the room, there is usually need to control glare—that strong, almost aggressive invasion of brightness—which frays the nerves and fills the room with harsh shadows. Glare should be controlled sufficiently for the user to feel comfortable facing the window, yet still permit soft daylight to flood the room. For this purpose, casements of mesh, closely-woven sheers or any open construction fabric, are required. Usually these are in white or off-white blends. If the expanse of glass is large and the glare intense, very dark sheer casements can be used as an alternative to blocking the light entirely.

View Control

Windows with interesting views need little or no covering during most of the day. Too many windows in our environment, however, have no idyllic view, and the requirement is to make the outline of the view, or simply the daylight, as interesting as possible. In these applications, textured sheers or open grid patterns can be effectively used. They must be carefully suited to the room's character, and add dimension and airiness to the space, while shutting out the less than pleasant view.

Unless the night view is of a lighted garden or a panorama of city lights, then the visual transition is from solid walls to black void. Sheer casements can dispel this view but afford no privacy. If privacy is a requirement, or if the user wants to give the room a changed appearance for nighttime, then opaque draperies should be available to draw across the windows' glass area. The fabric for these can be drawn from a wide range, depending on other requirements, tastes and budget. This blocking of the window at night, if not required for privacy, may be necessary to shut out unwelcome street lighting, or a collage of neon.

The view of the window from outside is usually of minimal importance to the occupant, but a window exposed to neighbors or passers-by, particularly in the presence of street lighting, should present a finished look on the back side as well.

Privacy

Privacy is a precious commodity. In some cases, a hard choice must be made between an unobstructed daytime view and a need for privacy. Fortunately, it is much easier to see out through a sheer than it is to see in.

Night privacy may require an opaque drapery. Some fabrics may reveal the occupants as moving shadows. If this is too 'exposed', then heavier fabric or increased lining will be required.

Ventilation

Windows which open for ventilation or which are fitted with an air conditioner, require special attention. Casements must be hung based on the window's method of opening so that they may be moved out of the flow of air. If an air conditioner is to function freely, it must not be blocked by fabric. However, it is often desirable to camouflage the equipment when not in use. If the conditioner projects into the space, this will pose further problems.

INSULATION

Insulation needs may be thermal or acoustical, or both, and the designer should assess and advise in this regard.

Thermal Insulation

Even with triple glazing, windows in northern climates lose interior heat in winter. Conversely, direct sun penetrates layers of glass with ease and will heat every surface it reaches in the interior. Knowing these facts, and armed with technical as well as basic information, the designer can specify window treatments that will conserve the client's heat in winter and/or air conditioning in summer.

Energy conservation has become a specific science. Technical information must be obtained pertaining to the local climatic region, and the window in question assessed as follows:

EXPOSURE: Orientation to the sun and wind.

EXTERIOR SUNBLOCKS: Awnings, shutters, overhead screens, architectural projections, trees and adjacent buildings.

WINDOW COMPONENTS: Size, type of operation, slant, if any, glazing, weather stripping, applied films, etc.

Any layer of fabric is effective in slowing heat transfer. Drapery fabric may have **Fabric Fenestration Data,** information relating to the transmission of solar energy through glass to a building interior. Casement fabrics may come with a **shading coefficient,** a numerical rating that measures transmission related to temperature flow. The lower the number, the more effective the fabric in blocking heat transfer.

Even a sheer can block a significant amount of heat. A practical test is simply to observe whether the fabric prevents the sun's rays from penetrating. If it does, then the radiant effect is blocked.

Greater insulation is provided by heavier, closely constructed fabrics. The most effective thermal insulation is obtained by using fabrics with linings or interlinings of closely constructed material with a thermal finish. Fiber batting and foam-backed linings are also effective.

Acoustical Insulation
Acoustical insulation may be necessary to muffle a noisy interior, or to block sounds from outside. To lessen indoor sounds, draperies and/or casements made of fabrics with lofty yarns and noticeable air spaces are most effective. To restrict outdoor noises from penetrating the glass, draperies with linings and interlinings are needed.

Protecting from Sun Damage
Protecting interior furnishings and carpeting against destruction by sunlight may be a necessity, if these items have not been covered with sun-resistant fabrics or given sun-resistant finishes. The only solution is to block the sun from entering.

AESTHETICS
'I like it' and 'I don't like it' are the measures of success and failure in meeting a client's aesthetic needs. Why and how are the responsibility of the designer.

The prime aesthetic consideration for the user is a feeling of comfortableness (not to be confused with comfort). The window treatment must have a comfortable unobtrusive feeling.

Several specific and distinct factors need consideration in order to satisfy both the client and the space.

Color
Color is a powerful, but often unconscious, source of feeling. Used with discretion it can lift the spirits, and contribute to an overall feeling of contentment or security. The use of color over a window, where the quality will vary with the light intensity and the time of day, should be approached with caution. Both the site and the exposure dictate whether casements in particular should be nearly neutral, very dark, very light, or colored.

Texture and Pattern
Texture and pattern are most effective in breaking up the large flat expanses often encountered in commercial and institutional settings. The range of textured sheers, patterned openwork, extruded film, and novelty yarn fabrics is exceedingly broad and can be utilized to great effect.

Pattern and texture are nearly limitless in fabrics which can be used for draperies.

Harmony, Balance and Scale
These design concepts apply as fully to window treatment as to any other area. It goes without saying that the choice of casements and draperies must complement the surroundings. The development of fabrics with the appearance of weight and strong texture is of interest for applications where excessively strong architectural details (striated concrete, for instance) dictate an equally strong window treatment. Similarly, the production of fabrics in formerly unattainable widths, assists in the treatment of whole walls of glass or multi-storey windows.

Camouflage
Very often an interior is considerably less than perfect. Irregularly placed or poorly proportioned windows, beams, radiators, air conditioners, all interfere with the overall unity of the space. Often the least arduous and expensive solution to such problems is the use of draperies and/or casements to conceal the problem.

PERFORMANCE CRITERIA
Performance data is an essential part of the information about any fabric, and was outlined

in chap. 11. Casement and drapery requirements are specific, and different in some respects to the performance requirements of textiles for other uses.

Dimensional Stability

The ability to retain shape is of paramount importance in fabrics that hang freely. Sagging, shrinking and hiking (alternate sagging and shrinking) are serious faults and will not be tolerated by any client.

SAGGING is elongation of the fabric and is more common in heavy, loosely constructed cloth. Weight is another factor that causes sagging, particularly if the fabric is heavier across the grain. Fabrics that hang should have greater strength and weight in the warp direction—lengthwise.

SHRINKING is shortening of the fabric and often does not occur until the cloth is washed or dry-cleaned. Most fabrics are either inherently resistant to shrinkage, or are preshrunk. Shrinking more commonly occurs with laundering, and it is anticipated that expensive and/or weighty casements and draperies will be dry-cleaned. Shrinking may also occur if the interior atmosphere is mechanically (or, less frequently, naturally) changed too quickly. An air conditioner set at high cool in a room full of moist warm air can produce instant shrinkage in some fabrics.

HIKING occurs with **hydrophilic fibers**—those that absorb moisture readily. The hiking, or **yoyo effect,** results from the fabric shrinking in moist air as the fibers swell with water, and then sagging, as the humidity lowers and the fibers release water and relax. Fabrics with strong warp yarns are less susceptible to hiking. **Hydrophobic fibers**—which do not absorb moisture at all (such as fiberglass)—are not affected by shrinking and sagging.

Sun Damage

Direct sunlight fades, weakens, degrades, or disintegrates fabrics, so a fabric's resistance to sun is a prime consideration in choosing fabrics and draperies.

Draperies should be protected with a sun-proof lining. If the draperies are of sun-susceptible fabric, the turned-back edge will rot. To forestall losing the entire drapery, extra fabric should be obtained at time of initial purchase so that a replacement of the edge can be done when necessary.

Casements in full sun for an extended time will be extremely vulnerable to damage. Fabrics of fibers either totally sun resistant (like fiberglass) or at least highly resistant should be chosen, or, alternately, a sun-proofed fabric.

It cannot be assumed that these protective measures will be completely effective. Sun, and the build-up of heat between glass and fabric, are both very destructive. Furthermore, the damage is not usually evident until the fabric is laundered or dry-cleaned, and then it literally falls apart.

Flame Retardance

Flame retardance for casements and draperies for use in public places is a safety specification required by law. Requirements are available for all areas of the country, and should be familiar to the designer.

For safety's sake, in applications where there is no legal requirement, precautions should be taken to assure that the window is not sporting a veritable 'Molotov cocktail' just waiting for a lighted cigarette or a spark. Flammability depends on fiber content and fabric construction. Shaggy or loosely constructed fabrics encourage the spread of fire, whereas smooth, closely constructed fabrics resist flame spread.

Key terms in this area are as follows:

FLAMMABLE (or inflammable) means easily set on fire.

FLAME-RESISTANT is used for fabrics which are hard to ignite, which burn slowly, and sometimes self-extinguish.

FLAME-PROOF OR NONFLAMMABLE means inherently fireproof—fabrics such as asbestos, metal or fiberglass.

FIRE-RETARDANT describes those man-made fibers which are considered flame resistant. **Finishes** may also render fabrics fire-retardant.

Microorganisms

Damage from microorganisms may occur in warm, moist conditions to fabrics which are susceptible. However, both air circulation and light discourage attack from moths, etc. As well, bacteriostats—finishes and/or treatments to prevent such damage—are widely used and effective. If wool products are under consideration for casements and draperies, labels should be checked to ensure that they are moth-proofed.

Slippage

This problem is one peculiar to loosely constructed fabrics, where the warp yarns and filling yarns can be separated. Particularly in the case of smooth fibers, slippage can cause distortion and sometimes snagging. In public places, people may thoughtlessly separate the yarns, causing unsightly gaps.

Installation
There are dozens of ways of hanging case-ments and draperies, and very specialized fittings are available. Overall design of a space and the practical problems of interior and exterior elevations, tracking and hardware, are not the concern of this book, but are, of course, intimately related to the successful use of cloth casements and draperies.

Upholstery

The bed was probably the first piece of furniture. Four substantial posts, fastened together and lashed with cord to support the sleeper, formed the basic sleeping platform, and cushioning and covers were soon added for comfort. Seating moved from squared blocks of wood or stone to the addition of a soft pillow. Backs and arms were gradually added, with padding and distinctive coverings for some. The sofa started as a bed, which was covered to make it appropriate for daytime seating. It, too, evolved into grand forms, some were padded and covered for comfort, others were for show. The two—comfort and appearance—were not so often combined.

Today, the range of upholstered furnishings is immense, and the range of quality, cost, comfort and appearance is there for whatever preference and budget one has.

The manufacture of upholstered furniture can be done in two ways: standard, good quality upholstery can be applied on an assembly line with adhesives, heat setting devices, and power staplers; fine upholstery, however, is still a task for a skilled upholsterer, armed with needle and thread, a hammer, and a mouthful of tacks.

USER REQUIREMENTS

In the case of upholstery, actual needs and aesthetic requirements are closely related. For purposes of this review, 'needs' will deal only with actual requirements regarding value and life expectancy. The many other factors will be counted as aesthetics and performance criteria.

Cost Effectiveness
A client's requirement for upholstery is based, naturally enough, on a predetermined need for seating. Given that decisions have been made to incorporate X number of chairs, sofas, or specialized seating units, the decision that follows is 'what covering'? The investment in fabric and labor must fit a predetermined budget, in most cases, and the client/user and designer must assess the possible solutions with an eye to value. Whatever the eventual decision, the client must be satisfied that he has paid for upholstery that will give him a reasonable term of wear, and that he has purchased goods that will return him comfort and eye appeal; in other words, that he has received value for his money.

Function
This is the first area which must be clarified. The client and the designer together should have a clear perception of the exact functions of the space, who will use it, what degree of use it will receive, where it is to be located, and what particular, and hidden, needs it is intended to serve.

Seating in a hotel lobby, a pediatrician's waiting room, a veterinary clinic, and a family room will have very different intended use patterns.

Life Expectancy
The intended use will dictate, to some extent, a range of life expectancy. The client, understandably, wants a reasonable lifespan. Depending on the user, this may be a totally unrealistic number of years, or an appreciation of the fact that a change in upholstery fabric will give a new look and extend the life of the seating.

The life expectancy of any fabric must take into account all of its physical characteristics, because life expectancy means the period of time it looks and feels good, as well as the time it takes to 'wear out'. Many fabrics can endure, endlessly, but at some point they become faded or uncleanable. Life expectancy should therefore be measured in terms of good appearance and responsiveness to cleaning.

Maintenance
This factor relates to intended use as well. Maintenance must take into consideration who is to have the responsibility of keeping the upholstery clean, how often it is to be done, and whether there will be anyone to spot clean if necessary.

AESTHETICS

The aesthetics of upholstery fabric choice are distinct and numerous because it is an area where nearly all of our senses are involved. We see and feel upholstery, but we may also hear it and smell it.

Appearance

The type of fabric used to cover a piece of furniture determines its character, its impact, its 'staying power' and its price. It can quite easily make identical chairs acceptable in the bedroom and the boardroom.

Color and/or Texture and/or Pattern

These factors evoke immediate response. The elements must be — and must be seen to be — in keeping with the piece of furniture, in tune with the room, and appropriate to the intended use. This is not to say the choice of fabric must be 'safe'; it may be surprising, or different, or just unexpected.

Some of the particulars here are as follows:

HARD LOOK VS. SOFT LOOK can also be stated as tailored vs. casual, or severe vs. comfortable, or even, chaste vs. sensuous. The impression should be fairly clear which side of the scale a particular upholstered piece fits. To a large extent, the construction, padding, and cushioning of a piece dictates whether the covering is taut and square, or loose and flexible. This should be generally adhered to, and need not lessen the flexibility in appearance noted earlier.

VISUAL FLATNESS is a way of describing patterned fabrics with balanced, structured, compact, or disciplined patterns. These are preferable on pieces of furniture to patterns that seem to have movement, or a random, unbalanced, free-floating design.

SCALE refers to the cloth itself, and the texture, as well as the pattern. Each must complement the piece of furniture it covers, and the environment.

Touch

Because upholstery fabrics are touched and sat upon, how they feel to the hand and the body are important aesthetic considerations.

Hand Contact

Upholstery fabrics can be relatively neutral to the touch, or have a definite character. Most are in the neutral range, neither pleasant nor unpleasant. More definitive textures will evoke subliminal responses. If the response is conscious, such as physically drawing away from a prickly plush — the fingernail on the blackboard effect — then the fabric is demonstrably wrong for that application. Hand contact should be 'pleasant' to the client, whether it is a nubby tweed, glazed cotton, velvet or satin. If any of these are rated 'unpleasant', which is a wholly individual response, then they are also wrong for the intended application.

FUZZING AND PILLING can add unpleasant texture where it did not originally exist. Fuzz results when abrasion works fibers out of the fabric, creating patches of loose, dirt-collecting surface. Pilling occurs when this fuzz gets rolled into tight balls, or pills. Woolens may fuzz and pill, but it is temporary and the pilling is easily removed. Some synthetic fibers, however, form pills that seem impossible to remove, and they add a most uncomfortable feel and look. Fabrics with a tendency to pill should therefore be avoided for applications where there will be abrasion.

SNAGGING occurs when yarns are pulled out of the fabric. It is a common occurrence with loosely constructed fabrics or those with long floats (satins), particularly if the constituent fibers are smooth and slippery. Pets allowed on furniture can snag yarns with their toenails, and idle or nervous people (children and adults) may unconsciously pick at fabric. The use, and users, of a piece of furniture should be assessed before choosing a snag-prone fabric.

On a more positive note, occasional snags are not serious as long as they receive prompt attention, and are mended back, pulled through, or cut off. Fabrics that may snag should not be totally discriminated against.

Body Contact

The degree of comfort or discomfort felt while sitting on an upholstered surface is dependent on two things: the texture of the cloth and its porosity.

TEXTURE affects body comfort if it is extreme, so rough or prickly as to be felt through thin clothing, or so slippery that leaning back causes the body weight to slide forward. Temperature accentuates these adverse reactions. In hot weather or in an overheated room, the prickly effect is particularly irritating. Similarly, a slick surface will feel uncomfortably cold in a cool or air-conditioned room.

POROSITY is a measure of a fabric's capacity to transmit air and moisture. This ability to breathe, or the lack of it, is experienced in direct proportion to the length of time the occupant is in contact with the upholstery. The porosity of a piece of upholstered furniture depends on the fabric's fiber content, its method of construction, finishes applied to the fabric, and the density of the cushioning. Fibers which are highly absorbent breathe; non-absorbent fibers do not. Open construction allows air and moisture to pass through; tightly formed fabrics, or films, do not. Finishes may seal the surface of otherwise porous fibers and may even block the tiny air passages in an open construction cloth. Finally, the cushioning material may not breathe at all, and thus would negate to a great extent the effect of a porous covering.

A further disadvantage of lack of porosity is the possibility of generated static. Fibers or construction which do not absorb moisture are subject to a build-up of electrons, and there is no easy conduction of electricity. This may cause sparking, with friction, but is more likely to evidence itself in a tendency to make clothing cling to the upholstered surface, or to pass the static from the upholstery to the occupant's clothing.

Where periods of extended use are expected, as in conference room seating or residential living rooms, all the above factors should be considered. Where short term use is anticipated, porosity is less important.

PERFORMANCE CRITERIA

The particular requirements of upholstery fabric have to do with strength, stability and abrasion resistance. These are the factors that most affect day-to-day use and life span.

Strength

Fabrics may vary in strength depending on their fiber content, yarns and method of construction. It is unlikely that an inherently weak fabric would be selected for upholstery. It is possible, however, that finishes can adversely affect a fabric's strength, making it 'tender'. Sunlight is capable of completely destroying some fabrics, so if placement in the sun is inevitable, then sun-resistant fabrics or those so treated will be the only choice.

Slippage

Although slippage is not common in upholstery fabric, some slippery yarns within a fabric may have a tendency to give. This will occur at seams, with the seam stitches holding firm and the adjacent fabric yarns pulling apart. Yarns may also ravel out of cut edges. These are serious problems. Slippage tendencies should be recognized before the fabric is made up so that workroom procedures can attempt to overcome the problem. Such procedures would include: machine stitching the pattern edge before assembling, allowing ample seam widths, reinforcing the seams with fine cotton, and sewing with a double row of stitches.

Because seam slippage or raveling is virtually impossible to repair, fabrics liable to slip, or give, under stress should generally be avoided for upholstery purposes.

Dimensional Stability

An upholstered fabric's dimensional stability is the ability to maintain a neat fit without wrinkling, sagging or tearing. It must have **resilience** in order to expand when weight is put upon it, and contract when the weight is removed.

An important factor here is the under-cushioning. Obviously, if the undercushion allows for more give than the fabric covering has, the upholstery will be strained in direct proportion to the weight put upon it. The second aspect of undercushion importance is its shape and size. Large slab cushions, for instance, must depend on the fabric's own resilience to keep it in place. Often, the pattern of use causes the fabric to work itself over an edge, totally destroying the squared look. Similarly, sculptured furniture requires a snugly-fitted resilient covering. The option exists in these cases for the fabric to be stabilized on the cushioning by buttoning, tufting or channeling. **Buttoning** is securing, with a minimum of tension, the layers of fabric and cushioning with a thread and a button on the surface. **Tufting** is similar to buttoning except that the button is pulled tight, causing characteristic folds in the fabric. **Channeling** involves folding and securing the fabric to the cushioning in parallel rows.

Abrasion Resistance

A fabric's ability to withstand abrasion (rubbing, grinding, friction) is based on fiber, yarns, construction, backing, and undercushioning. These were more fully discussed in chap. 11 but, generally, positive factors in abrasion resistance are:
—strong, smooth filaments
—tightly twisted yarns
—plied yarns
—close-set weave
—heaviness, or thickness

Factors peculiar to upholstery applications are points of vulnerability, undercushioning and color abrasion.

POINTS OF VULNERABILITY are those areas on a piece of furniture that will show wear first. These are the front and inside edge of upholstered arms, the top front edge of the seat, and any welts used in construction, particularly in the areas just mentioned. These factors, in turn, are influenced by the degree of tautness in the fabric. A tightly pulled cloth is naturally more susceptible to abrasive wear.

UNDERCUSHIONING plays a related role; soft undercushioning will permit the fabric to give and thereby resist some of the grinding action. Fabric pulled over a sharp or hard edge will very quickly be abraded.

COLOR ABRASION is due to insufficient penetration of the dye into the fabric, and the effect is to show the ground or natural color at points of abrasive wear. This is most noticeable in dark colors or nubby surfaces. **Crocking** is a related problem—the rubbing off of excess dyestuff from the surface of the fabric. It is temporary and does not affect the cloth, but chemical dye inadvertently deposited on clothing or hands is certainly not welcome. Dry crocking can be tested by rubbing a clean white cloth over the material. Test for wet crocking by rubbing with a damp cloth.

The degree of abrasion resistance needed for a particular upholstery application will depend on the anticipated use. A bedroom chair may be covered in a tender fabric because the degree and type of use will not be abusive. In a family room, a considerably more abrasion resistant fabric will be needed. In a restaurant or an airport lounge, use will be constant and relatively careless, and fabric choice will be limited to those with exceptional strength and abrasion resistance.

Walls and Ceilings

Cloth may be used on walls and ceilings for a number of reasons. It is not a new idea, but has never been widely used. It was limited, in the distant past, to luxurious surroundings; panels of tightly-gathered fabric or full wall tapestries provided richly elegant treatment for walls, and the tent canopy effect of fabric-draped ceilings had a period of high style in France in the Napoleonic era.

The purely aesthetic reason for using cloth on walls and ceilings is still viable. In addition, fabric can contribute excellent acoustic control. On a purely practical basis, fabric is a superior cover-up for ugly interior surfaces.

AESTHETICS

With today's dry-wall construction, factory made panelling, plain moldings and square corners, the texture and suppleness of fabrics offers a unique combination of 'strong-yet-soft'. It is impossible for a cloth-covered wall or ceiling to be bland or monotonous. Whether it is applied flat, plumply padded, shirred on tracks, or framed in a variety of ways, fabric will absorb and reflect light differently than any hard surface, and is therefore always changing.

Apart from the tactile pleasure, the visual effect of cloth-covered surfaces is one of warmth and intimacy.

ACOUSTIC CONTROL

Fabric can be used with great effectiveness to absorb sound, and to prevent sound transmission from room to room. Fabrics chosen for this purpose should be thick, with a relatively open construction, the idea being to provide air spaces which will trap and hold sound waves rather than bounce them back into the room. Wall fabrics for this purpose are available, or any deeply textured fabric may be used. Alternately, fabrics which are less bulky may be hung or mounted in such a way as to provide an air trap between the fabric and the wall or ceiling. The deadening effect can be heightened by using foam, batting or acoustical boards behind the fabric.

Besides the actual sound deadening characteristics, there is a psychological effect: fabric surroundings have a feeling of intimacy, people tend to talk more quietly and to be conscious of making incidental noise.

Fabrics may be mounted permanently in some situations, with proper soil resistant finishes, and careful maintenance such as frequent vacuuming. The area receiving such a permanent installation would obviously not be placed where it would be subject to smoke, greasy air or excessive moisture. Fabrics mounted on tracks, within frames, or directly on the surface with tape, tacks or other removable devices, may be taken down for periodic cleaning and renovation.

CONCEALMENT

Poor plaster, dry wall seams, nail holes, cracks and uneven finishes often call for drastic cover-up treatment. If lack of time or funds for complete refinishing of an interior wall or ceiling is a factor, the designer may call upon a broad choice of fabrics and a variety of application techniques to work an effective concealment. Similarly, if proportions are wrong, say, a too high ceiling in a small space, then removable panels of fabric are a viable choice.

Plain textured fabrics are particularly effective in rooms where art or artifacts are hung and frequently changed. The cloth will conceal nail holes, but will not reveal the 'ghost' of a painting that has been removed.

Some richly patterned, large-scale fabrics are of such beauty that applying them flat to a wall, or using them to line an alcove, provides visual impact that cannot be duplicated by any other means.

METHODS OF INSTALLATION

Several methods of installing fabric on walls and ceilings have been devised, both permanent and removable.

Permanent Application

These are the simplest and least expensive, and involve various paste-up techniques.

PAPER BACKING may be laminated to the fabric, which is then hung like wallpaper with a water-based adhesive. In this technique, the fabric may be dry stripped (separated from the paper backing) for easy removal.

FOAM BACKING may be applied to the fabric (or a foam-backed fabric used) and the material applied full width with a vinyl adhesive. Removal is by separating the fabric from the foam. However, the foam is difficult to remove from the wall.

ACRYLIC BACKING: In this method acrylic is coated on the reverse of the fabric to stabilize it, and it is hung by applying vinyl adhesive to the wall. Some upholstery fabrics are prepared with an acrylic backing in which case no additional coating would be required.

Applying paper, foam or acrylic to a fabric should be done by a professional laminator.

Removable Application

All of the following use techniques that permit removal of the fabric for cleaning or replacement.

TRACKS, as in drapery installation, may be used at top and bottom to secure shirred or gathered fabric to the wall.

PANELS are utilized in two ways. In the **blind-tack system,** vertical wood laths are applied to the wall to correspond to the fabric width. The wrong side of the left edge of the fabric is then stapled to the lath, a cardboard or thin wood strip tacked over the staples to provide a sharp edge, and the fabric wrapped over and stapled to the lath to the right. The procedure is then repeated. The finishing right edge must be covered with molding or a fabric-wrapped lath.

Panels of wood, chipboard or other material may be **solid wrapped**. The fabric covers the panel and the edges are tacked or stapled on the reverse. The panels are then secured directly to the wall or to laths. They may be butted together, or a slight reveal left to give a floating illusion. To emphasize a padded effect, the solid panels may be first covered with some form of batting.

UPHOLSTERED WALLS are achieved by stapling fabric directly to the surfaces. The seams are then covered with molding, braid or welting. If the walls are not suitable for tacking, laths are used. Padding may be applied to the walls for a softer look and more acoustical value.

Art

Fiber art is a relatively new and certainly vibrant art form. Although the seeds for an unfettered use of fibrous materials were sown in the thirties at the Bauhaus school, the original artistic endeavors were slow to spread. It was not until the 1960's that significant showings of fiber art began to be displayed. Now, in the 1980's, the form is recognized as a late-twentieth century art.

Fiber art constructions are free form and use any type or combination of techniques to make a visual statement with fibers, yarns, fabrics, ropes, string, ribbons or other materials. Works may be intimate in size, or of gigantic proportions, and may be designed for wall hanging, free hanging, or be self-supporting. This flexibility permits their decorative use on a par with flat visual art forms and sculpture. They are a welcome and fascinating newcomer in art.

Representational fiber art is another new decorative commodity. Called **soft sculpture,** people and animals are constructed of any combination of mainly soft materials, and are as viable as interior accessories as sculptures of ceramic, stone or metals.

Fabrics have always been enjoyed as art. Artistic expression was often combined with utilitarian function, by necessity, and we should be appreciative of those who choose to make ordinary things beautiful. Quilts certainly fall into this category, many of them delightful combinations of color and individual patterns. Samplers of embroidery skills, bedspreads, tablecloths, and items of lace are all examples of fiber art of an earlier time.

In the past, European tapestries were outstanding examples of art and design. These were hung on walls and often recorded a family's history, important national events, or everyday life of a community.

In the earliest civilizations, Mediterranean peoples, and those from Persia and China, produced art on fabric. Contemporary with fabric development there, Peruvian natives were weaving intricate fabrics and composing distinctive designs which related their history and religion. Their culture existed from about 1200 B.C. to the Spanish conquest in 1532 A.D.—nearly 3000 years—and the domain of this Inca Empire covered some 350,000 square miles of South America.

We enjoy a very long history of fiber arts: tapestries and rugs, folk artifacts, and contemporary native weavings, as well as the products of today's craftspeople, artisans and artists. For decoration of contemporary interiors, the fiber field is truly as interesting as painted art or sculptured stone.

Maintenance and Cleaning

For classification, **maintenance** is regular ongoing care. Ideally, it prevents spots and stains and delays the build-up of soil on the fabric's surface. **Cleaning** is the necessary periodic removal of accumulated grime. Ideally, it renews the fabric close to its original appearance.

MAINTENANCE

Good maintenance of casements, draperies and upholstery fabrics makes cleaning less frequent. There should be regular removal of airborne dust by vacuuming, and prompt treatment of any substance that may spot or stain. At time of installation, the cloth's composition and finishes should be noted and provided to the client, along with manufacturer's recommended procedures for care. Ignorance in this area may not only compound maintenance problems, but may lead to inadvertent disasters if the wrong treatment is applied. Use of the wrong cleaning fluid or water-based cleaner can result in bleeding dye, dissolved sizing, chemical wicking from interlinings or backings, shrinking, fading or other calamities.

A fabric's life span is part of cost, and good maintenance is an important factor in life span, therefore it follows that for a client to maintain a fabric is both economically sound and protective of the initial investment. The designer's responsibility is to make sure that full and complete information, in writing, is given to the client.

CLEANING

Cleaning is done by laundering, dry-cleaning, or, in the case of upholstered furnishings, by specialized treatment by professionals.

Casements and Draperies

Casements and draperies attract dust, and absorb air and moisture-borne particles from cigarette smoke, air pollution and oily fumes. Depending on the location, casements and draperies may need only one yearly cleaning, or they may require attention much more frequently. There are two distinct cleaning methods: laundering and dry-cleaning. Laundering involves water plus a cleaning agent, dry-cleaning uses organic solvents. Each fabric has a best method of cleaning, and labelling on the fabric bolt, or information provided by the manufacturer, should be followed.

THE LAUNDRY PROCESS may use hot, warm or cool water, and may specify soap or detergent. Soaps are excellent cleansers, but only in soft water. Detergents are more commonly used and often contain water softeners, soil redeposition preventatives, brighteners and antibacterial agents. Bleaches are oxidizing agents (chemical reacting) and may be chlorine or non-chlorine. Chlorine bleaches are fast and effective as whiteners and stain removers, if they are recommended for that fabric. Non-chlorine bleaches are slower and costlier, but are generally safe to use on all washable fabrics. All bleaches weaken fibers, so that excessive use is unwise.

THE DRY-CLEANING PROCESS immerses fabric in cool or temperate organic solvent (instead of water and cleanser) and mechanically tumbles as in laundering. The principal solvent used is of the chlorinated hydrocarbon type—perchlorethylene—which is nonflammable. A few fabrics specify that petroleum based solvent (called Stoddard solvent) be used. This is a flammable product and requires careful handling and special equipment.

Solvents remove oily and greasy soils, but cannot remove water soluble soil. To remove both soil types, dry-cleaning solvents are **charged,** which means that a small quantity of water and detergent are added to remove water-based soil from the fabric. These quantities, and products used, are the concern of professional cleaners.

In addition to the dry-cleaning process, **spotting** is used to remove particular stains. The interactions between fiber, stain and chemical spot remover are exacting.

Vinyl or vinyl-coated fabrics will turn brittle if dry-cleaned. Laminated or bonded fabrics will carry labels stating whether or not the adhesives are solvent soluble.

Upholstery

The most important aspect of upholstery cleaning is knowing the fabric. Materials are so numerous, the range of finishes so large, and the possible stain removal and maintenance products so diverse, that only complete information will guarantee good care. It should also be known what linings, backings or undercushionings have been used. This information, provided by the designer to the client, will be used to direct the intelligent maintenance and the professional cleaning of upholstered furniture. In any event, test cleaning of an inconspicuous area is essential.

Spot Cleaning

Spots and stains need prompt attention. If immediate action is not taken, some stains may prove impossible to remove. If the stain is fluid, it should first be soaked up with clean tissue or absorbent cotton, with care taken not to rub the soil into the fabric. If the stain is solid or semi-solid, it should be scraped off with a knife-like object, then the residue lightly blotted with tissue or cloth. Work should proceed from the edges toward the center.

Most stains fall into one of three categories: water-borne, oil-borne or combination. The following indicates some stains which fall into each category, and the prescribed treatment.

STAIN	TREATMENT
Water-borne	
blood • candy • catsup • coffee • egg • fruit • fruit juice • grass • ink, fluid • iodine • liquor • milk drinks • mud • soft drinks • tea • urine • vegetables	Water-borne stains should be sponged off with clear water (use only cold water for blood; substitute alcohol for water and detergent for grass). If stain persists, it should be sponged or brushed lightly with water and detergent, and rinsed. Care should be taken not to saturate the backing.
Oil-borne	
butter • candle wax • cold cream • deodorant • fat • grease • hair oil • ink, ball point • lipstick • make-up • margarine • mayonnaise • oil salad dressing • shoe polish	Oil-borne stains should be sponged with the *recommended* spot remover solvent. Solvent should not be applied directly, but on a cloth or sponge. Excess solvent may be removed with a blotter or tissues.
Combination	
chocolate • gravy • ice cream • mustard • soup	Combination stains should first be treated as water-borne stains. Persistent stain should be treated with a spot remover. Some may require professional treatment.

14 RUGS AND CARPETING

Rugs began by necessity, were made of wool because it was available, and reached heights of colorful and symbolic design because, quite simply, humans have a need for texture, color and pattern.

In the rugged hills of the near east, while shepherds tended their flocks, they began knotting wool into heavy woven cloth. These early rugs were used to lie upon, as coverings, and as a tent against the cold nights. By day, they were easy to roll up and transport to the next grazing site.

Inevitably, color and design were added. Soon sultans and shieks directed the making of rugs with distinctive and intricate markings. Rug making spread eastward to China on established trade routes, where it became an established craft. The rise of Islam gave birth to the personal prayer rug, and its spread took rugs into Spain and eastern Europe. The Crusades further introduced eastern rug making into Europe. Later, Persians, supposedly captured by Turks, were settled in the Slavic countries and became skilled carpet artisans. The British started carpet making in the sixteenth century, with skills taught by captive Moslems brought to England by seafaring adventurers.

Early rug making was exclusively a handcraft. Many workers, tuned to the chanted instructions of the *khaidi,* or chief weaver, would simultaneously loop and knot individual tufts of colored wool into woven wool backing. The craft developed to a fine art form; patterns were exciting, colors vibrant, and a fine silk rug could have as many as 110 knots per square centimenter (700 per square inch).

The commercial carpet industry began in England, and the names of manufacturing towns like Axminster and Wilton became synonymous with rugs. Power looms were devised to weave carpeting, but 27" was for many years the only width available. In 1848, American Erastus B. Bigelow invented the United States' first power loom for manufacturing Wilton carpets. Woven wool carpets of oriental design dominated the field and were a luxury until after World War II, when the tufted manufacturing process was devised. The machinery was fast and efficient, and the product of excellent quality. In 1950, tufted carpets accounted for less than 10% of production; by 1980 their market share had grown to over 95%.

Orientals

Oriental rugs are still an important factor in contemporary interiors. A fine Oriental is often used as the focal point in a formal residential living area, or as an outstanding addition to a corporate boardroom or luxury hotel lobby.

The rugs have distinctive designs, and all are formed by knotting wool or silk yarns on a woven backing. Two types of knots—the **Senna** (Persian) and the **Ghiordes** (Turkish)—are used, but there are no visible distinctions on the face of the rugs. Both are tied to the back's warp yarns. Traditionally, straight line designs indicated tribal or village source, while curves, floral, medallions and animals designated town weavers.

Three basic forms dominate Oriental design: medallion on an open field, medallion on a designed field, and an all-over design. Borders take many forms, and within these broad guidelines, there are innumerable variations.

Weaving Centers

Rugs are named after the city or area of origin. Some of the more familiar from Iran, with their usual design type, are as follows:

KERMAN is in southern Iran, and rugs from the city and surrounding areas feature florals and graceful curving decoration. The highland Persian wool is fine and light in color, and the Kerman rugs are noted for their pastel backgrounds, as well as red and deep blue.

SAROUK is located in western Iran, and rugs from the area feature floral designs in gold, green and blue on deep rose or blue grounds. Sarouk rugs are very compact and heavy.

KAZVIN rugs are now woven in Hamadan and feature higher pile and a medallion and corner design. HAMADAN is a contemporary rug center, and up to twenty named rugs are woven there.

KASHAN rugs feature foliage designs in a balanced all-over pattern. Background is usually deep rose or blue, and they are very densely woven.

HERIZ, SERAPI, GOREVAN AND MEHREVAN are all woven in the Heriz district in northwest Iran. Their designs are geometric, with strong medallions and rectilinear corners.

TABRIZ was the old capital of Persia, located in northwest Iran. These carpets are finely woven with either medallion or all-over designs.

MESHED is in eastern Iran, and rugs from the area are in strong magenta and blue.

TEHERAN, present capital of Iran, features close clipped rugs with clear, distinctive patterns.

SHIRAZ rugs are tribal in origin, featuring bold medallions in bright red or blue.

SARABAND rugs have an all-over design of rows of pears, with stems alternating direction in each row.

YEZD is an ancient city, mentioned by Marco Polo. Yezd rugs are more restrained, with browns, ivorys and clear blues predominating.

Carpet Types

Contemporary carpeting may be divided into three main types—woven, tufted, and needle-punched. Flocked and knitted carpets are also made but have a more limited market.

WOVEN CARPETS

Woven carpets were originally made exclusively of wool. They are now constructed in nylon, acrylics and blends of fibers as well, and feature extremely dense pile on closely woven backing. They are frequently specified for commercial installations, and can be produced in custom designed patterns.

Axminster

The weaving of these rugs requires a complicated loom. The backing is heavy jute, cotton, or a man-made fiber, and forms lengthwise ribs. Spools of yarns deliver the various colors to the weaving area in predetermined patterns. The carpet has a smooth cut-pile surface.

Wilton

Wilton rugs are produced on a Jacquard loom, and feature a variety of surface textures, from level cut pile to multilevel loop pile.

Velvets

These rugs are not patterned, but may

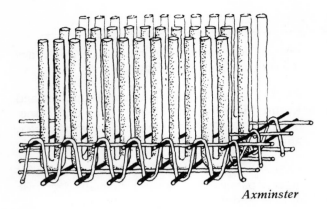

Axminster

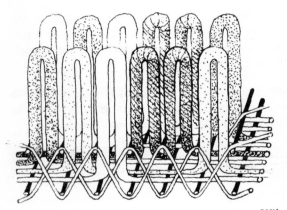

Wilton

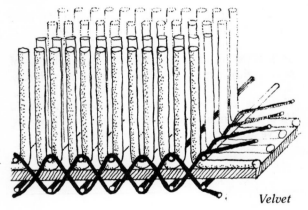

Velvet

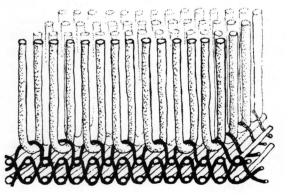

Chenille

feature various colors in an overall tweed look. Textures may be tight pebbly, cut pile, or multi-loop.

Chenille

Chenille carpets were devised in 1839 by a Scot, James Templeton. They are thick and soft, and can be woven in widths up to 9 meters (30 feet).

TUFTED CARPETS

As noted, tufting is by far the most common construction method. The tremendous growth in broadloom began in the 1950's and now accounts for over 95% of all carpet sales.

Manufacture

The tufting process was described under Fabric Construction (see chap. 8, page 75) which is the method used to produce tufted carpeting. Wide, multineedled machines can now manufacture 3.65 meter (12 foot) widths in a variety of fibers and blends, and in a wide range of patterns, gauges and colors.

LOOP PILE construction results in a surface of continuous loops.

CUT PILE construction has each loop as part of the production process, and the surface reveals the cut ends of the yarns.

CUT AND LOOP PILE combines both of the above construction techniques in the same carpeting.

PILE DEPTH is controllable by automatic machine adjustment of two factors: the tension on the feed-in yarn, and the distance between the backing and the loop-catching hooks.

PILE DENSITY is a factor in durability and cost, and is a measure of the number of tufts per unit square. This variable is controlled by machine adjustment of the tufting gauge and the stitch rate.

VERSATILITY is an important feature in tufting equipment, and allows for a selection of style effects. For an embossed surface, photoelectric cells activate a translucent acetate pattern drum to regulate the yarn supply, resulting in simultaneous construction of low and high pile. Twist can be introduced at set intervals to give various textured effects. The machinery is also adaptable to a wide range of carpet yarns in any fiber or blend.

BACKING MATERIALS may be jute, cotton, or synthetics. Polypropylene, woven or nonwoven, is the most widely used backing, with jute in second place.

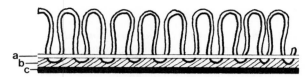

Backing on tufted carpet generally consists of two or three separate layers. The primary backing 'a' is the pre-formed fabric into which the tufts are stitched; 'b' represents a latex or thermoplastic layer which is heat set onto the primary backing to lock the tufts in place. These two layers may complete the backing, or a third layer 'c', may be added. It is called the secondary backing and can be a pre-formed fabric, either natural or man-made, or a foamed material.

The secondary backing may be of various quality, generally determined by the weight or density of the carpet face. It is laminated to the backing, and adds tensile strength, abrasion resistance and additional compression resiliency. It may also be treated for water resistance.

*T*ufted Carpet Pile Variations

Level loop *pile is formed with loops of yarn of uniform height. It usually has a tight, dense surface and may be solid color, multicolored or printed. Usually made of continuous filament yarn, it is hardwearing and easy to maintain.*

Multi-level loop *pile is formed of at least two levels of loops to produce random patterns, ripples or ribs. It has better soil hiding characteristics than level loop, but is slightly less durable as the longer loops take a disproportionate share of wear. It is usually constructed of continuous filament yarn.*

Plush *pile has all loops cut to a uniform height, giving a more luxurious appearance than loop piles. 'Shading' — the apparent change in color tone depending on the direction of the pile — may occur in plush carpeting. Usually made of staple fiber yarns, it requires more regular and thorough maintenance but it is long wearing. Plush pile is also called* **saxony** *or* **velvet**. *The plush surface may also be cut to form various surface contours. (See the accompanying illustration of Carpet Surface Contours.)*

Shag *pile has long cut tufts and is less dense than plush. It is subject to shading and crushing. Although it hides soil and footprints, it is time-consuming to maintain. Even in low usage residential areas, its popularity is limited. It may be constructed of staple fiber or continuous filament yarns.*

Hardtwist, or **frieze** *pile is formed of tightly twisted, heat-set yarns, either of staple or continuous filament fibers. It has a somewhat 'shag' appearance, but with greater durability and resilience. It has good soil hiding characteristics and is easily maintained.*

Level tip shear *pile has both loops and cut pile at a uniform height. It combines the long-wearing practicality of level loop with some of the luxuriant qualities of plush. It may be of staple or continuous filament yarn construction.*

Random shear *pile is a variation of the multi-level loop, but may be constructed of staple or continuous filament, with the highest loops sheared to form cut pile. The texture is similar to multi-level loop, and it may be similarly patterned.*

Cut and loop *pile may be very similar in texture to random shear, or it may present a carved or sculptured appearance. It is made of either staple or continuous filament yarns.*

Carpet surface contours

Carpet mills are able to produce carpeting with a variety of surfaces to give a three-dimensional effect to patterns such as medallions, scrolls, stripes and geometrics, and to accentuate colored designs.

Carved

Carved and bevelled

Hairline carved

Recessed

Recessed and bevelled

Embossed

Embossed and bevelled

Carved, multilevel

NEEDLEPUNCHED CARPETS

This system of manufacture is based on the fiber web method of needle felt fabric construction (see chapter 8, page 77). Webs of synthesized fibers are crosslaid for adequate strength. The barbed needles mounted in the needle board then repeatedly punch the web to produce a firm mass of entangled fibers. Latex is usually applied as a backing.

Needlepunched carpeting is the familiar indoor-outdoor type.

FLOCKED CARPETS

The electrostatic flocking process described in chapter 8—Fabric Construction—is used to produce carpeting. Flocking is fast, efficient and flexible, and contemporary machines are capable of producing more than 15 meters (50 ft.) of material a minute. The depth of the carpeting is determined by the length of the flocks—the chopped pieces of fiber—which are adhered to the backing. Pre-dyed, man-made fibers are most commonly used for flocked carpets. Natural fibers are also used to a lesser extent, and these carpets may be dyed or printed after production.

KNITTED CARPETS

Knitted carpeting is made on a raschel machine. The flexible warp knitter's capacity to stitch and lay-in yarns with multiple control bars produces plush carpets of various densities: textured, patterned or plain in a wide range of yarns.

Knitted carpets are fast and simple to produce and economical in use of yarn. They may well challenge the dominant position that tufted carpeting now holds in the market.

User Requirements

The use of carpeting in spaces formerly reserved for hard surface flooring has been made possible by the increased range of fibers and manufacturing techniques. The scope of possible application leads to an even wider range of aesthetic and performance requirements.

BASIC CONSIDERATIONS

Some basic considerations for carpet use are location, usage, maintenance and economics.

Location
Applications for carpeting have extended so greatly in recent years that soft surface floor-

ing can be installed almost anywhere—indoors and out. Interior use is not limited to selected areas in residences, offices, stores, schools, restaurants and institutions, but has moved into kitchens, bathrooms, stockrooms, school hallways and restaurant service areas, and even up the walls. With easy care carpeting treated for microorganism control and stain resistance, it has moved into hospitals, care facilities and food service areas.

Usage

These factors will dictate the type of carpeting installed. Obviously, there is a significant difference in use between a residential bedroom and the public areas of a downtown bank.

Maintenance

Maintenance of many of the new man-made fiber carpets, particularly with the absence of pile, is almost as routine as hard surface flooring. High power vacuums and wet-vac systems are effective in removing even tracked-in street dirt.

Economics

The economics of installing and maintaining carpet are becoming competitive with, or better than, many hard surface floorings. In extremely hard use areas, it will not have the staying power of slate, ceramic, or heavy duty vinyls with a comparable degree of care, but is considerably less expensive than these surfaces and can be replaced as needed. If acoustic control is important, a good argument can be made for frequent replacement of industrial-style carpeting as opposed to a lifetime investment in one of the extremely durable hard surface floorings.

In normal use areas, consumers generally are opting for the quietness, comfort, insulation and visual warmth of carpeting, and here investment in quality and in underpadding is undoubtedly a good one.

AESTHETIC ATTRIBUTES

Comfort, quiet and visual pleasure are the prime psychological benefits of any carpet product. Each factor takes in several distinct performance related requirements.

Comfort

Compared to hard surface flooring, any carpeting is more comfortable to walk and stand on. The degree of comfort wanted depends on personal preference and a realistic appraisal of the area to be carpeted. The degree of comfort

A Checklist of Performance-related Questions

- ☐ 1. What type of traffic is expected?
- ☐ 2. Will there be concentrated traffic patterns?
- ☐ 3. Will carpet be used on stairs?
- ☐ 4. Will carpet be exposed to direct sunlight?
- ☐ 5. What are the light sources—incandescent, fluorescent, natural?
- ☐ 6. Is flammability a factor?
- ☐ 7. Will a fireplace or other open flame source be nearby?
- ☐ 8. Will sprinklers or other fire prevention equipment be used in the area?
- ☐ 9. What is the occupancy load of the building?
- ☐ 10. Is static control a necessity?
- ☐ 11. Is static control for human comfort or as special precaution?
- ☐ 12. Will electric typewriters, computers and metallic office equipment be used?
- ☐ 13. Will there be some method of controlling humidity above 20%?
- ☐ 14. Are airborne noises important to consider?
- ☐ 15. Will there be music?
- ☐ 16. Will the area be used for public events or concerts?
- ☐ 17. Will a concentration of seating be prevalent?
- ☐ 18. What is the floor type: wood, concrete, terrazzo, other?
- ☐ 19. What is the grade level: above, ground level, or below?
- ☐ 20. Could a direct cement glue-down installation be used?
- ☐ 21. Is patterned carpeting considered?
- ☐ 22. Will access to sub-floor mechanical equipment be necessary?
- ☐ 23. Will any partitions be used? Fastened to the floor, or movable?
- ☐ 24. Will there be wheeled traffic—luggage carts, wheelchairs, stretchers? Directly from the street?
- ☐ 25. In office areas, will chairs have casters?
- ☐ 26. Is there a daily maintenance program?
- ☐ 27. Will the maintenance program include daily spot and stain removal?
- ☐ 28. Will smoking be permitted?
- ☐ 29. Will carpet be installed on street level?
- ☐ 30. Will carpet be exposed to 'walk-off' from street?
- ☐ 31. Are surroundings exposed to moisture?
- ☐ 32. Is food service available in the area, or directly adjacent?
- ☐ 33. Will beverages be consumed in the carpeted area? What kind?
- ☐ 34. Is carpet for use in a health facility?

attainable depends on the subflooring, the choice of underpadding, and the type and quality of the carpeting.

SUBFLOORING dictates the degree of comfort in some applications. If non-piled carpeting is glued down on concrete or other hard surface, it will certainly be more comfortable than a hard surface, but the major benefit in these applications is in acoustic control.

UNDERPADDING has a great effect, even the highest quality pile carpet is made much more resilient with suitable padding.

CARPET TYPES vary from very thin and nearly solid, through tightly woven low-looped pile, to thick, dense and luxurious cut pile. Comfort ranges accordingly.

Quiet

There is an enormous acoustic benefit when **impact noise** and **surface noise** (footsteps, furniture movement) are reduced with carpeting. In addition, carpeting muffles **airborne sound** within an area, equipment noise (typewriters, music systems, copiers), activity noise (food preparation, eating), and conversation.

Any carpet is effective for acoustic control, absorbing a minimum of 10% of airborne noise. The degree of sound deadening depends on the carpet type, carpet backing, and underlay.

CARPETS with dense piles and those with deep piles, absorb sound very well. A deep, dense piled carpet obviously is the best for sound deadening.

BACKINGS of woven wool, jute, cotton or kraft cord adds to acoustic effectiveness. Latexed backings have a lower noise reduction coefficient.

FOAM may be applied as a secondary backing. In this case, the urethane or other foamed material is laminated to the carpet back and forms an effective cushion for applications where no separate underlay is possible, such as in direct glue-down installations.

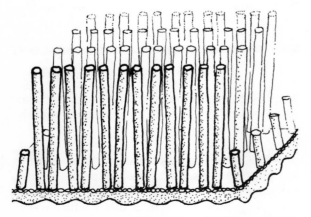

Tufted plush pile carpet with attached foam backing

UNDERLAYS make a large difference in sound muffling, with thick foam rubber, urethane foam and hair felt being most effective.

Visual Pleasure

This factor is, of course, a matter of individual preference. Generally speaking, however, a carpet which can maintain a neat appearance is preferable to one which shows overall grime, shedding, pile shading or **browning** (becoming flattened and off-color) in traffic paths. The quality and color of the carpet must be appropriate to the location and the end use in order to be maintained in a clean, new-like condition.

PERFORMANCE CRITERIA

The performance of any carpeting is based on the product's construction, and these basics must be assessed first. (Fiber choice is the prime basic, and it is discussed later.)

Construction

The factors for consideration are yarn count, yarn construction, and carpet construction details.

YARN COUNT is the fineness or coarseness of the finished yarn, and is measured by two systems:

— **Woolen count** refers to the number of running yards in 1 ounce of finished yarn.
— **Denier count** refers to the yarn weight measured in grams based on a standard 9000 meter length of yarn.

YARN PLY refers to the number of single yarns that are twisted together to form one plied yarn. Man-made fiber yarns may be twisted continuous filament. Yarns may also be given added fullness by various means, and are then called bulked yarns.

CARPET CONSTRUCTION is based on density factors. These are accumulated by the following measurements:

— **Stitches or tufts per square measure** refers to the count of stitches or tufts per square centimeter or inch. The more stitches per square, the denser the carpet.
— **Gauge** is the distance between rows of tufts across the width of a tufted carpet.
— **Pitch** is the distance between rows of tufts in a woven carpet, but it is counted on a 27-inch width (68.6 cm).

Function

The functional qualities required for all carpeting are strength, abrasion resistance, compression resiliency, appearance retention, maintenance and cost effectiveness. For special applications, increased levels of static control and sanitation are required.

In any carpet specification, **flame retardance** is an essential consideration; this was discussed in detail in chap. 12 under the heading 'Fire Regulations.' Whether regulated by law or not, the flammability aspects of any proposed carpeting should be carefully considered.

Strength

The strength of a carpet structure has a great deal to do with overall durability. Strength represents a combination of factors.

PILE HEIGHT refers to the distance from the backing to the top of the yarn. Generally, a lower pile height requires more stitches to the centimeter (inch) to obtain adequate coverage.

PILE WEIGHT, or face weight, is the weight of pile yarns and is measured, in the industry, in ounces per square yard. The FINISHED PILE WEIGHT includes the pile and all backing fabrics.

PILE DENSITY may be obtained by the following formula: 36″ x finished pile weight in ounces per yard, divided by the average pile height in inches. Alternately, the stitches per centimeter (inch) and the gauge or pitch may be assessed. Visually, the density can be estimated by bending the carpet sample. Whether the backing can be seen, and by how much, is a good indication of density.

CONSTRUCTION STRENGTH is based on the **tuft bind**—how firmly the tufts are secured to the carpet back; **delamination strength**—a measure of how well the secondary (laminated) backing is adhered to the primary backing; and **dry breaking strength**—how well a sample withstands mechanical pulling force. These factors are mechanically tested by carpet manufacturers, and test results are available for assessment purposes.

Abrasion Resistance

This is perhaps the major factor in durability. Resistance to abrasion depends on the carpet fiber, the thickness and twist of the yarns, and the density of the pile.

CARPET FIBERS rated in order of resistance to abrasion are nylon, polyester and olefins, then acrylics, modacrylics and wool.

YARN THICKNESS AND TWIST: The thicker the yarn, the better the abrasion resistance. Twisted yarns expose less continuous surface to be abraded.

DENSITY of the pile is naturally a factor—the more yarns, the less total abrasion. A loop pile is more abrasion resistant than a cut pile.

Compression Resiliency

This is the capacity of carpet fibers and yarns to return to original shape after deformation. Heavy traffic and furniture legs exert crushing force on carpets. In overall recovery, the ratings are nylon first, then wool, acrylics and polyesters.

Appearance Retention

The major factors here are soiling, stain resistance, fading and shedding. Crush resistance (mentioned above) is also an important factor in appearance.

SOILING is strongly fiber dependent, and has two elements: **real** and **apparent**. Real soil is the deposit of dust, dirt and grime on the fibers. Soil is naturally more visible on pale colors than on neutral or dark ones. Soil retention is also affected by the electrostatic properties of fibers. A build-up of static causes dirt to be attracted and cling to the fibers.

Apparent soil is a term used for the magnification of real soil that occurs when dirt is deposited on individual man-made fibers that are nearly transparent, as is some nylon. Round fibers are the only ones subject to apparent soil, as the dirt shows through easily and is magnified by the fiber's contour. Carpet fibers made more opaque by a change in cross-sectional shape or improved dyeing methods, show less apparent soil. The use of delusterants sometimes assists by making the fibers seem more opaque, but these may also give the carpet fibers a somewhat chalky appearance. The problem of apparent soil is well known and manufacturers of man-made carpet fibers now use trilobal, or other cross sectional shapes. In addition, carpet nylon fibers are now generally manufactured with voids within the fiber which scatters light and makes see-through and magnification impossible.

STAIN RESISTANCE is fiber dependent. If staining is a possibility, the type of stain must be matched to the type of fiber best able to withstand it and to recover from stain removal techniques.

FADING is a problem if a carpet is to be exposed

to sun or strong daylight, air pollution, or frequent and extensive wet cleaning. Manufacturers' tests are the best source of information for these particular situations.

SHEDDING is a problem with carpet yarns made from staple fibers. Some shedding is to be expected; dependent on fiber, this may be temporary and easily removed, or too persistent and difficult to remove. Continuous filament fibers are inherently resistant to fuzzing and shedding.

Maintenance

This is a factor in appearance and cost effectiveness as well as a concern in its own right. Particulars of maintenance and cleaning will be dealt with later in this section. However, it must be considered at time of specification. Obvious maintenance concerns are color selection, fiber choice, carpet construction, and placement of the carpet. The requirements of use and location will determine the range of suitable choice available for reasonable maintenance.

Cost Effectiveness

Cost effectiveness is a performance factor as it relates to value. The investment in carpeting is a large one, and initial cost, installation, maintenance, and expected life span must be taken into careful consideration based on other needs of the user and requirements of the space.

Static Control

Static electricity on carpeting may be an occasional annoyance or of real concern. In some situations—computer and data processing areas, care facilities where oxygen or heart monitors are used—its control is of vital importance.

In electrical terms, **conductors** are substances that offer little resistance to the flow of electricity. They do not generate or hold static. **Insulators** are non-conductors, or substances that offer very high resistance to electrical current flow, and so are prime targets for static buildup.

STATIC ELECTRICITY is so named because it remains stationary (or static) on some surfaces

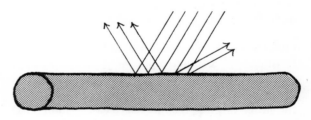

Pigmented round filament

Soil-hiding synthetic fibers

The first synthetic fibers were produced in round, smooth filaments. As these filaments were often nearly transparent, soil which collected on one surface was magnified and appeared on all surfaces. The phenomenon is called 'apparent soil'.

Several methods have been introduced to overcome apparent soil. Additionally, reshaping the filament's cross-sectional contour was discovered to have an effect on the fiber's ability to shed soil. The following representations outline the industry's progress in this area.

Color added to the round filament was successful in overcoming the magnification of soil. However, a somewhat chalky appearance was the result of the opaque pigment. As well, eventual soil build-up made the carpet look very dirty.

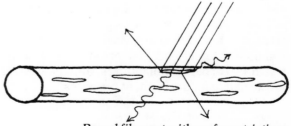

Round filament with surface striations

This modification was a take-off on the soil hiding efficiency of wool, with its natural serrations. The filament was produced with lengthwise voids in the round fiber's surface. While it was successful in hiding soil initially, it was found that the carpet darkened greatly when dampened, and re-soiling after cleaning was faster than previously.

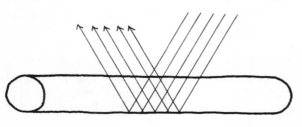

Clear, round filament

rather than flowing through like electrical current. When materials which are carrying dissimilar charges (negative or positive) are brought into contact, particularly in a frictional manner, an excess of electrons builds up and jumps to a grounded object, or a less charged one, at the first opportunity, causing the characteristic jolt or spark.

STATIC GENERATION in textiles is based on fibers and pile type, backings, atmospheric conditions, and on the types of materials in contact with the carpet.

Fibers with no moisture absorption are poor conductors. They offer more resistance to electrical current flow and are thus more susceptible to static build-up. Moisture-absorbing fibers are better conductors, and are less prone to static accumulation in the presence of sufficient humidity. Cut pile generates more static than loop pile.

Carpet backings may be made into better conductors of electricity by the addition of carbon or metal fibers. Metals are generally excellent conductors.

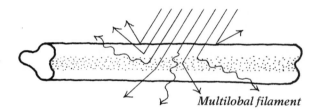

Multilobal filament

T*his development was very successful in combatting the magnification phenomenon. With sustained use, however, the indented portions tended to trap and hold soil.*

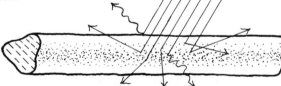

Pigmented trilobal filament, or 'delta'

T*his variation of multilobal filament eliminates the indentations found in other trilobals, exposing less soil-trapping surface.*

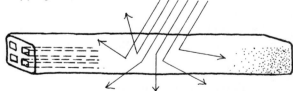

Square filament with longitudinal tunnels

A *popular cross-sectional shape is the round-cornered square. The smooth surface does not trap soil. The longitudinal tunnels refract light from the inner surfaces and avoid the apparent soil effect.*

Atmospheric conditions. When relative humidity is 50% or higher, static is seldom a problem.

Contact materials. Shoe soles of leather and heels of rubber usually generate more static than other types, but this is dependent on the carpet fiber as well. Furniture of steel and plastic tends to generate static, especially in low humidity conditions.

EXTRA SENSITIVITY: **Computers** are particularly sensitive to static. Static discharges may occur on the equipment frames, or the machines' high speed or frictional action may attract sparks from across a room. Erroneous keyboard entries, memory data changes, and upsets in terminal displays have all been linked to static.

Flammable or explosive materials need protection from static charge. Areas where these materials are stored or used are always protected by ground conductors, as the static problem is well known. The designer must be aware of the problem in case it is overlooked at a later date (for instance, a renovation of a hospital area with the addition of carpeting).

CONTROL METHODS include increasing humidity, and the use of anti-static fiber coaters. The inclusion of permanent electrostatic conductors is the surest way to combat the problem. Conductors are usually metals or carbons. Polymeric fibers may be infused with carbons, or metal fibers, such as copper, aluminum or stainless steel, may be tufted into carpets with the fibers, or woven into the backing. The most effective control is a combination of carpeting with carbon-infused fibers and conductive backing.

Sanitation

Carpet in health care facilities is a comparatively recent phenomena. Careful research in hospital settings of bacteria growth in carpets as opposed to hard surface flooring has indicated that vacuuming carpets reduced the number of bacteria present, while wet mopping of the tile floors actually fostered bacterial growth in dirt-clogged seams. Some fifteen years of such testing has led to a substantial use of carpeting in hospital and nursing home corridors and patients' rooms. Operating rooms, treatment areas, intensive care units and utility rooms are not carpeted because of the quantity of spillage.

Benefits of carpeting in these institutions are: increased safety for patients, noise level reduction, lower maintenance costs, better appearance, thermal advantages and better bacteria control.

Fiber Selection

A review of any project will reveal the major functional requirements, traffic levels, environmental conditions, thermal and acoustical needs, maintenance and economics. Determining the fiber best suited to these needs should be the first decision, before yarn and carpet construction factors are considered.

Carpet fibers are larger in cross section than cloth fibers, which gives them greater crush resistance. Carpet fibers may look very much alike, but their properties vary greatly.

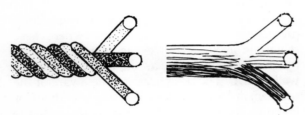

Multicolored carpet yarn construction showing the plied look (at left) where three or more colored yarns are twisted together. Each color remains quite clearly defined. The heather look (at right) is achieved by entangling colored filaments. Multiple colors may be used and the result is an integrated color union, or 'heather effect'.

Fibers for carpet yarns are similar to those for cloth yarns but are generally of greater weight and, in the case of synthetic fibers, of larger cross-section.

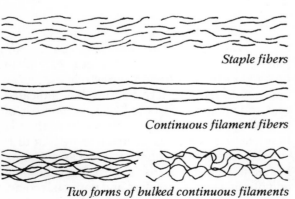

Staple fibers

Continuous filament fibers

Two forms of bulked continuous filaments

Crimped continuous filament fibers

Wool

Wool was once the major carpet fiber. The sheer quantity of carpeting now produced is one of the factors which has caused it to lose its top place. Wool has many good qualities. It is highly resistant to greasy stains, both because they show less and because they are relatively easy to remove. Abrasion resistance is good. Fuzzing may be a problem with a new carpet, but the shed fibers are easily removed, and wool carpets may wear nearly threadbare and still retain appearance. It is inherently fire resistant.

Nylon

Nylon is an exceptional carpet fiber. Manufactured in trilobal cross section, it has good opacity, a silk-like sheen and hand, bulk without weight, and exceptional recovery from crushing. Continuous filament nylon is inherently resistant to pilling and shedding. Some trade names are DuPont 501, Monsanto's Cadon and Cumuloft, and Enkaloft.

Staple cut nylon fibers, manufactured in round cross section with microscopic voids within the fiber, are used in a blend of deniers in cut pile carpets. DuPont Antron 837 and 839 are common trade names. Nylon outsells all other carpet fibers.

Acrylic

Acrylic carpet fibers are staple cut, mechanically crimped or bicomponent self-crimping. They have very good durability and good crush recovery, and are usually modified in the solution stage for fire retardance. Some trade names are DuPont Orlon Type 33, Acrilan Type 85, Creslan 83 and 85.

Modacrylics

Modacrylic carpeting uses mechanically crimped staple cut fiber. They have excellent weather and fire resistance.

Olefins

Polypropylene fibers are widely used for indoor/outdoor carpets, and as an alternate to jute for carpet backing. Some trade names are Herculon, Marvess and Polycrest.

Polyester

Polyester is a relatively new fiber for carpet use. It has high durability, good crush resistance, and high resistance to waterborne soil. One of the successful blends of polyester and nylon is the biconstituent carpet fiber trade-named Source by Allied Chemical.

Padding

Carpet underpadding is available in a variety of types and sub-types, and is generally recognized as a requirement in most carpet installations.

PADDING REQUIREMENTS

Traffic Classification

The amount of wear a carpet and underpad installation will receive is perhaps the most important consideration. **Heavy traffic** is the expectation in entrance foyers and halls in commercial buildings, hotels and schools, etc. If the traffic is constant, day and night, and, in addition, if carts or other objects are wheeled through, as in hospital entries and transportation terminals, the classification would be **extra heavy traffic**. **Medium** and **light** are other classifications.

Note must also be taken of the type of traffic, whether it is directly from the street, and factors such as anticipated spillage or staining (as would occur from salt-treated icy sidewalks).

Acoustic Control

An evaluation of noise levels and, if applicable, any other noise reducing components in the space, must be undertaken. These factors should be considered in conjunction with the user's anticipated sound-deadening expectations.

Thermal Consideration

Carpeting/underpadding combinations contribute to insulating value on a varying scale. The relative importance of this factor must be considered.

Life Span

Carpet life is extended by the use of underpadding. An underlay prevents loss of carpet thickness due to abrasion, pile crushing, and the cutting and fraying of fibers which occurs as dirt is ground in. Carpet maintenance is also aided with an underlay that allows more effective vacuuming.

Comparison of Properties: Major Carpet Fibers

	FIBER					
PROPERTY	WOOL	NYLON	ACRYLIC	MODACRYLIC	OLEFIN	POLYESTER
ABRASION RESISTANCE	good	excellent	good	good	excellent	good
RESILIENCY	very good	very good	very good	very good	good	fair
COLOR RETENTION	fair	very good	good	good	excellent	good
PATTERN RETENTION	good	very good	good	good	good	fair
TEXTURE RETENTION	good	very good	good	good	good	fair
STAIN AND SOIL RESISTANCE	good	good	good	good	excellent	good
STAIN AND SOIL REMOVAL	good	good	good	good	excellent	good
HEAT/FLAME RESISTANCE	excellent	very good	good*	very good	good	good
MOISTURE ABSORBENCY	high	low	low	low	very low	low
MOLD/MILDEW, INSECT RESISTANCE	†	high	high	high	high	high
STATIC RESISTANCE	low	low	medium	medium	excellent	low

†requires treatment   *if treated

Installation Assistance

Underpadding may be effectively used as a camouflage for less than perfect flooring, hiding cracks, nail holes, trowel marks, etc., and permitting carpet installation without repair of these faults, because such surface imperfections have a tendency to show through carpeting over time.

PADDING TYPES

Four categories of carpet padding, and many sub-types, guarantee a wide selection of cushioning materials for different needs and situations.

Felt

Carpet felts are formed either by heat and agitation of natural fibers or, more commonly today, by needlepunching. They provide a very firm dense cushion for heavy, moderate and light traffic classifications. Felts are available in various weights, from about 1200-3220 grams per square meter (32-86 ounces per square yard) and in widths up to 3.7 meters (12 feet).

HAIR FELT is composed of 100% animal hair, usually washed cattle hair.

COMBINATION FELT is made of animal hair and other fibers.

FIBER FELT is composed of 100% fibers.

RUBBERIZED FELT may be any of the above with the addition of a rubber coating on one or both sides.

Sponge Rubber

Sponge rubber padding is manufactured of combinations of natural and synthetic rubber with various fillers and a 'blowing agent' which forms the characteristic cells. A synethetic fiber facing is applied to the top side so that the carpet may more easily slide across the rubber surface during installation. The degree of cushioning or firmness is dependent on the formulation of the sponge, and whether it is flat or waffled. Waffled is applicable for light to medium traffic, flat sponge is for light to heavy traffic. It is available in 3.7 m (12') widths, in weights from 1535-4500 g/m² (41-120 oz/sq.yd.). Thickness may be from 1.6-8 mm (1/16-5/16").

FLAT SPONGE is formed in a continuous sheet and has a smooth surface.

WAFFLED SPONGE is formed and then expanded on a chain belt to form the desired rippled or waffled surface.

Urethane Foam

Urethane foam is manufactured by various methods, and provides padding to suit light to heavy traffic.

PRIME URETHANE FOAM is manufactured by mixing polymeric materials and curing in blocks. These are cut into sheets of various thicknesses (6.4-19.1 mm or ¼-¾") and densities, and a facing is applied to one side.

DENSIFIED PRIME URETHANE FOAM has a modified structure, with various densities controlled by cellular configuration. It is formed and then cut into rolls of the desired thickness, and a facing material is applied to one side. Thickness varies from 6.4-19.1 mm (¼-¾").

BONDED URETHANE FOAM is made from trimmed waste material of prime urethane foam. It is granulated and then bonded together in blocks, sheets or rolls. Some **debris** may be used as additives — vinyl, fabric backed foam, wood chips, paper — and coloring may be added. Designers should not permit more than 1% of debris, and be cautious that added color is not of a type that may bleed into the carpet.

Foam Rubber

This is a medium weight padding providing a good degree of firmness. It is manufactured in flat sheets up to 3.7 m (12') wide, from a latex rubber base, either natural, synthetic or a blend. It has a facing applied to one side. Weights are from 1086-2168 g/m² (28-65 oz/sq.yd.). Thickness ranges from 3.2-15.9 mm (⅛-⅝").

Because underpadding is a hidden element, extra care must be given to its specification and installation in order to forestall problems in the carpeting which may become evident later. Padding should be installed in the largest possible lengths, with a minimum of seaming. It should be placed flush with tackless strips and have the applied facing (if any) on top. If installed over concrete, it should be cemented down; over wood, it may be stapled in place. Seams should be taped together and should not occur directly under carpet seams.

Carpet cushioning should not be over-specified, as far as density or thickness is concerned. Too much give under a carpet places a strain on the carpet backing and may accelerate carpet wear.

Installation

Carpet manufacturers provide specific installation recommendations. The designer, however, must be familiar with the terminology and the basic methods of installation. There are two ways to install carpeting: stretching and securing over underpadding, or glueing down.

METHODS

Tackless Strip

This method involves stretching the carpet and securing the edges with tackless strips. These strips are water-resistant plywood containing two or three rows of angular rust resistant pins set at a 60° angle, and long enough to penetrate the carpet backing and provide a firm attachment. The strips are secured around the perimeter of the area to be carpeted, by various means. On wood floors, the strips are nailed down with closely spaced nails long enough to provide a secure hold. On cement floors, the strips may be applied with adhesives, by drilling holes through the strip and into the floor and plugging the two together, or by direct nailing into the floor.

The carpet must be stretched sufficiently to assure that it will not buckle or pucker after a few weeks of installation. Tackless strips are used across doorways, and if there is a transition to hard surface, the carpet edge must be covered and further secured with carpet molding strips (called metal binders).

Direct Glue-Down

This method is useful in extra heavy traffic areas, and in any other installation involving tight, low surface carpets with high density foam backings, those with jute or nonwoven backings, and those with backings finished with latex, polyvinyl chloride or polyurethane compounds. No separate underpadding is used in this method.

Carpet is held securely to the floor with specific adhesives, and does not shift under heavy traffic. Occasionally, carpeting is adhered to a built-up wooden floor which may be lifted in sections to provide access to underfloor services (computer wiring, for instance).

Direct glue-down is successful only if careful consideration is given to the location's environmental conditions, the condition and pre-preparation of the sub-floor, adhesives, the type and quality of carpet construction and its constituent fibers, and the seaming.

ENVIRONMENTAL CONDITIONS must include relatively stable temperatures and relative humidity. Drastic temperature changes may cause buckling, and excessive humidity may stretch or shrink the fibers.

SUB-FLOOR preparations are more important for glue-down installation because of surface irregularities and adhesive bonding criteria. Concrete is commonly the flooring surface for glue-down installations. It is classed as **suspended** if it is above grade, **on-grade** if it is in contact with the ground, or **below grade**. Moisture transmission from the ground up through on-grade or below grade concrete must be blocked by pre-preparation compounds. Wood, terrazzo, ceramic or quarry tile will necessitate floor preparation techniques to fill cracks or grout lines. Radiant heated floors must be maintained at specified levels while adhesive drying takes place after installation.

ADHESIVES used for carpet glue-down are of four types: natural latex, synthetic latex, solvent-based rubber adhesive and alcohol solvent resins. Each has particular characteristics, compatabilities and application techniques.

CARPET TYPES: The carpet construction should be tight, with a good face weight. Generally, low level loop surfaces are amenable to this installation technique and the areas where it will most likely be applied. The carpet's backing must be one that will remain stable and provide a secure bond with the adhesive. Jute and non-woven synthetics are among the most successful. Fibers should be selected for abrasion resistance. Nylon, acrylic, wool and olefin carpets have been successfully used in direct glue-down installation.

SEAMING must be secure. The carpet should be tightly constructed to prevent edges from fraying. Seams should be sealed with latex-type glue before installation.

OTHER CARPET PARTICULARS

Nap

Carpet nap is the direction that the pile tends to lie. The nap direction affects the appearance, in that a slightly different color will be seen depending on whether the carpet is viewed with or against the nap.

Ideally, nap should run in the same direction for an entire installation. Cuts and sides, where seaming has been necessary, must not show a nap change. On stairs, the carpet should be installed with the nap running downward. This provides for longer wear as well as the most pleasing appearance.

Seam Placement
Planning the seam placement in a carpet installation is one of the most important considerations. Designers should request that the contractor or installer submit a seaming diagram prior to work being undertaken. Seams should be avoided across areas of heavy traffic, such as halls. They should not run into doorways, although across a doorway is often necessary. Seams should not be placed at locations where people change directions, or pivot.

Carpet seams must be as strong as possible to withstand stretching during installation and during use.

HAND SEWING with coarse linen thread and curved needles is an exacting task, and it is only feasible on carpet with backing which can be penetrated. The completed seams are ironed with a special heating device, and coated with latex adhesive.

HOT MELT TAPE produces a flat, invisible seam that is very strong. An adhesive-surfaced tape bonds the seams together when heat is applied. It is useful only on specified fibers, and must not be used on carpet with low melt point fibers, rubber or latexed backings, or in conjunction with foam or sponge underlays which permit the seam to become apparent on the carpet surface. Seams should be accurately fitted before the tape is applied.

LATEX TAPE is a similar method, but no heat is necessary and latex becomes the binding agent.

Patterned Carpet
Patterned carpets present special problems in seaming. The pattern must be accurately measured and the match planned accordingly. Patterned carpets are designed in three ways:

SET MATCH indicates that the pattern elements are in a straight side-by-side match across the width of the carpet.

DROP MATCH indicates that pattern elements are situated in a diagonal across the carpet.

QUARTER DROP MATCH is usually found in 27" woven carpets, with four pattern blocks (4 quarters) in every length repeat, with one block (1 quarter) dropped in each repeat.

Maintenance and Cleaning

Carpet maintenance has changed over the years from a semi-annual cleaning to programmed regular cleaning to prevent dirt and abrasive soil from settling in the fibers.

PREVENTIVE MAINTENANCE
A program of maintenance may be planned based on knowledge of the expected soil sources and areas of the carpet which will receive extra wear.

Types of Soil
These have been defined as water soluble soils and solvent soluble soils. The sources of the soiling are airborne, shoe surface and spillage. If any of these are extensive and not removable by vacuuming, cleansing (and thorough removal of the cleansing agent and the soil) should be done as soon as possible.

Soil Areas
Areas which require daily maintenance and more frequent special attention are:

TRACK-OFF AREAS: This is where people walk in from the outdoors, or from adjacent hard surface flooring. It should be vacuumed daily, and walk-off mats, both inside and outside, are necessary to prevent the tracked in soil from spreading into the space.

FUNNEL AREAS: These are areas where foot traffic takes a specific, concentrated course, such as the center of a hallway. These require daily vacuuming, spot cleaning as necessary, and frequent cleaning of the whole area.

Maintenance Activities
VACUUMING is the single most important activity related to carpet care. In commercial buildings and institutional settings, it is usually done with

a heavy duty upright vacuum equipped with brush agitators.

SPOT REMOVAL should, ideally, be undertaken as soon as spots or spills occur. Many manufacturers make available spot cleaning kits equipped with the proper chemicals and instructions for use.

CORRECTIVE CLEANING

The accumulation of oily airborne soil is one of the main reasons for undertaking overall cleaning. Carpeting should first be thoroughly vacuumed, and the floor area then cleaned by one of the following methods:

WET CLEANING, with water-based cleaners, takes several days to dry thoroughly, so scheduling is very important. It is not advisable to require wet cleaning in areas where traffic cannot be stopped. A detergent solution is usually recommended by the carpet manufacturer. If a non-recommended detergent is used, it should be tested on an inconspicuous area before proceeding.

DRY FOAM CLEANING is a simultaneous procedure. Dry foam detergent is deposited on the carpet just before it is vacuumed with an agitating reel type brush. Overwetting is prevented, and use may resume within an hour.

HOT WATER EXTRACTION uses a hot detergent solution under pressure to quickly wet the carpet. The solution is immediately extracted by vacuum, along with the soil. Sometimes overwetting occurs, involving long delays in the re-use of the cleaned area.

POWDER CLEANERS are absorbent powders with detergents and solvents added. The powder is sprinkled on the carpet and allowed to sit for a very short time before being vacuumed. The method is very fast.

ULTRASONIC CLEANING is, at this time, a cleaning plant technique for carpeting which can be removed. A practical on-site application of high frequency sound waves to attract soil from the carpet fibers is still being investigated.

The investment in carpeting is a large one, and the installed carpeting deserves knowledgeable care and attention. Maintenance factors must always be considered, both for the user's satisfaction with the carpet's appearance, and as a factor in life cycle costing.

15 SUMMARY

The future of environmental textiles is assured. They are versatile, easy to handle, economical and aesthetically pleasing. They are an essential part of the built environment as well as being an integral part of the personal environment of each of us.

It has been shown throughout this book that the forces of history — particularly the pressures of changing societies — shaped and determined the desirability of certain textiles, and that textile manufacturers then provided a dependable supply. Consumer demand, as it is now called, has played a starring role in the world-wide distribution of fabrics. In the seventeenth century, the demand for cottons from India and America made them popular and available in England, despite the Crown's attempts to keep the country exclusively in wool. In recent history, consumer demand contributed to a proliferation of low cost textiles that could be discarded without the earlier twinges of thrift. More recently, energy conservation has led consumers to demand insulating draperies, and pollution awareness has led to a welcome retreat from the throw-away era.

The future of textile demand is therefore to be found, in part at least, in current societal trends. Whether these trends continue and develop further or change course entirely is not predictable; the textile industry evaluates and plans production; designers observe and anticipate. A crystal ball would help!

The issues and priorities of the mid-1980's are economic recovery, inflated energy costs, continuing concern with air, water and soil pollution, and increasing awareness of alienation, crime and violence. Being both realistic and basically optimistic, people-priorities of our times are to obtain good value for money spent, to conserve energy, to be more careful of our natural resources and to have a growing appreciation for what is being called 'the old values' — conservation, thrift, a personally rewarding quality of life and a more conscientious sense of community. These trends will influence demand and spending on all levels for all products.

Considering the current trends, there appears to be a need for quality textiles manufactured efficiently with concern for water and air pollution. Maximum performance products at reasonable cost is an ideal which the textile industry has conscientiously tried to attain, and it has had considerable success. The market is large and expanding. It has been estimated that about 13% of disposable income is spent on textiles, and that textiles for interiors occupy roughly one third of that percentage. A large share of the latter expenditure is for carpeting, with use in public places continuing to increase, and a large replacement market now on stream.

Developments in technology are made yearly to meet changing demands, though emphasis now is focused on fabrication techniques and finishes rather than new fiber development. Technical developments in weaving are unlikely. Knitting as a fabrication technique is both faster and more efficient, and possibilities are greater for new fabric structures and greater diversity of design. Raschel knitting machines have incredible flexibility, as was discussed; they are capable of producing complex designs and of utilizing speciality yarns; 'down time' is minimized as the machinery can be adapted to changes in design and/or yarn weights in minutes rather that days.

Improvements may be made in the no-element fabric field; there are many exciting possibilities as yet unexplored such as fabricating directly to furniture shape. No-element fabrics are simple and economic to produce. As carpeting, they give adequate to excellent performance at low price.

The activity in the tufted fabric field will undoubtedly continue. The majority of all carpets now sold are produced on tufting machines, which are more than eight times faster and more efficient than woven pile carpet looms. There also may be increased research in producing upholstery fabrics on tufting machinery.

Finishing technology is expected to continue apace. Meeting new requirements for insulating factors and natural fiber enhancement will be activities of importance to consumers; streamlining production and reducing costs will be of importance to the industry to minimize inflation in their area. Recently developed dyeing and printing techniques are still being tested to save time, water and energy. Microjet printing, which forces color into the tufts of a pile carpet and other such bulky fabrics, is being seen as both efficient and cost effective.

Soil and static control finishes will continue to be improved, especially in carpeting. These finishes improve a fabric's range of use and life span and so will add value to purchased textiles.

Fire resistant fabrics, being not only desirable and necessary but also required by law, will ensure that research on flame retardant finishes continues at a constant pace. There will undoubtedly be set flammability standards for upholstery fabric and upholstered furniture which will have a considerable impact on designers.

Natural fibers have had a substantial revival in the last few years. The uniqueness of cotton, linen, wool and silk is appreciated by those who are seeking less artificiality in the built environment. They cannot regain their previous pre-eminent position, mostly because the demand would far outstrip the supply, but their new appeal is an interesting phenomenon. As fibers, they are indeed unique; being much more complicated in structure they combine aesthetic attributes and performance characteristics that have yet to be matched by a single man-made fiber. Cotton is definitely in a resurgent position. Both treated for durable finish, and untreated, it is currently a favored fabric. 100% cotton, as well as cotton/polyester blends are edging up in the space most recently occupied by polyester/cotton blends and 100% polyester.

Rayon, as the nearest relative to cotton, is being re-examined and may become a revitalized fabric of the future. Made of wood pulp cellulose, it is in no danger of becoming scarce, and utilizes a renewable natural resource.

Wool was at a low of about 1% of total fibers used in 1980. Since then it has increased slightly. It has remarkable qualities—resilience, durability and flame retardance—as well as unmatched aesthetics, and is also known to absorb sulphur dioxide, one of the major air pollutants. Sulphur dioxide originates from the burning of oil and coal and the manufacture of steel, and is a common ingredient in the air of city environments. While many of the man-made fibers and finishes are attacked by air pollution chemicals, such natural materials as wood, brick, cellulosic fibers, and especially wool, are able to absorb the substances without damage to the material itself. Interiors which feature quantities of natural materials are thus healthier than those in which only man-made textiles and products are used.

Interior designers should be aware of textile trends as they relate to consumers' needs. The emphasis for the late 1980's is expected to be on quality, higher prices, and a challenging balance between aesthetic consideration and the demands of performance and energy-related criteria.

Professionalism is a responsibility as well as a status. Familiarity with technical developments, awareness of legislative regulations and an appreciation of the economic times, will each be of benefit to the designer in dealing with clients. Knowledge of textiles today is freedom to use them tomorrow, and designers who appreciate the very special history and wonderful flexibility of fabric will do justice to a remarkable medium.

BIBLIOGRAPHY

Adrosko, Rita J. and Cooper, Grace R., *Spinning and Weaving.* Smithsonian Institute Press, Washington, D.C., 1977.

All About Textiles. American Textile Manufacturers' Institute, Charlotte, North Carolina, 1978.

American Association for Textile Technology, *Textile Fibers and Their Properties.* Burlington Industries Inc., Greensboro, North Carolina, 1977.

Burnham, Dorothy K., *The Comfortable Arts, Traditional Spinning and Weaving in Canada.* National Gallery of Canada/National Museums of Canada, Ottawa, 1981.

✓ Crane, Catherine C., Editor, *Residential Interiors Today.* Whitney Library of Design, New York, 1977.

Caplan, Ralph, *The Design of Herman Miller.* Whitney Library of Design, New York, 1976.

Craft House, *Williamsburg Reproductions.* The Colonial Williamsburg Foundation, Williamsburg, Virginia, 1976.

Eldringhoff, Sylvan F., *A Survey of Factors for Drapery Specification.* Thesis, Faculty of Graduate School, University of Missouri, August 1968.

Facts About Fabrics. DuPont DeNemours & Co. Inc., Textile Fibers Department, Wilmington, Delaware, undated.

Faulkner, Ray and Faulkner, Sarah, *Inside Today's Home*, 4th Edition, Holt, Rinehart and Winston, New York, 1975.

Friedman, Arnold, Pile, John F. and Wilson, Forrest, *Interior Design — An Introduction to Architectural Interiors*, 2nd Edition. American Elsevier Publishing Company, New York, 1976.

Guide to Man-Made Fibers, Man-made Fiber Producers Association Inc., Washington, 1977.

Gutcheon, Beth, *The Perfect Patchwork Primer.* Penguin Books Ltd., New York, 1977.

Heckenlaible, Darlene Fae, *Development and Documentation of a Catalogue of Historic American Textiles in the Related Art Division Permanent Collection.* Thesis, Faculty of Graduate School, University of Minnesota, August, 1969.

Hollen, Norma and Saddler, Jane, *Textiles*, 4th Edition. Macmillan Publishing Co. Inc., New York, 1973.

Interplay — The Story of Man-Made Fibers. Manmade Fiber Producers Association Inc., Washington, 1975.

Joseph, Marjory L., *Introductory Textile Science*, 3rd Edition. Holt, Rinehart and Winston, New York, 1977.

Larsen, J. L. and Weeks, Jeanne, *Fabrics for Interiors.* Van Nostrand Reinhold Company, New York, 1975.

Lewis, Alfred Allan, *The Mountain Artisans Quilting Book.* Macmillan Publishing Co., Inc., New York, 1974.

Man-Made Fibers Fact Book. Man-Made Fiber Producers Association, Inc. Washington, 1978.

Miller, Edward, *Textiles, Properties and Behaviour.* B. T. Batsford Ltd., 1968.

Pizzuto, Joseph J., *Fabric Science*, 5th Edition; revised by Arthur Price and Allen C. Cohen. Fairchild Publications, New York, 1978.

Propst, Robert and Wodka, Michael, *The Action Office Acoustic Handbook.* 2nd Edition. Herman Miller Research Corporation, 1975.

Reznikoff, S. C., *Specifications for Commercial Interiors, Professional Liabilities, Regulations and Performance Criteria.* Whitney Library of Design, New York, 1979.

Snook, Barbara, *The Creative Art of Embroidery.* The Hamlyn Publishing Group Limited, London, 1972.

Swan, Susan Burrows, *Plain and Fancy, American Women and Their Needlework 1700-1850.* Holt Rinehart and Winston, New York, 1977.

Textiles From Start to Finish. American Textile Manufacturers' Institute, Charlotte, North Carolina, undated.

Textiles Our First Great Industry. American Textile Manufacturers' Institute, Charlotte, North Carolina, undated.

The Textile Industry and Burlington's Position in It. Burlington Industries Ltd., Greensboro, North Carolina, 1975.

GLOSSARY
INDEX

A

abaca   fiber obtained from the leaf stalk of the banana plant. Also called Manila hemp. *20*, 28

abrasion resistance   ability of fabric to withstand damage from rubbing and wear. 51, 106, 110, *117*, *119*, 139, 151, *155*

absorbency   the ability to take in moisture. 23, 106, 108, *114*, *117*, *155*

acetate   generic term for a man-made fiber composed of acetylated cellulose. *20*, 36, 83, *91*, 106, 110, *112*, *114*, *116*, *120*, 128

acid dyes   class of dyes used primarily for protein and nylon fibers. 91, *91*

acoustical insulation   insulation employed to reduce sound or noise. *117*, *119*, 133, 135, 140, 150, 155

Acrilan   trade name of an acrylic fiber produced by Monsanto. 40, *112*

acrylic   generic term for a man-made fiber composed of acrylonitrile units which are derived from petrochemical by-products. *20*, 40, 51, 90, *91*, *112*, *114*, *116*, *120*, 154, *155*

additive finishes   general term for finishes that are chemical rather than mechanical, typically used to modify a fabric's appearance, hand, or function. 87, *118*

alpaca   long, fine, natural protein hair fiber obtained from the domesticated South American alpaca, a member of the camel family; a wool variant. *20*, 30

angora   goat native to Turkey from which the natural protein fiber, mohair, is obtained; a wool variant. *20*, 30, 31

animal fiber   general term for natural protein fiber of animal origin, such as wool (sheep) or silk (silkworm). 17-23, 28-32

antibacterial finishes   chemical treatments (bacteriostats) applied to finished cloth to repel mildew and other microorganisms. 88, 110, *118*, 136

antique satin   cloth of sateen construction with an exaggerated slub filling and a fine warp. 70

antistatic finishes   chemical treatments for reducing static electricity in synthetic fibers. 88, 110, *118*

Antron   DuPont's trademarked term for trilobal nylon, a strong, delustered synthetic fiber. 37, *112*

apparent soil   term used for the magnification of real soil deposited on individual, nearly transparent man-made fibers. 151, *152*, *153*

aramid   generic term for a modified nylon fiber. *20*, 39, 87, *112*

Arnel   trade name for a triacetate fiber produced by Celanese. 51, *112*

asbestos   natural mineral fiber used for its inherently flame resistant property. *20*, 21, 32, 87

Italicized page numbers refer to charts/illustrations.

ASTM   the American Society for Testing and Materials.

ASTM Standards   minimum standards set by the ASTM.

Avisco   trade name of a rayon produced by FMC.

Avril   trade name of a high-modulus rayon produced by FMC. 35

Axminister   cut pile woven woolen fabric used for carpeting. 12, 144, *146*

azlon   generic term for man-made fiber composed of regenerated natural protein.

azoic dyes (naphthol)   class of dyes used on cellulosic and selected man-made fibers. 90

B

backfilling   supplementary filling yarn used to pad or support a cloth. 69

backing   a semi-liquid latex or plastic sprayed or rolled on fabric back to increase stability and prevent seam slippage. 78, *120*, 141, 146, *147*, 150

backing fabric   fabric that is bonded or laminated to the reverse side of a face fabric. *147*

bacteriostats   general term for microorganism repellents. 88, 110, *118*, 136

Banlon   trade name of a process for texturizing filament yarns, licensed by Joseph Bancroft. 58

bar, barre, or color bar   a flaw in cloth—a line of off-shade color running crosswise in a fabric caused by a change in loom tension or irregular dyeing. 122

barathea   twill variation with a broken rib weave on one face and a pebbly texture on the other. 70

bark cloth   a) roughly woven drapery fabric with a bark-like texture. 70; b) nonwoven material made from soaked and beaten inner bark of tropical trees such as tapa. 79

basic dyes   class of synthetic dyes effective on acrylics, modified nylon and modified polyester. Also called cationic dyes. 91, *91*, 92

basket weave   balanced plain weave in which two or more warp yarns interlace with two or more filling yarns to resemble the surface of a woven basket. 66, 70

bast fibers   woody fibers from the stems of plants such as flax, jute and hemp. 21, 26, 27

batik   resist print in which wax is drawn or blocked onto a fabric before dyeing. 5, 93

batiste   fine, sheer, plain-woven cloth of combed and carded long-staple cotton. 70

batten   see 'beater'.

batting   layers or sheets of fiber used for lining quilts. 82

beaker dyeing   dyeing of small fabric samples during color development.

beam   cylinder attached to a loom, on which the warp is wound. 63, 64, *64*

beater   movable frame on a loom that holds the reed and packs the filling yarns into place. 64

Bedford cord   a weave with padded ridges parallel to the lengthwise grain of the fabric. Originally wool, now made in a variety of fibers. 69

beetling   a pounding action that flattens linen yarns to a ribbonlike profile and adds surface luster.

Bemberg   trade name of a process for producing cuprammonium rayon fibers, now produced by Beaunit. 34, 35, 70

Berber yarn   hand- or machine-spun wool yarn with a mottled, natural color and irregular diameter.

Beta   trade name of an extremely fine bulked-glass fiber with improved abrasion resistance and flexing properties, manufactured by Owens-Corning. 45

bias   invisible line at a 45° angle to the grain of a fabric; the diagonal. 65

bicomponent fiber   single fiber formed by extruding two different modifications of a polymer solution as one filament, usually to build in crimp or bulk. 49, *49*

biconstituent fiber   single fiber formed by extruding two generically different polymer solutions as one filament. 49, *50*

bird's eye   a dobby loom weave. Pattern is a diamond with small center dot. 70

blanket   a textile sample showing a series of patterns or colors all on the same warp.

bleaching   basic finishing process to whiten grey goods. 13, 83

bleeding   a fault in which dye runs from one pattern area into another. 105

blend   a) yarn of two or more staple fibers spun together. 51, 52; b) fabric containing blended yarns in the warp and filling. 83, *91*

block printing   general term for a hand-printing process using wood or other solid material blocks into which patterns have been cut. 96

blotch printing   open-screen roller-printing process by which the plain background of a printed fabric can be colored. 94

bobbinet   fine net with a six-sided mesh. 12

bobbin lace   single-element construction, originally handmade on a pillow with numerous threads.

bolt   an entire length of fabric, usually rolled full-width on a tube; sometimes folded before rolling. 13

bonded fabric   fabric formed by combining an outer face fabric with a backing fabric using an adhesive or thin foam lamination. 77, 80, 81, 109, *117*

bonded web   bat of loose fibers that is compressed with heat and an adhesive. 77

bonding   process of laminating two fabrics, or a fabric and a backing. 77

bouclé   a) a looped and crimped novelty yarn. 59; b) fabric with a knotty, looped surface, woven with a bouclé yarn.

braid   flat or round, woven or plaited fabric used for trimming. 75, *75*

breaking load   maximum force applied to a fabric in a tensile test.

broadcloth   tightly woven, lustrous cotton fabric in a plain weave with a fine crosswise rib, or wool fabric with a close twill weave, brushed and sheared to give a uniform, slightly felted, smooth appearance. 6, 7, 70

brocade   jacquard-woven fabric with a supplementary warp and/or filling which creates an all-over design; background is satin or twill weave. 70, 123

brocatelle   satin-faced jacquard-patterned cloth in which a supplementary backing weft is used to raise the

surface. 70

broken end   a cut or untied warp yarn in a fabric. *122*

broken twill   twill weave with diagonal lines reversed in alternate directions to form a pattern. 70

brushing   finishing process in which fibers are raised to obscure the construction of the fabric. 83

buckram   plain-woven, sleazy cotton fabric stiffened with sizing.

bulking   chemically or mechanically plumping up filament yarns to increase their loft. 48, *154*

burlap   plain-woven cloth of retted, single-ply jute. 27

burling   removal of extraneous substances such as knots, loose threads, or burrs from a woven fabric. 84

burn-out   printing process to produce an opaque or translucent pattern by applying acid which dissolves fibers supplemental to the ground cloth. 96

buttoning   method of securing upholstery fabric on a padded surface. 139

C

cadet cloth   wool broadcloth specially made for military cadets, heavily milled and cropped to produce a compact, durable fabric.

calendering   standard finishing process in which cloth is pressed heavily and/or repeatedly under steel rollers to produce a polished surface; also used to emboss fabrics. 85

calico   ancient, basic woven cotton cloth. 4, 9, 12, 70

camel's hair   natural protein fiber obtained from the undercoat of the Asiatic camel; a wool variant. *20*, 30

cane   a grass or reed fiber.

canvas   dense cloth, originally cotton, in twill or plain weave. 70

Caprolan   trade name of a textured nylon fiber produced by Allied Chemical. 38, *112*

carbonizing   finishing process to destroy vegetable matter in wool cloth. 84

carded yarn   yarn spun from a carded sliver of fibers. 57, 108

carding   process used for all natural fibers, in which they are separated and brought into general alignment prior to spinning. 11, 25, 29

carpet   general term for fabric constructed to be used as floor covering. 119, 120, *147, 148, 154,* 144-159

casement cloth   general term for sheer drapery fabric. 76, *119, 120,* 133, 134, 142

cashmere   fine, natural protein fiber obtained from the undercoat of the Himalayan Kashmir goat. *20*, 30

cationic dyes   see basic dyes.

cavalry twill   smooth-surfaced, 63° diagonal twill fabric with pronounced ribs, usually of worsted wool. 70

Celanese   trade name of acetate yarns produced by Celanese. 38, *112*

cellulose   organic fibrous substance found in all vegetation that is the basic constituent of both natural and man-made fabrics.

cellulosic fibers   such as cotton, linen, jute and rayon. 19, *20*, 21, 24-28, 34-37, 82-90, 110, *128*

chain stitch   ornamental stitch resembling the links of a chain.

challis   sheer, plain-woven, lightly brushed fabric of woolen, worsted, or similar-textured man-made yarns.

cheesecloth   cotton in loose, plain weave with a very low thread count, originally used as wrap for cheese. 81

chemical finishes additives used to modify the appearance or hand of fabrics. 87, *118*

chenille a) fuzzy, caterpillar-like yarn of cotton or man-made fibers, produced by locking short, cut fibers at right angles to the core thread. 60; b) fabric woven with chenille yarn in the weft, producing a cut-pile surface. 70; c) as carpeting, 146, *146*

chevron twill weave with a zigzag repeat. 42

chiffon sheer fabric, especially of silk. 70

chintz close, plain-woven cotton, either printed or dyed, with a glazed surface. 70, 86

Chromespun trade name of a solution-dyed, acetate filament yarn manufactured by Eastman. *112*

ciré high-luster glaze on silk, cotton or synthetics, produced with wax or resin and hot rollers.

cleaning a) dry: immersion of fabric in petroleum or synthetic solvents to remove oil or grease. *119*, 124, 142, 143, 158, 159; b) wet: removal of waterborne soil or stains by a soap or detergent and water process, done usually on a flat surface with a brush, not to be confused with laundering by immersion. *119*, 158, 159

cloth general term used for any pliable material whether woven, knitted, felted, knotted, or extruded. 3-10, *117*, *119*, *120*, 133-143

cloth count see thread count.

coated fabric fabric coated, or treated, with a substance such as rubber, vinyl, plastics or oil.

cohesiveness ability of fibers to adhere to one another in yarn manufacturing process. 18

coil term used to describe a type of configuration given to a yarn in order to make it stretchable.

coir coarse and extremely durable fiber obtained from the outer husks of coconuts. 20, 28, *114*

color a hue, as contrasted with white, black or grey. *23*, 47, 90, *91*, 92, 100, *101*, 102, 105, 110, *122*, 135, 138, *155*

color abrasion loss of color, particularly in pigment prints or from poor dye penetration. 94

colorfast term applied to fabrics colored in such a way as to prevent color fading from light or cleaning. 90, 91, *105*, *119*, 123, 124

color card a series of swatches attached to a sample of fabric to show the complete color line. 14

color line the range of colors available in a particular fabric.

color way one individual coloration from the full color line.

color value the lightness or darkness of a color.

C.O.M. customer's own material. 129

combed yarn yarn spun exclusively of long fibers in parallel conformation which produces the strongest, smoothest staple fiber yarn. 57, 108

combination dyeing general term for a dyeing process involving cloth made of two or more different fibers.

combination filament yarn yarn composed of two or more different filaments. 50, *50*

combing the process of making carded fibers parallel and removing impurities and short fibers before spinning. 25

complex yarns any yarns constructed in such a way as to produce a bulky or uneven or otherwise special appearance. 59, *59*, 108

compound cloths cloths layered in two or more thicknesses. 79, 109, *117*

construction the particular manner in which yarns or fibers are interlaced to form fabric. *117*, 150

conversion broad range of processes such as finishing, dyeing, printing, embroidering or embossing which change the basic appearance of a fabric.

converter individual or company that buys grey goods, applies finishes, and sells the finished fabric to a wholesaler or retailer, 13, 82

cord fabric general term referring to a fabric with a pronounced horizontal or vertical rib. 69, 70, 108

corduroy cloth made of either natural or man-made fibers, with cut-pile ribs (or wales) running the length or width of the fabric. The ribs are produced by weft yarns that are carried over the fabric face and then cut. *68*, 70, 85

cord yarn yarn made of two or more ply yarns twisted together. *56*, 57, *57*

core a base yarn which is wrapped with a second and sometimes a third yarn. 49, 50, 60

core spinning yarn spinning process in which an elastomeric filament under pre-determined tension is enrobed in a sheath of staple fibers. When tension is removed, the sheath fibers are pulled into a compact formation, and the yarn is thereafter stretchable to the extent of the pre-determined tension of the core filament. 45

coronizing process in which foreign matter is burned out of fiberglass fabric and the fiber is heat-set for stability and abrasion resistance.

cotton natural vegetable fiber composed of pure cellulose. 3-10, *20*, 24, *24*, 25, *25*, 57, 61, 82, *91*, *114*, *116*, *120*, *128*

count see thread count.

course the horizontal element in a knitted fabric. 71, *72*

covert medium or heavy-weight wool fabric, usually of two colors, closely woven with a steep twill, and finished with a smooth face. 70

cramming process in which extra warp or filling yarns are forced into a cloth.

crease a line in a fabric caused by a fold.

crease resistant finish a resin finish heat-set on cellulosic fabrics to inhibit wrinkling. *118*

crepe a) yarn that is overtwisted to create a crinkled profile and stretchy resilience. 57; b) fabric woven of crepe yarn, which has a matte surface texture and slight stretch. 67, 70, 108

Creslan trade name for an acrylic fiber produced by American Cyanamid. 40, *112*

cretonne plain-woven printed cloth similar to unglazed chintz. 70

crewel a hand embroidery technique from Kashmir in which fine, loosely twisted two-ply yarn is stitched on cotton. 79, 81

crimp the waviness in a fiber, either natural (as in wool) or imposed on man-made (nylon, etc.). *38*, 48, *48*, 49, 58

crimping process in which natural or synthetic fibers are set in wavy coils for resilience, wrinkle resistance, and natural cohesion in finishing.

crocking the rubbing off of color due to improper or insufficient dye penetration or fixation. Crocking may occur under wet or dry conditions. 91, 105, *119*, 124, 140

cross-dyeing piece-dyeing fabric composed of two generically different fibers with two different dyes to produce a pattern characteristic of yarn-dyed fabric. 51, 93, 100

crushed fabrics pile fabrics treated with heat, moisture and pressure to distort the pile formation.

Cumuloft trade name of a texturized nylon produced by Monsanto. 38, *112*

cuprammonium rayon   a type of rayon made from cellulose dissolved in an ammonium copper solution. 34, 35

custom services   work performed to special order.

cut   the cutting module or unfinished panel length of a window or wall fabric.

cut and loop   a tufted carpet pile variation. *147*

cut order   fabric ordered to a specific measurement. 13

cut-pile fabric   cloth with a three-dimensional surface produced by double weaving or by looping an additional warp or filling thread into the basic weave, and then cutting the loops. 69

cutting   a small sample of fabric.

cut wire   rod with a blade that is inserted under the extra warp or filling yarn during the weaving of a cut-pile fabric. As it is withdrawn, it cuts the loop, producing a cut-pile surface. 69

D

Dacron   trade name of a polyester fiber made by DuPont. 40, *112*

damask   woven pattern based upon contrasting warp-face and filling-face cloths. 70, 133

decating (decatizing)   basic finishing process that includes light scouring and single calendering. 85

degumming   removal of natural gums from silk yarn or fabric by boiling in a mild alkaline solution.

delamination   undesirable separation of the components of bonded or laminated fabrics.

delamination strength   term used in testing how securely the secondary backing is adhered to the primary backing of carpeting. 151

delustering   chemical process in which the luster of man-made yarn or fabric is reduced by changing the character of its light-reflecting capacity, either before spinning, by inserting colorless pigments into the solution, or during spinning, by altering the contour, cross-section, or density of the filament. 20, 48, 87

denier   a unit of weight indicating the size of a filament. The higher the denier the heavier the yarn. 61

denim   yarn-dyed cotton cloth woven in a warp-faced twill, usually with a dyed warp and a natural filling. 70

density   the measure of the set of a cloth—the total number of ends and picks. *23*, 108, *114*, 151

dent   the space between the teeth in the reed of a loom.

diaper   all-over repeating pattern produced by combining herringbone weave and a reversed twill. 70

dimensional stability   ability of a textile to maintain its original shape and size. *23*, 51, 106, 107, 110, *117*, *119*, 136, 139

Diolen   trade name of a German polyester.

direct dyes   class of dyes used for cellulosics which need no fixatives. 90, *91*

direct glue-down   method of installing carpet securely to floor. 157

direct printing   general term for a process in which color is applied directly onto the fabric. 95

discharge printing   process in which pattern is obtained by bleaching portions of already dyed cloth. It may be left white or dyed another color. 96

disperse dyeing   process for coloring acetate, acrylic, nylon and polyester in which a slightly water soluble dye is dispersed in the fiber solution. Sometimes subject to fume-fading and sublimation. 91, *91*, 92, 105

dobby   a mechanical loom attachment that can regulate as many as forty harnesses to produce small, geometric patterns. 69, 70, *117*

Donegal tweed   thick, homespun woolen fabric, originally hand-woven in Donegal, Ireland, of characteristically rough yarns with flecks of many colors.

dope dyeing   trade jargon for solution dyeing.

dotted swiss   sheer cloth with a spaced dot pattern, produced by dense areas of supplementary filling in a swivel weave. The dots may also be clipped. 70

double cloth   compound cloth based on two sets each of warp or filling yarns held together at regular intervals by a warp or filling thread passing from one fabric to the other. 68, 70

doubleknit   knitted fabric made with a double set of needles to produce a double thickness of fabric which is consequently denser and has greater stability than a single knit. 72

double weave   fabric woven with two sets of warp and filling yarns, with an extra yarn to loosely hold the two cloths together. The connecting yarn is cut, and two cut-pile fabrics are produced.

doubling   joining together an S twist yarn with a Z twist yarn to create a plied yarn free from torque.

douppioni   silk yarn reeled from two cocoons that have grown together, resulting in a slubbed, interrupted texture.

downtown house   fabric house that sells to retailers and uptown and regional houses. 14

draft   chart indicating the relationship of warp and weft yarns of a cloth.

Dralon   trade name of a German acrylic made by Bayer. 40

drapery   general term for fabric used as opaque window or other surface covering. 133, 134, 142

draw   a) to shape or stretch out a fiber or yarn. 54; b) in weaving, to move warp threads through the heddles in the proper order to produce a pattern.

drill   strong cloth, originally cotton, of twill construction.

drip-dry   cloth that can be hung to dry without spinning or wringing and thus needs no ironing; may be inherent in a fabric or induced with special finishes.

dry-cleaning   removal of dirt from fabrics by treatment with solvents. *119*, 124, 142, 143, 158, 159

dry spinning   a) spinning fiber, particularly linen, when dry to produce a lofty, soft yarn;   b) extruding man-made filaments from a spinnerette into warm air. 20 36, 39, 41, 43

duck   compact, durable plain-woven cotton fabric. 70

durable press   finish applied to fabric by means of resins in solution or gaseous form, and cured under conditions of controlled heat to set the shape and make it wrinkle-resistant in machine laundering. Also called *permanent press.* 86, 90, 110, *118*

dye affinity   the susceptibility of a fiber to various dyestuffs. 91, *91*

dye house   facility where grey goods are colored through dyeing or printing.

dyeing   the process of applying color to fiber, yarn or fabric with natural or synthetic coloring agents. 4, 5, 13, 47, 90, 93, 110   See also: cross, jig, package, piece, skein, solution, space, stock, top, union and yarn dyeing.

Dynel   trade name for a modacrylic fiber produced by Union Carbide. 42

E

Egyptian cotton fine grade of cotton known for its long staple.

elasticity ability of a stretched material to recover its original size and shape. 21, *23*, 106, *114*

elastic recovery a factor in the dimensional stability of fabrics. *23, 114.* See also: recovery.

elastomer elastic synthetic fiber with the physical properties and strength of natural rubber. *20*, 21, 44, 45, 60

element a single yarn or set of yarns in a constructed fabric.

elongation the stretch capacity of a fiber, yarn or fabric. *23*, 106, 107, *114*

embossing decorative fabric finish produced by patterned rollers. 86

embroidery basic cloth embellished with ornamental needlework. 79, 81, 109, *117*, 133, 142

end a) a single strand of warp yarn. 65; b) a short length of fabric.

end-and-end fabric woven with two alternating colors of warp yarns.

Enjay trade name of a saran (monofilament or slit film only) produced by Eastman.

Enkaloft trade name of a high-bulk texturized nylon produced by American Enka. *112*

Enkalure trade name of a multilobal nylon produced by American Enka. 38, *112*

Enkrome trade name of an acid-dyeable rayon produced by American Enka. *112*

Enkron trade name of a polyester produced by American Enka.

Estron trade name of an acetate produced by Eastman. *112*

extruded fabric nonfibrous fabric, related to film that is made directly from a polymer solution. 78, 79, 109, *117*

F

fabric general term for any woven, knitted, knotted, felted or otherwise constructed material made from fibers or yarns. Cloth, carpet, caning and matting are all defined as fabric. 63-81

fabric construction 102, 106, 109, 110, *117*, *119*

fabric width crosswise measurement of cloth.

face the side on which a fabric is finished. 66

Fade-Ometer a testing machine that determines the colorfastness of a fabric. 124

fading color loss due to light, pollutants, cleaning, etc. 105, 151

faille lightweight fabric, originally silk, with a pronounced transverse rib. 70

fault an inconsistency in an entire piece or lot of fabric. 122, *122*

felt a) non-woven fabric made of fibers joined through the application of heat, agitation and moisture, or by mechanical treatment. 3, 76, 109, *117*, 156; b) woven fabric that has been treated with heat, moisture and pressure to achieve greater strength and fullness.

fiber the basic element of cloth. Any tough, hair-like substance, natural or man-made, that can be spun or thrown to form yarn, or felted or otherwise joined into a fabric. 17-23, 102, 105, 107, 108, 110, *114*, *116*, 120, 151, 154

Fiberglas trade name of a glass fiber produced by Owens-Corning. 44, 45

fiberglass man-made mineral fiber extruded in continuous filaments. *20*, 44,87

fiber web fabrics cloth constructed from a mat of fibers secured with adhesives and/or heat. 73, 77, 148

filament fiber of indefinite length, either natural (silk) or man-made. Silk filament is the actual thread of a silkworm's cocoon; man-made filaments are produced by forcing a solution through a spinnerette. 17-23,37, *38*, 47, *48*, 56, 61, 62, 108, *152*, *153*, *154*

filling (or weft or woof) in weaving, the crosswise yarn or yarns that interlace at right angles with the lengthwise warp. 10, 12, 65, 68

filling-faced a term used to describe fabrics in which the filling picks predominate over the warp ends. The filling may conceal the warp completely. 65, 67, 70

film non-fibrous, no-element fabric primarily used as a substrate or laminate. 78, 109, *117*

finish any treatment given to a fiber, yarn or fabric to alter its original or grey goods state. See also: additive finish, beetling, bleaching, calendering, carbonizing, decatizing, delustering, mercerization, mothproofing, napping, pre-shrinking, shearing, silicone finish, tentering, weighting, wet finish. 82, 102, 110, *118*, 136

fireproof fabric cloth which is impervious to burning.

fishnet diagonally knotted fabric sometimes used for casements.

flame lamination see foam flame bonding.

flame-resistant fabric a fabric whose fiber content or topical finish makes it difficult to ignite and slow to burn. *116*, *119*, 128, 136

flame retardant chemical applied to fiber, yarn or fabric to reduce its tendency to burn. 87, 110, *116*, *118*, 128, 136 151

flame-retardant fabric man-made fabric whose fiber content is officially acceptable for most situations.

flammable, or inflammable easily set on fire. 136

flammability code specifications indicating the highest amount of burning, charring, smoke density, or flame spread a fabric may exhibit to meet an approved standard. 125, 126

flammability test any one of several tests to determine a fabric's resistance to burning, conducted under specific atmospheric conditions. See also: Methenamine Test, Steiner Tunnel Test. *116*, 125, 126, 127, 129

flannel medium weight, slightly napped plain or twill-woven cloth, most often of wool or cotton. 70

flaw defect in a fabric. *122*

flax plant from which linen is produced. 5, *20*, 26 *26*, 57, *114*, *116*

fleece a) the woolly coat of a sheep, usually clipped in one large piece; b) fabric with a deep soft woolly pile.

flexibility capacity to be bent repeatedly without breaking; pliability. 18, *23*, 62, *114*

float portion of warp or filling yarns covering two or more adjacent yarns to form a design or satin surface. 65, *117*, *122*

flocked fabric fabric in which the entire surface is covered with flocking to produce a velvet-like or suede-like texture. 148

flocking process by which a velvety pile surface is formed by securing short fiber ends to a fabric with adhesive. 85, 110

foam man-made, no-element fabric primarily used as a

substrate or backing for another fabric. 78, 109, *117*, 128, 150, *150*, 156

foam flame bonding   one of the two basic processes used in fabric-to-fabric lamination. (The other is wet adhesive bonding). The foam takes the place of an adhesive and is made tacky by heating with a gas flame. In the process, the thickness of the foam is reduced but not eliminated entirely. This method may also by used to build up face fabrics. 81

Fortisan   trade name for a filament rayon produced by Fiber Industries (a division of Celanese). 35

Fortrel   trade name of a polyester fiber produced by Fiber Industries (a division of Celanese). 40, 112

frieze (or frisé)   durable uncut warp-pile fabric often woven with a wool face and cotton back. 70

fulling   a finishing operation dependent on the felting properties of wool, that shrinks the fabric to make it héavier and thicker. 84

fume fading   term used to describe color loss or change caused by gases or other pollutants. Also called atmospheric, or gas, fading. 91, 92, 106, 124

functional enchancement   improvement of the factors which affect durability, strength, life span, etc. 47-52, 87

fusing   process in which thermoplastic fibers or yarns are melted together, as in ribbons, or heat-sealed, as in joinings, to form a fused edge.

fuzzing   gradual raising of fiber ends in a fabric due to wear on the surface, forming patches of matted fibers. These retain soil, are unsightly in appearance, and may lead to pilling. 105, 138

G

gabardine   fabric of fine worsted yarns closely woven in a diagonal twill and finished with a high sheen. 57, 70

gas fading   see fume fading.

gauze   openly constructed, transparent cloth of any fiber.

generic fibers   universally accepted classifications of chemically distinct families of fibers. *20*, 21, 37, 61, *112*, 125

gimp   a silk or metallic yarn spiral-wrapped closely around an inner core to cover it completely.

gingham   yarn-dyed, combed or carded cotton fabric woven into a series of simple patterns in two or more colors, such as checks, stripes and plaids. 70

glass   raw material from which fiberglass fibers are made. *114, 116, 120, 128*

glazing   general term for a polished finish on cloth, often using waxes or resins and hot rollers. 85, *85*

Göbelin   tapestry made at the Göbelin works near Paris.

grain   the alignment of vertical (lengthwise) and horizontal (crosswise) elements in a fabric to form a right-angle relationship. 65

grass fibers   general class of fibers that includes abaca, sea grass, grain straw, bamboo, rattan and cane.

grey goods (or greige)   woven fabric as it comes from the loom: unbleached, not dyed or printed, unfinished. 13, 70, 82

grin   a) ground cloth of a pile fabric visible when it is folded or creased. 151;   b) small area of ground color that shows through if the print is off-register. 94

grosgrain   a) heavy, corded ribbon or cloth. 70;   b) large-scale frieze cloth with a heavy, regular warp pile.

grospoint   non-directional warp-looped, uncut pile fabric, extremely resilient and hard wearing.

H

hackling   combing process as it applies to flax. 26

hair fibers   animal fibers that lack the crimp and resilience of wool, cashmere, or camel's hair, such as rabbit hair and fur fibers.

hand   the tactile quality of a fabric. 51, 105, 110, *114*, *119*, 138

hand-spun yarn   yarn spun by hand on a spinning wheel.

handwoven fabric   cloth woven on a hand or foot-powered loom, or woven by hand without a loom. 69

hardtwist   a tufted carpet pile variation. *147*

harness   rectangular frame on a loom that holds the heddles through which the warp yarns pass. The harnesses raise and lower the heddles in predetermined patterns so that the filling yarns can be inserted through the shed to produce a desired weave. 64, *64*

Harris tweeds   highly durable woolens handwoven on the Outer Hebrides Islands off the coast of Scotland, rough textured and made in narrow fabric widths.

heather mixture   yarn composed of a mixture of fibers dyed in different colors.

heat setting   process in which fabrics made of thermoplastic fibers are tentered under controlled heat to stabilize dimensions and minimize future shrinking or stretching. *38*, 58, 85

heddles   needle-like wires on a loom through which the warp yarns are drawn. They are mounted in the harness, which is raised and lowered during weaving. 63 64, *64*

Helanca   trade name of a stretch-nylon process developed by Heberlein. 58

hemp   coarse natural cellulose fiber. *20*, 28, *114*

Herculon   trade name of a polypropylene fiber produced by Hercules. 42, *112*

herringbone   twill weave which has a zigzag pattern formed by alternating the direction of the twill. The chevron pattern runs selvage to selvage. 67, 70

high wet modulus rayon   a modified rayon with greater dimensional stability in washing. 34, 35

hiking   the alternate sagging and shrinking of casement panels due to humidity changes. 106, 136

homespun   originally, a plain-woven fabric from hand-spun yarns; currently, a machine-woven fabric with irregular yarns to simulate the original textures. 7, 10

Honan   lustrous tussah silk, originally hand-woven in the Honan province of China.

honeycomb   hexagonal woven pattern, resembling the cells of a honeycomb. 70

hopsacking   coarse basket-weave fabric of jute, hemp or cotton. 70

horizontal operation   a textile business involved with a single aspect of fabric production, which it sells to a varied market. 13

horsehair   narrow upholstery fabric woven with a filling of long, single tail hairs. *20*

houndstooth   variation of a twill weave, with a broken check pattern. 70

hue   color, shade or tint of a color.

hydrophilic   moisture absorbent. 89, 105, 106, 136

hydrophobic   moisture repellent. 105, 106, 136

I

Ikat   fabric woven with tie-dyed yarns. 93

indigo   natural vegetable dye used to color fabric blue. 67

insulating   general term for any material used to lessen the transfer of noise, heat or cold. See also acoustic and thermal insulation. 89, 110

intensity   the brightness or darkness of a color.

interlining   a layer of fabric between the outer, decorative fabric and the lining. 78, 135

International Grey Scale   standard used to measure color fading on a Fade-Ometer.

intimate blend   blend of two or more compatible fibers that are carded together so that no one characteristic dominates. 51

J

jacquard   loom attachment that uses a punched card system to raise and lower single heddles. It permits the weaving of fabrics with complex patterns such as tapestry and brocade. 12, 68, 69, 70, 73, *117*, 145

jean   sturdy cotton fabric, finer and softer than drill. 70

jobber   person or organization that buys large lots of finished fabrics for resale in smaller quantities. 13

jute   coarse natural cellulose fiber, used primarily in burlap and carpet backing. *20*, 27, *114*, 120

K

kapok   natural cellulose fiber, extremely light, which is used 'as is', not spun. *20*, 28

kemp   coarse wool fiber found in the fleece of mountain sheep and domestic goats. Because it does not absorb moisture, it appears paler than other fibers in a fabric when dyed.

kersey   heavily milled woolen fabric with a lustrous nap.

kiss coat   a light latex backing on a fabric.

knit fabric   textile produced by continuous interlooping of one or more yarns. 71-75, *73*, 109, *117*, 148

knot   weaving flaw; broken yarns which are tied, and usually pulled through to the back of the fabric. *122*

Kodel   trade name of a polyester staple fiber produced by Eastman. 40, *112*

L

lamb's wool   first fleece sheared from a young sheep. The previously unclipped fiber ends are tapered, producing a very soft texture. 29

laminated fabric   fabric created by bonding two or more layers of material together. 78, 81, 109, *117*

lappet   three-element woven fabric similar to discontinuous brocade. 69, 70

lawn   lightweight, sheer, fine cotton or linen fabric. 70

leno weave   open weave used for casements, which achieves extra stability by twisting the warp yarns around each other. 60, 69, 70, *70*, *117*

level loop   a tufted carpet pile variation. *147*

level tip shear   a tufted carpet pile variation. *147*

lightfastness   resistance to fading due to exposure to sun or light. *119*

line   long linen fibers that have great luster and strength. 57, 108

linen   a) natural cellulose yarn made from flax fibers, noted for strength, cool hand and luster; low resilience;
b) fabric woven from linen yarns. 3-10, *20*, 57, 82, *91*, *120*, *128*, 133

lining   material attached under the principal material of a cloth or article.

llama   South American animal of the camel family whose fleece is produced in a variety of colors, similar to but coarser than alpaca. *20*, 31

loft   bulk or resilience of a fabric, yarn or fiber. 48

loom   machine that produces woven textiles by interlacing warp and filling yarns at right angles to each other. 11, 12, 63-65, *64*

Lurex   trade name of a slit-film metallic yarn produced by Dow Badische. 45, *112*

luster   the gloss or sheen on the surface of a fiber, yarn or fabric. *23*, 62, 104, *114*

Lycra   trade name of a spandex fiber produced by DuPont. 45, *112*

M

macramé   coarse, single-element construction employing a variety of knots in a geometric pattern.

macromolecule   large molecule formed by hooking together many monomers; a polymer. 17-23,37

Malimo   nonwoven multiple-element fabric construction in which hundreds of stitching yarns knit the weft onto the warp. 74, 109, *117*

man-made fiber   inclusive term for manufactured fibers, natural or synthetic in origin.

marquisette   leno-woven sheer of cotton or synthetic yarn used for casement cloths. 69, 70, *71*

Martindale Test   a wear abrasion test used extensively in Europe. The fabric's warp and weft are abraded at the same time.

match   the relative constancy of shade from one dye lot to another; also pattern match.

matelassé   jacquard-woven cloth with a quilted-like surface, usually cotton or rayon. 70

melt spinning   extruding man-made filaments through a spinnerette in a melted form, which immediately harden when cooled. 20, 38, 42, 43

memo sample   sample of fabric, generally 30 cm. (1 ft.) square.

mercerization   caustic soda treatment for cotton and linen, which makes the yarn or cloth stronger, and increases luster and dye affinity. 25, 84, *84*

Merino   breed of sheep yielding a high grade wool used for fine woolen and worsted cloth. 4, 6, 7

metallic   descriptive term for any fiber, yarn or fabric using a metal (gold, aluminum, steel, etc.) as part of its structure. *20*, 45, 60, 108, *112*, 114, *116*, *120*

Methanamine Pill Test   a flammability test. 126

mildew-resistant fabric   fabric of inherently resistant fibers, or one treated to resist deterioration by mildew and mold.

Milium   trade name of an aluminum-powder backing produced by Deering Milliken, which is applied to window fabric to reflect heat. 89

mineral fiber   natural or man-made fiber derived from a mineral, such as asbestos or fiberglass. 19, *20*, 21, 32, 44

Mitin   trade name of a permanent mothproofing process for wools and wool blends, produced by Geigy. 88

modacrylic   generic term for a modified acrylic fiber composed of copolymers of acrylonitrile and other materials such as vinyl chloride, which enable the fiber to be softened at low temperatures. *20*, 42, 87, *112*, *114*, *116*, *120*, *128*, 151, 154, *155*

mohair a) processed fiber of the long, silky hair of the Angora goat. *20*, 30, *114*; b) velvet or plush fabric with a mohair pile and cotton back.

moiré a wavy pattern. 86

moisture regain term used to designate the moisture content of a fiber under prescribed conditions. It is expressed as a percentage of the bone-dry weight. *23*, 108

moleskin heavy, sateen-weave wool fabric, napped to produce a sheared or sueded effect.

monk's cloth basket-woven cotton fabric. 70

monofilament one silk or synthesized filament; also a yarn composed of a single untwisted and unplied synthetic filament. 20, *38*, 56, 60, 108

monomer single unit, or molecule, from which polymers are formed. 17-23

mordant a metallic salt used to fix dyes.

mothproofing general term for any additive finish which makes natural fibers unappealing to insects. 88, 110, *118*

motif a pattern unit, usually repeated. 93, 94, 101

Moygashel trade name of fine Irish linen cloths produced by Moygashel.

multi-level a tufted carpet pile variation. *147*

multifilament yarn composed of several, or hundreds of, extruded filaments. 20, *38*, 56, 108

muslin plain-woven, uncombed cotton fabric, ranging from sheer to coarse. 4, 53, 70

Mylar trade name for a polyester available as a clear film or as a metallic laminate produced by DuPont. 45, 105

N

nap the cut pile or fuzzy surface finish of a cloth or carpet. 85, 110, 157

natural fiber any textile fiber obtained from an animal, vegetable or mineral source, such as wool, cotton or asbestos. 17-23, 24-34

Naugahyde an expanded vinyl leather-look fabric produced by UniRoyal. 78

needle-punching form of no-element fabric structure in which webs of fibers are laid down in various ways and stitched together by hundreds of barbed needles, which push the fibers into a closely entangled arrangement. The thickness of a web determines its end use — from light open-work effects to a dense mesh used for carpeting. 77, 148

net a) general term for a lacy diamond-shaped mesh; b) coarse, open-mesh fabric made by diagonal square knotting. 76

ninon smooth, sheer, plain-woven fabric for casements. 70

no-element fabrics fabrics which are either fibrous, but not made into yarn form, or non-fibrous, made directly from a solution. 76, 109, *117*

Nomex trade name for a flame-retardant and heat-resistant aramid fiber produced by DuPont. 39, *112*

nonwoven fabrics see no-element fabrics.

novelty yarns see complex yarns.

novolid generic term for a new type of man-made fiber with inherently high flame resistance. *20*, 44, 87

nub random clot of short, dense fibers incorporated during spinning.

nylon generic term for synthetic polyamide fiber. *20*, 37, 51, 90, *91*, *112*, *114*, *116*, *120*, *128*, 151

nytril generic term for a synthetic fiber composed largely of vinylidene dinitrile. *20*

O

off-grain finishing fault in which the horizontal structure is not at right angles to the vertical. 65, 83, *122*

olefin generic term for synthetic fibers produced from either polyethylene or polypropylene. *20*, 42, *112*, *114*, *116*, *120*, *128*, 151, 154, *155*

oleophilic tendency to absorb and retain oily substances. 40.

organdy sheer, plain-woven cotton cloth with a crisp hand. 70

organza similar to organdy, but made of silk, rayon or nylon.

Oriental term generally used alone to denote a type of rug first handwoven in the Middle East. 145

Orlon trade name of an acrylic fiber produced by DuPont. 40, *112*

ottoman heavy, horizontal-ribbed fabric, usually with a densely set warp of silk, acetate or rayon, and a cotton or wool weft. 70

outline quilting form of quilting in which the stitching follows the motif of a printed fabric. 80, 109

Ozite trade name of a felted fabric of coarse animal hair produced by Ozite, generally used as an underlay for carpets. 77

P

package dyeing form of yarn dyeing in which the dye fluid and the rinse bath are forced through a large number of 0.45 kg. (1 lb.) packages of yarn. 92

panné mechanical finish for velvets and velours in which heat and pressure lay the pile on a steep diagonal, thus increasing pile cover and luster.

pattern a) the arrangement of form, design or decoration in a fabric. 69, 93, 101, 102, 135, 138, 155; b) guide for cutting fabric.

pattern repeat a total design unit. 94, 95, 101, 103

peel bond strength see delamination strength.

Pellon trade name of a nonwoven backing or interlining produced by Pellon

percale fine, plain-woven cloth of closely set, combed and carded long-staple cotton. 70

pick in weaving, a single passage of filling yarn through the warp shed. 64

piece one entire length of woven cloth, usually 30, 45 or 55 meters long (33, 50 or 60 yards).

piece dyeing dyeing of cloth after production. 92

pigment insoluble powdered coloring agent carried in a liquid binder and printed or padded onto the surface of a cloth. 47, 94

pile velvety surface produced by an extra set of filling yarns that form raised loops, which may be cut and sheared or left uncut.

pile fabric cloth with a three-dimensional surface of cut or uncut loops of yarn. 69, 72, 75, 85, 146, 151

pile weave construction in which cut or uncut loops protrude from the ground cloth; loops may be warp or filling yarns, and be produced by a double weave or with wires. The wire method uses round-tipped, re-

Glossary / Index / **171**

movable wires to raise loops for uncut pile, and sharp-edged cut wires for cut pile. 68, *68*, 70

pilling formation of fuzzy balls on a fabric surface by the rubbing and matting of loose ends of fiber. Depending on the fiber, pills may or may not be easy to remove. 47, 105, 138

pina crisp, grassy fiber from the leaves of the pineapple plant. *20*, 28

piqué durable fabric, either ribbed or in a honeycomb or waffle weave. 69

plaid pattern of unevenly spaced repeated stripes crossing at right angles. 70

plain weave simplest method of interlacing warp and weft yarns to make cloth. Each filling (weft) passes alternately under and over the warp yarns to produce a balanced construction. It is strong, inexpensive to produce, and the best ground cloth for printing; the thread count determines the fabric's strength. 66, *66*, 70, 109

plastic as fabric, extruded vinyl plastic sheeting comes in various weights from very thin to fairly heavy. It may be fused to a knit backing for greater pliability and stability. 125, 128

plied yarn yarn formed by twisting together two or more single strands. *56*, 59

plissé puckered design effect formed by shrinking fabric in selected areas with a caustic soda solution (cotton) or with heat (synthetics). 85

plush a) cut-pile construction with higher, less dense pile than velvet and velour. 70; b) a tufted carpet pile variation. *147, 150*

ply a) a single strand of yarn; b) to twist two or more strands of yarn together. 55, 61, 108

polished cotton combed and carded fabric, usually of twill or satin construction, which is calendered to produce a high luster.

polyester generic term for a manufactured fiber in which the fiber-forming substance is a long-chain synthetic polymer composed on a complex ester. *20*, 39, 51, 90, 91, *112, 114, 116, 120, 128*, 151, 154, *155*

polyether foam urethane foam produced from polyether resins, primarily used in furniture, bedding, automotive and other non-apparel fields.

polymer chemical compound consisting of repeating structural units; the basis of most synthetic fibers. 17-23, 37, *38*, 49, 56, 78, 109

polymerization conversion of monomers into large molecules or polymers. 17-23, *38*, 47

polypropylene olefin fiber made of propylene monomers. 43, 90, *91*

pongee plain-woven raw silk fabric with an ecru heather effect caused by natural color variation within the fibers.

poplin plain-woven, warp-faced fabric with a fine crosswise rib. 70

porosity the ease with which air and water can pass through a cloth. 139

preshrinking deliberate shrinking of a fabric during manufacture to reduce later shrinking in laundering. 83

primary colors red, yellow and blue. All other colors are derived from combinations of these.

printing application of color designs to the surface of cloth. 8, 12, 13, 93, 94, 110

protein fiber natural fiber originating from an animal such as a sheep (wool) or silkworm (silk). 19, *20*, 21, 28-33

PVC (polyvinyl chloride) or vinyon generic term for a

synthetic fiber composed primarily of vinyl chloride. *20*, 43, *114, 116*

Q

Qiana trade name of a luxurious silk-like nylon produced by DuPont. *112*

quilting compound fabric construction of two layers of cloth with a layer of padding (batting) between, stitched through all three layers. 79, 80, *80*, 109, *117*

R

railroading applying fabric to furniture so that the weft or filling runs vertically to avoid intermediate seam detailing.

ramie fine, oriental bast fiber. *20*, 27

random shear a tufted carpet pile variation. *147*

raschel knit fabric woven on a raschel warp-knitting machine. 73, *117*

ratiné a) novelty yarn constructed by twisting a heavy yarn around a fine yarn. 59; b) textured fabric woven in a plain weave with ratiné yarns.

raveling fraying of yarn at the cut edge of a fabric. 70, *117*, 139

raw fiber textile fiber in its most natural state, e.g., cotton before ginning, wool before scouring.

raw silk silk that is not fully degummed. It is stiff, tacky and caramel in color.

rayon generic term for a man-made fiber derived from regenerated cellulose. 8, 19, *20*, 34, *35*, *36*, 51, 83, *91, 112, 114, 116, 120, 128*

reactive dyes class of dyes that react chemically with fiber molecules and produce fast, bright colors. 91, *91*

recovery ability of a stretch yarn or cloth to return to its original shape or size. 106, 107, *114*

reed comb-like device on a loom through which the warp ends pass. See beater. 64, *64*

reedmark vertical streak in woven fabric caused by a bent wire in the reed. *122*

reeled silk continuous filament silk as it is reeled off the softened cocoon of the cultivated silkworm.

regenerated cellulose cellulosic material derived from cotton linters or wood pulp and dissolved, purified, and extruded to form rayon, acetate and triacetate.

registration the alignment of print screens or rollers to make a precise pattern. 94

remnant leftover yardage from a bolt of cloth, usually less than three meters or yards.

rep plain-woven fabric characterized by distinct ribs running crosswise, produced by weaving large filling yarns through the warp yarns. 70

repeat the amount of surface a single pattern covers on a fabric.

reprocessed wool wool produced by recarding and re-spinning shredded scraps of unused fabric and yarn. 29

resilience a fiber's or fabric's ability to return to its original shape after stretching or crushing. 21, *23*, 106, 108, *114*, 139, 151, *155*

resin synthetic finishing substance applied to fabric to add water repellence, resistance to crushing, luster or other durable finish. 85, 86

resist printing general term for printing processes in which the motif or the ground is treated with a dye-resistant substance before dyeing the fabric. 93

retting soaking of bast fiber plants to permit bacterial or chemical breakdown of the outer bark, which loosens the fibers. 26

reused wool wool spun from shredded used fabrics, commonly blended with other fibers. 29

Rhovyl trade name of a French polyvinyl-chloride fiber produced by Rhone-Poulenc.

rib raised ridge running lengthwise, crosswise or diagonally on a fabric, usually formed by the insertion of a heavy thread, also formed by embossing with rollers.

rib weave a) modification of plain weave in which fine warp ends are closely set and two picks (or one heavier pick) interlace as one. 66; b) any woven fabric construction with a horizontal rib or cord. 70

roller printing mechanical printing of fabric with engraved rollers. 95, *95*, 96

rotary-screen printing a fast and accurate printing process in which the cloth moves under a series of large, patterned cylinders. 95, 96

roving bundle of fibers that are carded and combed and arranged in parallel alignment before spinning. 54, 56

rubber generic term for fibers composed of natural or synthetic rubber. 19, *20*, 21, 32, 33, 156

S

sagging elongation, common to many fabrics and dependent on fiber content and cloth structure. 106, 136

sailcloth lightweight, plain-woven cotton duck. 70

Sanforizing trade name of preshrinking process for cotton and linen fabrics, produced by Cluett Peabody.

saponified rayon rayon filament created by reconverting cellulose acetate to cellulose. 35

saran generic term for a man-made fiber composed of at least 80% polymerized vinylidene chloride. *20*, 43, *114, 116, 120, 128*

sateen filling-faced satin-woven fabric with horizontal rather than vertical floats. 70

satin warp-faced fabric in a satin weave. 70, 133

satin weave basic weave in which the fabric face is composed almost entirely of warp or filling floats, producing a smooth, lustrous surface. 67, *68*, 70, 109

schiffli embroidery machine-made embroidery in which the decorative yarns are held in place by a binder thread on the reverse side of the cloth. 79

Scotchgard trade name of a fluorochemical stain- and water-repellent finish produced by 3M. 87, 89

scouring washing of fiber, yarn or fabric to remove grease, dirt, sizing or color. 29, 84

screen printing hand or machine printing process in which a pattern-making stencil or screen held in a frame is positioned on the cloth and coloring agent applied. 94

scrim theatrical gauze of sheer, plain-woven linen or hemp.

seam placement a factor in the proper installation of carpeting and underpadding. 158

seam slippage the pulling apart of sewn fabrics at the seams because of loose fabric construction or slippery yarns. 139

secondary colors orange, green and violet, obtained by blending two primary colors.

seconds imperfect fabrics having weave, finish or dyeing flaws.

seersucker plain-woven cloth, often striped, with puckered or blistered vertical rows produced by a shrinking differential in two groups of warp yarns. 70

selvage reinforced edge on either side of a woven or flat knitted cloth, finished to prevent raveling. 65, *122*

selvage legend printed copy (firm, designer, pattern, color key) sometimes found running lengthwise on the fabric edge. 94

serge smooth-finished fabric in a balanced twill weave, identical on face and back. 70

sericulture raising of silkworms and production of silk. 4, 6, 31

set density of a fabric's warp and filling.

shade dark variation of a color. See hue.

shading apparent gradations of color in cut-pile fabrics caused by variations in light reflection. It is not a defect but a desirable characteristic of these fabrics.

shading coefficient the amount of heat and light deflection achieved by a casement cloth, a factor in calculating a room's sun resistance and/or air-conditioning requirements. 135

shag a tufted carpet pile variation. *147*

shantung dense, plain-woven silk cloth with a slightly irregular surface due to uneven, slubbed filling yarns. 70

sheath fibers fibers which form a sheath around the elastomeric fiber used in core spinning. 49, 56

shed the space formed as the harnesses of a loom raise some warp yarns and lower others, through which the shuttle passes to lay in the filling. 63, *64*

sheer very thin, transparent, or semi-opaque fabric. 87, 133

sheeting plain-woven cotton of various qualities, the traditional ground for chintz and a basic cloth for printing. 70, 103

shot see pick.

shrinkage contraction of fiber, yarn or fabric due to heat and/or moisture. 106, 136

shuttle device on a loom to carry the filling yarn through the shed to interlace it with the warp. 10, 11, 63, 64, *64*

shuttleless loom loom on which the filling is carried across the warp by other than a shuttle, allowing faster production. 64, 65

silicone finish applied finish to resist dry and water-borne soil.

silk natural protein fiber unwound from the cocoon of the silkworm. Also, any fabric of silk fibers. 3-10, *4*, 19, *20*, 31, *31*, 83, *91, 114, 116, 120, 128*, 133

singeing basic finishing process, particularly for wool fabrics, in which unwanted surface fibers are burned off by passing the cloth under gas jets. 83

single a single-ply yarn. 55, *56*, 59, 61, 108

sisal strong natural cellulose fiber used in making cord and matting. *20*, 28, *114, 120*

sizing a) starch applied to warp threads to strengthen them for the weaving process, usually removed by scouring during finishing; b) starch applied to cotton or linen cloth that is removed when the fabric is washed. 66, 83

skein a loosely coiled length of yarn.

slippage the sliding of filling threads over ends, or the shifting of warp threads which results in open spaces in the fabric. 122, 136, 139

slit film ribbon-like yarn in which metallic and other films are commonly available; see tape yarns.

slub lump or knot in a yarn; may be a defect or purposely spun to produce a textured surface in cloth. 59, *59*, 122

slug fabric flaw caused by filling yarn doubling back on itself. *122*

snagging yarns or fibers catching or pulling out of the cloth surface. 137, 138

soil release finish chemical finish applied to fabrics to facilitate the release of soil during laundering. 89, *118*

soil resistant see stain and spot resistant.

solid wrap system a method of securing fabric to walls. 141

solution dyeing dyeing process in which color is added to man-made fibers before extrusion into filaments, resulting in a tendency to superior colorfastness. 92

soutache narrow, decorative braid with a herringbone pattern.

space dyeing dyeing technique in which parts of a long skein are dipped into different color baths. 92, 100

spandex generic term for synthetic elastic fibers composed of segmented polyurethane. *20*, 45, 60, *112*

special finishes finishes that determine the character of a fabric.

specific gravity ratio of the weight of a material to the weight of an equal volume of water.

specification a) detailed description of a fabric's composition, including style, width, pick and end count, weight per meter or yard, color and finish; b) directive to choose. *100*

spinnerette metal disc with numerous fine holes through which a chemical solution is extruded to produce synthetic fibers. 19, *19*, 31, 34

spinning a) drawing out and twisting fiber into yarn or thread. 3-10, 11; b) extruding man-made filaments through a spinnerette. 54; See dry spinning, melt spinning, wet spinning.

spun-bonded no-element fabric made from thermoplastic filaments that is formed in a directionless mass and bonded with heat. 77

spun yarn yarn spun from staple-length fiber, either natural or cut synthetic filaments. 53, 55, 57, 62, 108

squeegee a heavy rubber blade used to push color dye onto the fabric in screen printing. 94, 95

stability retention of size and shape in a fabric.

stabilize to treat fabric to retain size and shape. 84

stain and spot resistance ability of a fabric to resist water and oil-borne stains, either through natural fiber characteristics or treatment with a resistant finish. 89, 110, *117*, *143*, 151, *155*

standard accepted quality and color of a fabric.

standard conditions in laboratory testing, 65% relative humidity at 21.1°C (70°F). *23*

staple natural or man-made fiber that has a relatively short length. 18, 24, *38*, 48, 54, 57, 61

static the build-up of electrons on any surface; the release of electrons which have built up on any surface. 88, 105, *119*, 139, 152, 153, *155*

Steiner Tunnel Test a flammability test. 126

stock dyeing dyeing of staple fiber prior to spinning. 92

strength see tensile strength.

stretch fabrics fabrics constructed of stretch yarns to have much greater than normal stretch and recovery characteristics. 'Comfort stretch' is a designation for fabrics with up to 30% stretch and recovery; 'power or action stretch' describes fabrics with 30-50% stretch and recovery. 58

stretch yarn yarn with a durable, springy elongation and exceptional recovery. 58, 60, 108

striae irregular variations of color in a fabric, forming muted stripes.

strike-off a trial for color or pattern. 94

stripe narrow section of a fabric differing in color or texture from the adjoining area.

S twist clockwise direction in which yarn is twisted. 56, 61, *61*, 108

sublistatic printing see transfer printing. 96

substrate fabric underlayer, generally of synthetic foam. 78

suedecloth woven fabric with a flat, napped surface finished to resemble suede.

sulphur dye dye that produces heavy shades of black or brown in cellulosic fabrics. 91, *91*

sun rot deterioration caused by sun or light. 107, 135, 136

surface treatment any mechanical or chemical finishing process which affects the appearance or hand of a fabric. 85, 110

swatch card see color card.

Syl-mer trade name of a silicone finish produced by Dow Badische. 87

synthetic fiber textile fiber made from a petrochemical rather than a natural base. All synthetic fibers are man-made, but not all man-made fibers are synthetic. 17-23, *20*, 21, 37-45, *38*, *41*, 47, 83, *152*, *153*

T

Taber Test textile abrasion test; the specimen is placed on a rotating platform and is mechanically rubbed by two abrasive wheels.

tackless strip method of installing carpet which is secure but easily removed. 157

taffeta crisp, plain-woven fabric in which the filling is heavier than the warp, producing a fine, lustrous rib. 70

tapestry jacquard-woven fabric with supplementary multi-colored yarns which form a design. 70, 142

tape yarns yarns produced by finely slitting an extruded sheet of polymerized chemicals. 55, 56, 60, 108

tear strength the force required to begin or continue a tear in a fabric.

Teflon trade name for a highly heat-resistant fiber produced by DuPont. *112*

tender goods fabric that is especially susceptible to tearing, usually because of improper finishing. *122*

tensile strength ability of a fabric to withstand tension without tearing or breaking. 18, *23*, 51, 62, 107, *114*, *117*, 139

tentering controlling fabric width by stretching the selvages on tenterhooks during finishing. 83

Tergal trade name of a French polyester fiber produced by Montedison. 40

terrycloth uncut warp-pile fabric, plain or jacquard-woven of cotton, linen or rayon. 68, 70, 110

Terylene trade name of a British polyester fiber produced by Imperial Chemical Industries. 39, 40

tertiary colors colors obtained by mixing three primary colors, or by mixing one or two secondary colors with black.

testing standard procedures used to determine the specific performance characteristics of a fabric. 122

textile   orginally, a general term for any woven cloth; now, a general term for any fabric made from fibers or yarns, natural or man-made. 110, *117*

textured yarn   man-made yarn that has been mechanically or chemically bulked or crimped. 58, 108

texturing, or texturizing   process by which a fiber is given a permanent curl to make it lofty, resilient, and more natural in appearance. 13, 48, *48*, 58

thermal insulation   insulation used to reduce heat transfer. 99, *117*, *118*, *119*, 133, 155

thermoplastic fiber   a fiber that softens or fuses with heat and hardens again when cooled. 39, 58, 77

thermosetting   see heat setting.

thick-and-thin yarn   complex yarn that is given an uneven profile in spinning. 59

thread   a strand of plied and twisted yarn with a smooth finish that is used in sewing and stitching. 57

thread count   the number of warp and filling yarns per square measure. 65, *117*

throwing   slight twisting of filament yarns. 7, 10, 55

ticking   heavy, strong, linen or cotton twill with a colored warp stripe, used in upholstering and as a covering for mattresses or pillows.

tint   a pale variation of a color.

toile   plain, coarse twill-woven fabric, often linen. Most noteworthy were the toiles de Jouy, 18th century French fabrics printed in scenics with one color on pale cotton, linen or silk. 96

top dyeing   form of stock dyeing in which a loose rope of parallel wool fibers is dyed prior to spinning. Also, dyeing over another color. 92

tow   a) short or broken fibers of flax, hemp or synthetic materials used for yarn, twine, or stuffing;   b) thick bundle of continuous filaments assembled without twisting into a loose ropy strand for cutting into staple. 18, 48, 55, 57, 108

trade name   name given by manufacturer to distinguish a product produced and sold by that manufacturer. 61, *112*, 125

trademark   word, letter or symbol used in connection with a specific product originating and owned by a particular manufacturer. *112*

transfer printing   printing process in which a pattern is printed on waxed paper and transferred to the cloth under heat and pressure. 96

trapunto   decorative quilted design in high relief that is worked through two or more layers of cloth by outlining the design in a running stitch and padding it from the underside. 80, 109

treadle   lever or pedal on a loom that activates the lowering or raising of a harness.

Trevira   trade name of a multilobal-polyester fiber produced by Hoechst. 40, *112*

triacetate   generic term for a man-made fiber that is a modification of acetate with a higher ratio of acetate to cellulose. *20*, 36, 83, 110, *112*, *114*, *116*, *120*

triaxial weave   woven fabric composed of three sets of yarns meeting at 60° angles. 70, *71*, 109, *128*

tricot   plain, warp-knit fabric with a close, inelastic vertical knit. 73

tuft   soft, fluffy threads in a fabric which are cut off short and used as a decorative feature.

tufted fabrics   fabrics, especially including carpeting, constructed by a tufting process. 75, 93, 109, 144, 146, *147*

tufting   system of securing yarns at right angles to a

woven or knit backing, extensively used for the production of carpeting. 75, 139, *150*

Tunnel Test   a series of three tests to measure the flame retardance of carpeting and wall coverings. 126, 127

tussah   brownish silk fabric from uncultivated oriental silkworms. 32

tweed   medium-weight, rough woolen fabric, usually twill-woven. Named tweeds such as Donegal, Connemara, Harris and Galashiels are produced in Ireland and Scotland. 7, 57, 70

twill   basic weave that produces a surface of diagonal lines by passing filling threads over two or more ends in a regular progression. 66, 67, 70, 109

twist   the tightness and direction of the twist spun into a yarn. 'S' twist is a clockwise twist and is the most common; 'Z' twist is a counter-clockwise twist. 61

twisting   winding two or more strands of fiber or yarn together to make a single multiple-ply yarn. 55

twistless yarn   yarns formed by combining fibers by means other than twisting. 55, 56, 108

U

uniformity   similarity in length, width, flexibility and spinning quality. 19, *23*, 62

union dyeing   general term for a dyeing process in which a solid color is obtained in a cloth made of two or more different fibers with different dye affinities. 92

upholstery   general term for fabric intended for use as a covering for furniture. *120*, 137, 142

uptown house   a fabric house that sells cut orders to the trade. 14

urethane   chemical family of cross-linked polymers subject to reactions which cause foaming. The foams are used for bonding and laminating fabrics. Also called polyurethane. 78, 128, 156

V

vat dyeing   process in which alkaline-soluble dyes are oxidized to produce excellent colorfastness in cellulosic fibers. 91, *91*

v-construction   in a pile weave, catching the pile loops under one shot of weft.

vegetable fibers   natural textile fibers of plant origin, such as cotton, flax or hemp.

velour   cut warp-pile fabric, usually of cotton or wool, with higher, less dense pile than velvet. 70

velvet   a) close-cropped, warp-pile fabric with a smooth, rich surface, produced by double weaving or with wires. Originally woven in silk, now made with cotton or synthetics as well. 70, 133;   b) a type of carpeting. 145, *146*

velveteen   single-woven weft pile fabric with a dense cut surface. 70

Verel   trade name of a modacrylic fiber produced by Eastman. 42, *112*

vermicelli   machine quilting technique that produces an overall pattern of noodlelike squiggles. 80, 109

vertical operation   a business involved with the entire production of fabric. 13

vicuna   small, wild Andean animal of the camel family, from the undercoat of which is derived a fine, lustrous fiber. *20*, 31

vinal   generic term for a man-made fiber composed largely of vinyl alcohol. *20*, 44

vinyl non-woven fabric made from a petrochemical solution; thick or thin, it is usually soft and pliable.

vinyon see PVC.

virgin wool new wool; not reused, reprocessed or respun. 29

viscose rayon the most common rayon, formed by converting cellulose into a soluble form and regenerating it into fiber. 34, 35

voile soft, sheer cloth, plain-woven of fine crepe yarns. 70

W

waffle weave three-dimensional rectangular pattern woven on a dobby loom. 66, 70

wale a) a horizontal, vertical, or diagonal rib in a fabric; b) the vertical rib on the face of a knitted fabric. 66, 71, 72

warp lengthwise yarns in a fabric, running vertically through the loom parallel to the selvages. 12, 63, 65

warp-faced fabric woven cloth in which the warp yarns predominate over the filling yarns. 67, 68, 70

warp knit fabric produced on a knitting machine in which the yarns run in a lengthwise but zigzag direction, producing excellent lengthwise stability. 71, 73, 109, *117*

water-repellent fabric cloth that is impervious to water, but still 'breathes'. *110, 118*

water-repellent finish additive finish to make cloth impervious to water. 87

w-construction in a pile weave, catching the pile yarns under one weft and over another and tying them down on the third to keep them from pulling out of the face of the cloth.

weave structural pattern in which yarns are interlaced to produce fabric. 66-70, *117*

weaving process of making a fabric on a loom by interlacing horizontal yarns (weft) at right angles with vertical yarns (warp). 3-10, 54, 63-66, 145

weft horizontal or crosswise element in a cloth. 63

weighted silk silk treated with metallic salts to increase the weight and apparent value, strictly controlled and now virtually obsolete. 84

welt fabric-covered cord sewn into an upholstery seam for aesthetic reasons or to improve the durability of the construction. 140

wet adhesive bonding process used in fabric-to-fabric bonding; a liquid adhesive is applied to the fabric and the bond is cured with heat. 81

wet spinning a) spinning fiber, particularly linen and hemp, while damp to produce a smooth, wiry yarn; b) extruding man-made filaments through a spinnerette into water or a chemical solution. 20, 34, 43

wet strength the relative resistance of a wet fiber, yarn or fabric to tension and abrasion.

wickability fiber property that allows moisture to move rapidly along a fiber's surface and pass quickly through a fabric.

Wilton multiple-element cut-pile carpeting. 144, 145, *146*

woof see weft, filling.

wool fiber or fleece from the coats of sheep. 3-10, *20*, 29, *29*, 83, 88, *91, 114, 116, 120, 128*, 151, 154, *155*

woolen fuzzy, loosely twisted yarn spun from carded short wool fibers. Woolen cloths are generally simple weaves and show coarser finishes than worsteds. 57, 61, 108

woolen system spinning process in which short wool fibers are carded and spun into soft, fuzzy, loosely twisted yarn.

Wool Mark stamp of approval issued by the International Wool Secretariat to denote selected 100% pure virgin wool.

worsted smooth, compact yarns spun from carded and combed long wool fibers. Worsted cloths are more closely constructed and have smoother finishes than woolens. 29, 57, 61, 70, 108

worsted system spinning process in which long wool fibers are carded, combed, and spun into smooth, compact yarns with average to high twist.

woven-double fabric velvet or plush fabric in which two ground cloths are woven one over the other, with the pile yarns woven up and down between them, and later cut to form two fabrics.

Wyzenbeek Test test used to measure a fabric's resistance to wear abrasion. A sample, pulled taut and weighted, is abraded with a cylinder covered with a fine wire screen or heavy cotton duck.

Y

yarn any form of spun, twisted or extruded fibers, natural or man-made, that can be used in weaving, knitting or knotting; may be monofilament, multifilament, or spun—single or plied. 53-62, *56*, 102, 106, 108, 110, *117*, 150, 151, *154*

yarn dyeing dyeing at the yarn stage of production, as opposed to solution, stock or piece dyeing. 92

Z

Zefran trade name of an acrylic fiber produced by Dow Badische. 40, *112*

Zefkrome trade name of a solution-dyed acrylic fiber produced by Dow Badische.

Ze pel trade name of a fluorochemical finish that resists water and oil-borne stains, produced by DuPont. 87, 89

Z twist counterclockwise direction in which a yarn is twisted. 56, 61, *61*, 108